Foundation Design in Practice

Karuna Moy Ghosh

CEng (UK), FIStructE (London), MIE (India) Civil Eng.

Formerly, Chief Structural Engineer
Kaiser Engineers and Constructors, Inc

PHI Learning Private Limited

Delhi-110092
2014

₹ 295.00

FOUNDATION DESIGN IN PRACTICE
Karuna Moy Ghosh

ISBN-978-81-203-3588-2

The export rights of this book are vested solely with the publisher.

Fifth Printing   ...   ...   **August, 2014**

Published by Asoke K. Ghosh, PHI Learning Private Limited, Rimjhim House, 111, Patparganj Industrial Estate, Delhi-110092 and Printed by Mudrak, 30-A, Patparganj, Delhi-110091.

Contents

Preface

During my experience of over 40 years in the management of design office and in the field in civil and structural engineering both in UK and other countries, I was deeply involved in the heavy civil engineering projects, namely Channel Tunnel, A 13 highway tunnel, Medway submersible tunnel, Heathrow Express tunnel link in England; Rashadiya cement plant in Jordan; Tabbo hydroelectric plant in Ivory Coast; Sardinia alumina plant in Italy; Noamundi iron ore plant, Jamshedpur, and Kanpur fertiliser plant in India. I have written this book based on the experiences and knowledge I accumulated from the above projects.

The soil supports the foundation structure. The behaviour of soil is closely interlinked with the behaviour of the foundation. The deformation of foundation depends on the parameters of soil, as we can see in the case of a isolated footing. If the loaded footing rests on incompressible soil (granular sandy), the intensity of contact pressure at the centre of the foundation is higher than the average pressure and lower at the edge. The distribution of pressure tends to be oval shaped. In the case of relatively compressible soil (say clay), the intensity of pressure at the edges is higher than the average pressure and lower at the centre of foundation. The distribution of pressure assumes the form of a shallow bowl.

Take another case of a retaining wall. During the process of backfill, the pressure develops due to the backfill and the wall yields. The end result of the value of pressure is dependant not only on the type of soil and the height of wall but also on the amount of yield the wall sustains. If the wall is of very high stiffness so that the yield is almost zero (no movement), then the pressure exerted on the wall is of full value and is considered as 'the earth pressure at rest'. If the wall yields, i.e. if the wall moves away from the backfill, then the whole mass of retained soil transforms from the rest to the 'active state of plastic equilibrium'. Thus, we can visualize that a 'soil-structure interaction' phenomenon takes place. So, before we start of analyzing and designing a foundation, one should have a clear concept of behaviour of soil subjected to loadings.

The analyses of soil and the analyses and structural design of foundations included in this book are performed, both based on BS codes of practice and Eurocodes, and the results are compared. In each chapter, examples on foundations are analyzed and structural design calculations are presented in a simple and lucid way with step-by-step procedures stating the design philosophy, functional aspects and the methods of construction and clarifying the referred clauses of codes of practice and also producing sufficient numbers of relevant sketches, figures and tables wherever necessary.

The author strongly feels that this book will be useful among the final year undergraduates and postgraduates of civil engineering, freshly qualified engineering graduates attached to the design office and preparing for the professional examinations, and also for practising engineers.

Karuna Moy Ghosh

Chapter 1

Principles and Practice

1.0 GENERAL

Foundation engineering is the engineering science that addresses the engineering aspects of foundations in dealing with the principles and practices in the analysis and design of structural foundations. The foundation may be defined as the substructure that acts as a medium to transfer the loads from the superstructure to the soil. The foundation distributes the loads from the superstructure to the soil to an area so that the pressure on the soil does not exceed the allowable value (bearing capacity), and with reasonable settlement, does not endanger the stability and safety of superstructure. The soil is the load bearing material. The distribution of contact pressure of soil under the foundation is dependent on its geotechnical properties.

1.1 CONTACT SOIL PRESSURE

Contact soil pressure may be defined as the pressure per unit area induced under the foundation base subjected to a vertical downward load acting centrally on the foundation base.

Consider that a vertical downward load W from the superstructure acts concentric on the footing foundation with a square base of size $b \times b$ and placed on the soil of homogeneous character for great depth. For equilibrium, an equal and opposite upward resisting contact force P from the soil mass will be exerted underneath the foundation base, as shown in Figure 1.1 (a).

Theoretically, the intensity of upward contact pressure p (average) is equal to W/b^2. But, the intensity of pressure in contact with foundation base, may not be uniform for the whole contact area of foundation.

The distribution of pressure (intensity of pressure) depends on the geotechnical properties of soil underneath the foundation.

For a relatively incompressible soil (granular soil), the intensity of contact pressure at the centre of the foundation base is higher than the average pressure p and lower at the edges. The distribution of pressure tends to be oval-shaped, as shown in Figure 1.1 (b).

In the case of relatively compressible soil (say clay), the intensity of pressure at the edges is higher than the average pressure p and lower at the centre of foundation. The distribution of pressure assumes the shape of a shallow bowl, as shown in Figure 1.1 (c) (Terzaghi and Peck [1.1]).

However, in compressible plastic clay soil with continuous loading over a sustainable period, greater degree of compaction of soil takes place, and thus it gradually brings an even distribution of contact pressure.

On granular soil, a slight deformation of soil at the centre of foundation due to loading will tend to decrease pressure intensity at the centre, whereas increasing the pressure intensity towards the edges, thus bringing an average pressure intensity over the entire area.

Following the above reasons, we may conclude that the average contact pressure p may be assumed for all practical design purposes, as shown in Figure 1.1 (d).

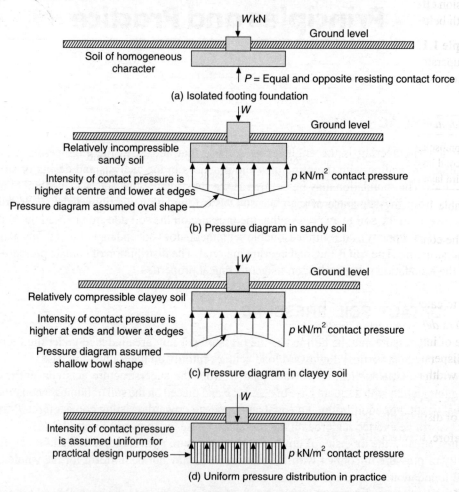

FIGURE 1.1   Contact pressure distribution in variable soils.

1.2 PRESSURE DISTRIBUTION

In the previous section, we discussed contact pressure, i.e. the pressure just underneath the foundation base. When the foundation is loaded, the pressure is not confined to the soil in contact with the base of foundation. The depth of column in mass of soil underneath the foundation base area try to transfer the load to the surrounding soil by the shearing stress of soil between the contact surfaces. As a result the contact pressure spreads the surrounding soil as we go down.

So, the load on the foundation disperses in all directions, spreading the load in a wider area as the depth increases. The angle of dispersion depends on the shearing strength and cohesion of soil. For the soil of low shear strength and cohesion, the angle of dispersion with the vertical is low and for soils of high shear strength of firm granular materials, the angle of dispersion is high. If the soil is made up of stratum of different geotechnical properties, the angle of dispersion will vary. Due to dispersion effect, the intensity of pressure decreases as the loaded area increases with the increment of depth below the foundation.

Example 1.1:   Consider an isolated square footing foundation of 3 m × 3 m subjected to a load from superstructure of 450 kN, as shown in Figure 1.2 (a). The foundation is placed on soil consisting of various strata of different geotechnical properties, as shown in Table 1.1.

TABLE 1.1 Showing geotechnical soil properties

Stratum	Depth below ground	Soil type	ϕ' in degrees
Topmost layer	2.5 m below ground	Very soft silty clay with fine sand	12
Second layer	10 m below ground	Medium to stiff clayey fine sand	30
Third layer	35 m below ground	Dense to very dense grey sand	35

Table 1.1 shows the angle of internal friction of various soil strata underneath the foundation base.

The contact pressure at foundation base

$$p = \frac{W}{a^2} = \frac{450}{3^2} = 50 \text{ kN/m}^2$$

Now, to calculate intensity of pressure at different depths:

At 5.0 m depth below the foundation base
Angle of internal friction of soil, $\phi' = 12°$ with vertical.
The dispersion on either side of original width = 5 × tan 12° = 1.06 m
Total width of dispersion

$$b_1 = 3 + 2 \times 1.06 = 5.12 \text{ m}$$

Area of dispersion $5.12^2 = 26.2 \text{ m}^2$

Therefore, the intensity of pressure

$$p_1 = \frac{450}{26.2} = 17 \text{ kN/m}^2$$

At 7.5 m depth below the foundation base
With $\phi' = 12°$; the dispersion on either side of original width = 7.5 × tan 12° = 1.59 m
Total width of dispersion

$$b_2 = 3 + 2 \times 1.59 = 6.18 \text{ m}$$

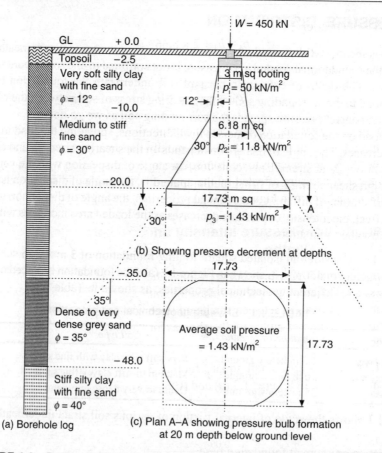

FIGURE 1.2 Pressure distribution of varying soil parameters below foundation.

Area of dispersion $\qquad 6.18^2 = 38.2 \text{ m}^2$

Therefore, the intensity of pressure

$$p_2 = \frac{450}{38.2} = 11.8 \text{ kN/m}^2$$

At 17.5 m *depth below the foundation base*
With $\phi' = 30°$ with medium to stiff clayey sand; the increase in dispersion $= 10 \times \tan 30° = 5.77$ m
Total width of dispersion

$$b_3 = b_2 + 2 \times 5.77 = 6.18 + 11.55 = 17.73 \text{ m}$$

Therefore, the intensity of pressure

$$p_3 = \frac{450}{17.73^2} = 1.43 \text{ kN/m}^2$$

At 32.5 m *depth below the foundation base*
With $\phi' = 30°$ with medium to stiff clayey sand; the increase in dispersion $= 15 \times \tan 30° = 8.66$ m

Total width of dispersion

$$b_4 = b_3 + 2 \times 8.66 = 35.05 \text{ m}$$

Therefore, the intensity of pressure

$$p_4 = \frac{450}{35.05^2} = 0.36 \text{ kN/m}^2$$

Thus, from the above results, we may conclude that as the depth below the foundation base level increases, the intensity of pressure decreases rapidly and approaches a negligible value and the shape of area of dispersion tends to be from square to circle, as shown in the plan in Figure 1.2 (b). The whole zone of pressure affected by the applied load forms a bulb of pressure encircled by curved surfaces, as shown in Figure 1.2 (c).

1.2.1   Variation of Pressure Intensity under Small and Large Foundation at Various Depths

The intensity of contact pressures between foundation base areas of small and large foundation may be the same. But as we go deeper below the foundation bases, the decrement of intensity of pressure varies significantly between small and large foundations. For small foundation base the pressure intensity decreases quite rapidly whereas for large foundation base the pressure intensity decreases not appreciably.

Example 1.2:   Consider a small square footing 3 m × 3 m and a big stiff foundation raft 25 m × 25 m, as shown in Figures 1.3 (a) and (b).

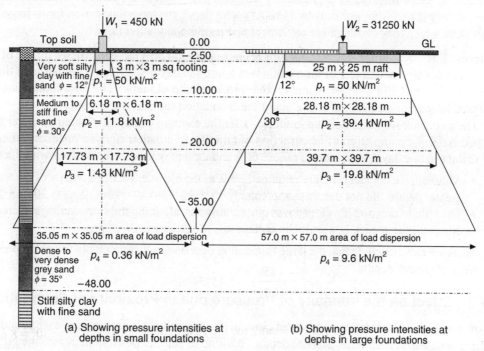

(a) Showing pressure intensities at depths in small foundations

(b) Showing pressure intensities at depths in large foundations

FIGURE 1.3   Variation of pressure intensity under small and large foundations at various depths.

Both the foundations are placed on the same type of soil as shown in Table 1.1.

The small footing is loaded with $W_1 = 450$ kN and the large raft foundation is subjected to a total load of $W_2 = 31250$ kN.

The intensity of contact pressure under the small footing

$$p_1 = \frac{450}{9} = 50 \text{ kN/m}^2$$

and the intensity of contact pressure under the large foundation

$$p_2 = \frac{31250}{25^2} = 50 \text{ kN/m}^2$$

So, the contact pressure under both foundations is the same. The intensity of pressures for these two foundations at various depths below the foundation bases are shown in Table 1.2.

TABLE 1.2   Showing pressure variations between small and large foundation

Intensity of pressure	For small foundation	For large foundation
At base level	50.0 kN/m²	50.0 kN/m²
5 m below base	450/5.12² = 17 kN/m²	31250/27.12² = 42.5 kN/m²
7.5 m below base	450/6.18² = 11.8 kN/m²	31250/28.18² = 39.4 kN/m²
17.5 m below base	450/17.73² = 1.43 kN/m²	31250/39.7² = 19.8 kN/m²
32.5 m below base	450/35.05² = 0.36 kN/m²	31250/57² = 9.6 kN/m²

The results in Table 1.2 show that at 32.5 m depth below the foundation base, the pressure intensity for small foundation is practically insignificant, whereas for large foundation base the pressure intensity has dropped only by 19%. At such a depth, the large foundation forms large bulb of pressure which may cause undue settlement and results foundation failure.

Example 1.3:   A medium size oil tank for a refinery was built on a raft constructed on soil of silty clay. The long-term settlement of foundation was found satisfactory. After a long period of time, it was necessary to build a larger diameter tank replacing the old tank. The new foundation was designed keeping the contact pressure under the foundation same as the old one.

The steel tank wall was built up gradually after the erection of staging floated on water filled in tank. After the completion of construction of tank the foundation showed unequal settlement and collapsed one day. The reason of failure of foundation may have been the following facts:

- Although the contact pressure remained same as the old one, yet the intensity of pressure at greater depths did not decrease appreciably.
- The bulb of pressure developed was quite enormous, affecting the surrounding soil creating unequal settlements, hence finally collapsed.

Thus, we may conclude that the large foundation base does not appreciably lower the pressure intensity at greater depths.

1.2.2   Effect on the Intensity of Pressure due to Proximity of Foundations

When a number of foundations is situated close by, the intensity of pressure from each foundation is superimposed on each other at some depth. This kind of superimposition increases the pressure intensity which may sometimes exceed the permissible value.

Example 1.4: Consider a number of isolated footing foundations of $3.0 \ \text{m}^2$ spaced at 6.0 m spacing [see Figure 1.4 (a)] is constructed on the soil of same geotechnical characters as shown in Table 1.2. At 17.5 m depth below the base, pressure intensity is $1.43 \ \text{kN/m}^2$ for single foundation. The next foundation is 6 m apart. The pressure intensities for three foundations overlap each other and pressure intensity at central 5.43 m width has increased 3 times $= 3 \times 1.43 = 4.29 \ \text{kN/m}^2$ [see Figures 1.4 (a) and 1.4 (b)].

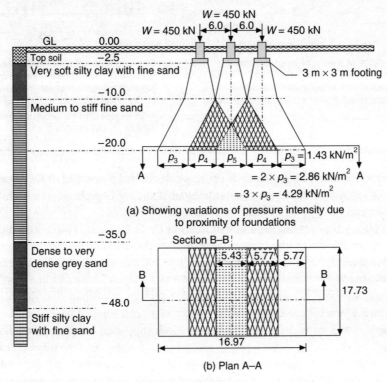

(a) Showing variations of pressure intensity due to proximity of foundations

(b) Plan A–A

FIGURE 1.4 Effect on the pressure intensity due to proximity of foundations.

1.2.3 Shear Stress in Soil

Consider that a foundation is placed at the ground level and is subjected to a vertical load W. The soil underneath the foundation is compressed and will try to squeeze out of all sides of the foundation in a parabolic pattern, as shown in Figure 1.5 (a). The shear stress developed between the sliding surfaces will prevent the movement of the soil mass. If the total shear and cohesive resistance of soil along the sliding surface is greater than the weight of sliding mass of soil, then the movement of ground will not take place. When resistance is overcome by the sliding mass of soil, the ground movement will occur due to shear failure and there will be formation of heave (uplift of ground surface) on the sides of foundation as shown in Figure 1.5 (a). As a result, the structure will settle.

  If the foundation base is placed below ground level, then the additional mass of soil between ground level and foundation base level will add to the shearing resistance against the sliding action, as shown in Figure 1.5 (b) (C.W. Dunham [1.2]).

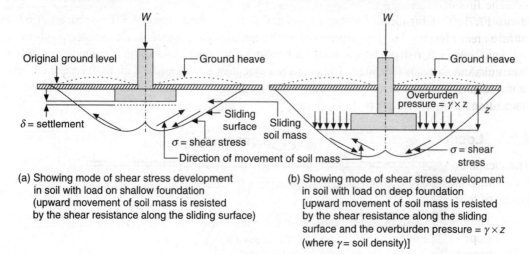

FIGURE 1.5   Development of a shear stress in soil due to foundation loading.

The resistance against sliding depends on the geotechnical properties of soil. For granular soil of high angle of internal friction, the resistance against sliding is high. So, the higher intensity of contact pressure can be applied without the failure of foundation.

In case of clayey plastic soil, the angle of internal friction of soil is quite low and we can only utilize the cohesion. So, the failure of foundation may occur with low intensity of contact pressure.

The surface area of shearing resistance depends on the shape of contact surface of foundation.

If we compare long rectangular foundation base and a square base of same base, we find that the long rectangular base creates greater frictional surface area than that of the square base. So, the resistance against shear failure is higher in rectangular-shaped base.

For example, let us consider two foundations, both subjected to a same load W, as shown in Figure 1.6.

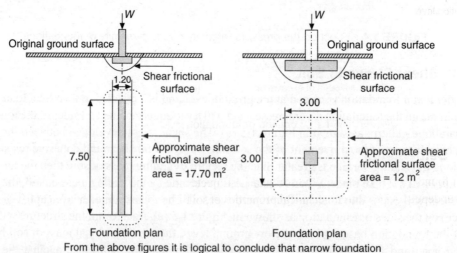

FIGURE 1.6   Comparison of shear frictional surface area of varying foundation base sizes.

The first one rectangular: base = 1.2 m × 7.5 m, base area = 9.0 m², and frictional surface area = 17.7 m²; and the other square: base = 3 m × 3 m, base area = 3 × 3 = 9 m², and frictional surface area = 12 m².

Thus, assuming that both the foundations are placed in the soil of same geotechnical properties, the results show that the rectangular base has got about 46% more frictional surface area than that of the square base, and so also has higher shear resistance against the movement of soil causing foundation failure.

1.2.4 Location of Foundation Near Excavation

The location of foundation near excavation face is important in the stability of foundation. The following points should be observed when placing a foundation near excavation area to avoid the failure of foundation:

- The shear failure of soil depends on the angle of internal friction of soil. So, the angle of slope of cut with the horizontal in the excavation should not be more than the angle of internal friction of soil, as shown in Figure 1.7 (a).
- In clay soil, the slope of cut may be made higher than its normal angle of internal friction and high cohesion value. This type of slope stands temporarily for a short period, but fails in the long term due to the loss of moisture content in soil.
- So, the foundation should be placed away from the edge of slope for a reasonable distance, at least half the height of excavation, as shown in Figure 1.7 (b).

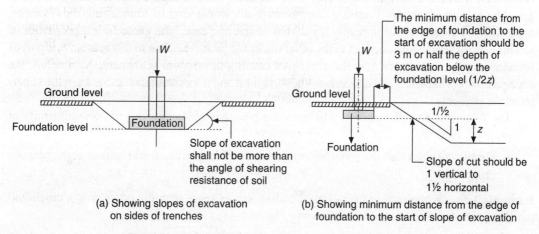

(a) Showing slopes of excavation on sides of trenches

(b) Showing minimum distance from the edge of foundation to the start of slope of excavation

FIGURE 1.7 Location of foundation near excavation.

1.2.5 Settlements

When a foundation is placed on the soil and is subjected to load, a certain amount of settlement will occur depending on the geotechnical properties of soil. The following points should be observed in deciding the types and location of foundation in view of attaining the reasonable settlement of foundation to avoid foundation failure:

- *Sandy soil of gravel, coarse and medium sand:* The settlement occurs immediately (instantaneous) in such a case but is of very low amount after the foundation is subjected to load. There is no more continuity of settlement afterwards. The subsidence is negligible to cause any structural damage.
- *Silty soil of fine sand:* In such soil, greater part of settlement takes place when the foundation is loaded. The residual settlement continues gradually over a period as the moisture content squeezes out in time. Sometimes, if the moisture gets a free flow path, the squeezing action takes place fast resulting unfavourable vertical and horizontal settlement which may cause failure of the foundation.
- *Clay soil:* In such soil, certain amount of initial settlement occurs due to compression when the soil is loaded. Most of the settlement takes place for a long period of time, but at a decreasing rate, as the consolidation process goes on with the squeezing out of water content in the clay. So, it is a very difficult task to predict the exact final settlement of foundation even by any complex method of analysis. Therefore, one should be cautious in designing the foundation in clay, particularly, the blue and London clay.

Differential settlements

When a foundation is placed on soil and is subjected to a load, the contact pressure under the base is constant with the assumption that the soil underneath the foundation base is homogeneous in geotechnical aspect and will settle uniformly over the whole area of foundation, thus creating apparently no problem. But in reality it may not be the true case. The geotechnical properties of soil may be different from one part to the other under the base area. Due to this reason, one part of foundation may settle more than the other part causing differential settlement. As a result, the superstructure will be subjected to stresses beyond limit and may create undue cracks in the super-structure elements.

The following few illustrations will show the types of settlements due to non-uniformity of soil properties and their effect on the superstructure.

- Firstly, consider that the foundation of a long building rests on soil of non-homogeneous properties.

Example 1.5: When one end of a long building settles more than the other end, a crack will develop at the top of mid length, as shown in Figure 1.8 (a).

Example 1.6: When one part of a foundation rests on soft plastic clay and the other part is placed on sandy soil, the soft clay soil settles more than the other part. As a result, an unsightly crack will develop all along the middle of the building with crack width widening at lower portion of the building, as shown in Figure 1.8 (b).

Example 1.7: When the middle part of the foundation rests on hard sandy soil and the ends of the foundation lies on soft soil, the ends settle more than the central part. As a result, a crack may open out at the centre of the building with increasing width as we go up, as shown in Figure 1.8 (c).

- Next, consider the foundation of a tall building resting on soil of non-homogeneous character. Differential settlements in foundation causes the building tilt. If the amount of differential settlement is excessive, the building becomes uninhabitable and may even collapse, as shown in Figure 1.8 (d).

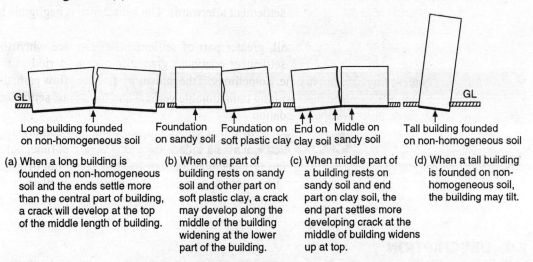

| Long building founded on non-homogeneous soil | Foundation on sandy soil | Foundation on soft plastic clay | End on clay soil | Middle on sandy soil | Tall building founded on non-homogeneous soil |

(a) When a long building is founded on non-homogeneous soil and the ends settle more than the central part of building, a crack will develop at the top of the middle length of building.

(b) When one part of building rests on sandy soil and other part on soft plastic clay, a crack may develop along the middle of the building widening at the lower part of the building.

(c) When middle part of a building rests on sandy soil and end part on clay soil, the end part settles more developing crack at the middle of building widens up at top.

(d) When a tall building is founded on non-homogeneous soil, the building may tilt.

FIGURE 1.8   Differential settlements of foundations.

Thus, after going through the above principles and practices, we find that the behaviour of foundation is closely interlinked with the geotechnical characteristics of soil, and hence, there exists a soil-structure interaction.

So, in order to get a clear conception of the behaviour of foundation and to design the foundation, we should thoroughly study the geotechnical properties of soil.

REFERENCES

[1.1]   Terzaghi, Karl and R.B. Peck, Soil Mechanics in Engineering Practice, Wiley USA, 1962.

[1.2]   Dunham, C.W., Foundation of Structures, McGraw-Hill, New York, 1950.

Chapter 2

Geotechnics

2.0 DESCRIPTION

Geotechnics is the soil engineering which primarily addresses the properties and behaviour of soil relating to foundations and underground structures, and includes the operations of soil exploration, obtaining soil samples from borehole logs, conducting field tests and finally carrying out laboratory tests. All the sequence of operations are then put in the Geotechnical Report.

The laboratory and field test results provide sufficient technical information about the geotechnical properties of soil necessary in the design of underground structures.

2.1 SITE EXPLORATION

Before we start the exploration of site, we have to establish the type of project and the types of required structures to be constructed for the said project. In heavy engineering project the superstructures and their foundations are heavy. So the site exploration needs careful considerations regarding surface and subsurface conditions of the site.

Surface exploration: The surface exploration of site consists of the following:

1. The top surface condition of soil including soft patches of very weak soil, dumping of loose household and industrial materials.
2. The groundwater table and seasonal variation of water table.
3. Any nearby river source that may create problems in excavation and foundation design.
4. Any natural springs.
5. Outcrop of rock.
6. Occurrence of floods in the region.
7. To obtain information about the site from the local authority and from the local residents.
8. To carry out field load tests at various locations of the site to obtain the bearing capacity of soil.

Subsurface exploration: The subsurface ground exploration of site comprises the following:

1. To prepare an area map locating the borehole positions. The locations should be chosen to identify the importance and type of foundation positions.
2. To carry out the operations of boring holes at the marked locations as shown on the map.
3. To collect and store borehole logs of undisturbed soil samples in the precise way with proper markings as used in geotechnical engineering.

2.2 LABORATORY TESTS

After the site exploration is complete, the borehole soil samples are taken to the soil laboratory, and various tests are carried out to obtain the soil characteristics at various soil strata. Then the results are put in a tabular form for ready reference.

Example 2.1: Table 2.1 showing various geotechnical data is prepared for the design of a underground highway tunnel in London clay.

TABLE 2.1 Showing geotechnical design data

Soil type	Depth below GL(m)	γ_b kN/m³	C_u kN/m²	C' kN/m²	ϕ' degree	K_0	K_a	K_{ac}	K_p	K_{pc}	K_s kN/m²	N
Made ground	0.0	18	20	0	25	0.6	0.36	0	3.2	0	5000	4
Alluvium	4.0	18	20	0	25	0.6	0.36	0	3.2	0	7500	4
Gravel river terrace deposits	7.0	20	0	0	35	0.5	0.27	0	3.7	0	7100	25
London clay	9.0	19	55 to 210	20	20	1.0	0.44	1.33	2.7	3.3	50000	4
Woolwich and Reading beds	20.0	20	150	0	29	0.5	0.35	0	2.9	0	7100	10

where

γ_b = bulk density of soil (in kN/m³)

C_u = undisturbed undrained shear strength (cohesion) (in kN/m²)

Referring to Figure 2.1, the lower bound line, and also mean bound lines are plotted from the laboratory test results of a number of soil samples of 102 mm and 38 mm diameter for London clay.

By using the correlation suggested by 'Stroud and Butler [2.2a], $C_u = 4.5 \times N$, the values of undrained shear strength may be obtained. These values agree well with the mean strength of 102 mm diameter specimens tested from the site. N are the values of standard penetration tests. The lower bound line of 102 mm diameter samples, the line of expressing $C_u = 4.5 \times N$, and also mean boundary line are shown in Figure 2.1. The minimum value of C_u is taken to be 75 kN/m² at top of clay stratum which is 9.0 m (average) from ground level.

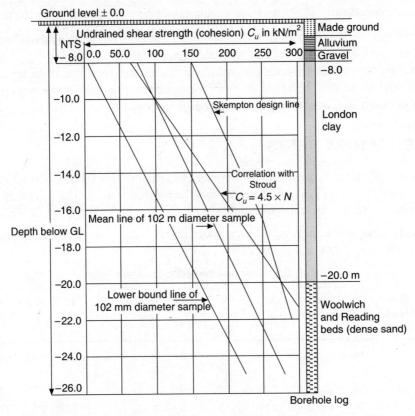

FIGURE 2.1 Graph showing undisturbed shear strength versus depth.

The value of C_u increases as the depth increases as set in the following expression:

$$C'_u = C_u + 12 \times z$$

where

z = depth from clay layer

C'_u = increased value of C_u at a depth z

Example 2.2: At a depth 20 m from the ground level

$$C'_u = 75 + 12(20 - 9) = 207 \text{ kN/m}^2$$

C'_u = Effective cohesion intercept in kN/m²

ϕ' = Effective angle of shearing resistance in degrees

δ = Angle of wall friction between soil and retaining wall surface in degrees.

Maximum effective wall friction may be taken as:

In active zone, $\delta = 2/3 \times \phi'$

In passive zone, $\delta = 1/2 \times \phi'$

K_0 = Coefficient of horizontal earth pressure at rest = $1 - \sin \phi'$

K_0 represents the stress state of the ground under conditions of zero horizontal strain, and it is defined as the ratio of horizontal to vertical effective stress in the soil at rest. In normally-consolidated clays the values K_0 varies between 0.5 and 0.6, but overconsolidated clays have higher values of K_0 which may sometimes exceed unity.

For sandy soil, K_0 varies between 0.4 and 0.6.

Example 2.3: Consider horizontal earth pressure at rest at a depth $z = 5$ m and the weight of soil is $\gamma = 20$ kN/m³ and $K_0 = 0.5$.

Then, horizontal earth at rest at 5 m depth $= p = K_0 \times \gamma \times z = 0.5 \times 20 \times 5 = 50$ kN/m²

K_a = Rankine active horizontal pressure coefficient

$$\frac{1 - \sin \phi'}{1 + \sin \phi'}$$

Example 2.4: If $\phi' = 35°$ for gravelly soil, then

$$K_a = \frac{(1 - \sin 35)}{(1 + \sin 35)} = 0.27$$

if the wall friction is considered with $\delta = 2/3 \times \phi' = 23.3$ in active zone, then referring to Figure 39 (prepared by 'Caquot and Kerisel, CIRIA Report 104' Design of retaining walls embedded in stiff clays [2.15]).

$$K_a = 0.23$$

K_{ac} = Active pressure coefficient for cohesion $= 2 \times (K_a)^{0.5}$

Example 2.5: If $\phi' = 20$ degrees for London clay, then

$$K_a = \frac{(1 - \sin 20)}{(1 + \sin 20)} = 0.49$$

Therefore,

$$K_{ac} = 2 \times (0.49)^{0.5} = 1.4$$

If the wall friction is considered with $\delta = 2/3 \times \phi' = 13.3$ in active zone, then referring to Figure 39 (Caquot and Kerisel) $K_a = 0.44$

Therefore, $\quad K_{ac} = 2 \times 0.44^{0.5} = 1.33$

K_p = Rankine passive pressure coefficient

$$\frac{1 + \sin \phi'}{1 - \sin \phi'}$$

Example 2.6: If $\phi' = 35$ degrees for gravelly soil, then

$$K_p = \frac{(1 + \sin 35)}{(1 - \sin 35)} = 3.7$$

If the wall friction is taken into account with $\delta = 1/2 \times \phi' = 17.5°$

then, referring to Figure 40 (Caquot and Kerisel) $K_p = 6.0$
(Design of retaining walls embedded in clays)
K_{pc} = Passive pressure coefficient for cohesion = $2 \times K_p^{0.5}$

Example 2.7: If $\phi' = 20$ degrees for London clay, then $K_{pc} = 2 \times 3^{0.5} = 3.46$
If the wall friction is considered with $\delta = 1/2 \times \phi' = 10°$ in passive zone,
then, referring to Figure 40 (Caquot and Kerisel) $K_p = 2.7$
Therefore,

$$K_{pc} = 2 \times K_p^{0.5} = 2 \times 2.7^{0.5} = 3.3$$

K_s = Modulus of subgrade reaction is defined as the resistance of the soil per unit area to unit displacement under load and is measured in kg/cm^2/cm or kN/m^2/m deformation.

The relationship between modulus of subgrade reaction (K_s) and undrained shear strength of stiff overconsolidated clay is given in Table 2.2.

TABLE 2.2 Showing the relationship between C_u and K_s

Consistency	Stiff clay	Stiff to very stiff clay	Hard clay
Undrained shear strength (C_u) in kN/m^2	50–100	100–200	> 200
Range of K_s in kN/m^2	15000–30000	30000–60000	> 60000

In our case, the London clay is considered as overconsolidated stiff to very stiff character. So, we have assumed the value of K_s for London clay = 50000 kN/m^2/m.

For other types of soil, say, gravel river terrace deposits, Woolwich and Reading beds, the value of K_s increases as the depth increases.

For practical design purposes, the following values of K_s may be assumed:

For silty soil: K_s = 4000 kN/m^2/m
For gravelly soil: K_s = 61000 kN/m^2/m

N is defined as the number of blows/300 mm penetration in standard penetration test (SPT). The value of N varies with the effective angle of shearing resistance of soil in degrees. Figure 2.2(a) shows the relationship SPT(N) versus depth for London clay from the samples taken at site. The line, shown in Figure 2.2(a), is the mean line of SPT values for London clay.

Figure 2.2(b), prepared by Peck, Hanson, Thornburn [2.1] shows the relationship between the angle of internal friction ϕ' of soil and the value of N in standard penetration tests.

Table 2.3 shows the relationship between relative density and standard penetration number in non-cohesive soil and clayey soil.

TABLE 2.3 Showing value of N and corresponding density for non-cohesive soil and clayey soil

Non-cohesive sandy soil		Clayey soil	
Number of blows	Relative density	Number of blows	Consistency
0–4	Very loose	0–4	Very soft–soft
4–10	Loose	4–8	Medium
10–30	Medium	8–15	Stiff
30–50	Dense	15–30	Very stiff
Over 50	Very dense	Over 30	Hard

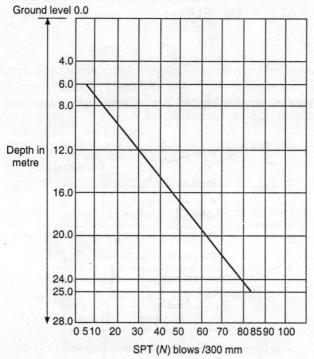

FIGURE 2.2(a) SPT (*N*) blows/300 mm versus depth for London clay.

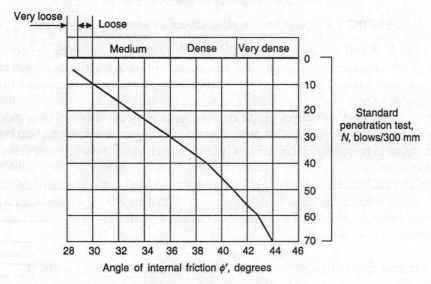

FIGURE 2.2(b) Relationship between angle of internal friction ϕ' and the value of *N* in SPT. Graph showing N/ϕ' (based on Peck, Hanson, Thornburn).

2.3 BEARING CAPACITY OF SOIL

2.3.1 Definition

Consider a foundation base of either continuous long rectangular shape or square or circular shape is placed on the surface of soil at ground level, and subjected to a load. Due to the application of loading the soil settles. There is a relationship between the settlement and the load per unit area of loading surface, as shown in Figure 2.3.

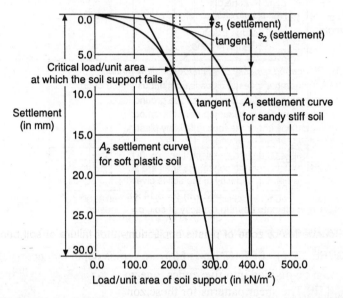

FIGURE 2.3 Graph showing load versus settlement of foundation.

If the soil is of stiff dense sandy type, the settlement curve is shown by the curve A_1. The critical load is the load per unit of length of a continuous footing of the load on a spread footing at which the soil suport fails. The abscissa s_1 of the vertical tangent to the curve may be defined as the bearing capacity of soil.

In the case of soil of soft clayey plastic type, the settlement curve is of similar shape but the bearing capacity is not well defined, as shown by the curve A_2. In this case, the bearing capacity may be assumed to be equal to the abscissa s_2 of the point at which the settlement curve becomes steep and straight.

The foundation base is not generally placed at the ground level, but at a certain depth, depending on the design criteria. The distance from the ground level to the base of the foundation is termed as depth of foundation z. The base of the foundation that has a width B equal or greater than the depth z is considered as shallow footing.

2.3.2 Plastic Equilibrium beneath Shallow Continuous Footing

Mathematical investigations concerning the state of plastic equilibrium beneath the continuous footing have led to the following general conclusions;

If the base of the footing is perfectly smooth, the loaded soil fails by plastic flow within the region located by the composite curve *abcde* as shown in Figure 2.4.

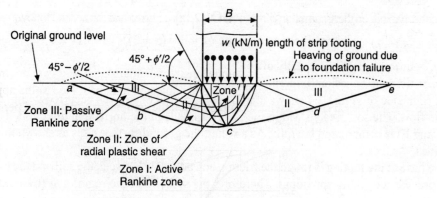

FIGURE 2.4 Boundaries of zone of plastic equilibrium after failure of soil beneath the continuous footing.

This region can be divided into five zones, one zone marked by I and the two pairs of zones marked by II and III. The shear patterns for these zones are shown on the left side of the figure. Zone I represents an active Rankine zone, and the zones III are passive Rankine zones, because the shear patterns within these zones are identical with those for the active and passive Rankine conditions.

The boundaries of the active Rankine zone rise at an angle of $45° + \phi'/2$ and those of the passive Rankine zone at $45° - \phi'/2$ with the horizontal. The zone II located between I and III are defined as zone of radial shear, because the lines that constitute one set in the shear pattern in these zones radiate from the outer edge of the base of the footing. These lines are fairly straight. The lines of the other set represent logarithmic spirals with their centres located at the outer edge of the base of the footing.

If the weight of the soil located within the zone of plastic equilibrium is neglected ($\gamma = 0$), the radial lines are perfectly straight, and the concentric lines are true logarithmic spirals, as shown in Figure 2.4.

Finally, if the unit weight of soil is taken into consideration ($\gamma > 0$), but $\phi' = 0$, the radial lines are arc of circles.

For the stability of foundation on saturated clay, immediately after completion of construction, it is a common practice to assume the undrained condition, that is, $\phi' = 0$.

For cohesive soil, on the assumption $\phi' = 0$, Prandtl [2.1a] analyzed and formed the following equation:

$$q_u = \text{Ultimate bearing capacity of soil} = (\pi + 2) \times c = 5.14 \times c \qquad (2.1)$$

where q_u = ultimate bearing capacity of soil

c = ultimate cohesion (undrained shear strength).

The right side of Figure 2.4 shows that the deformation of soil has occurred within the zones of plastic flow. The soil located within the zone I spreads in the horizontal direction. The soil in zones II and III is compressed laterally. As a result, the ground surface rises as shown through the dotted lines.

If the base of the footing is rough the friction and adhesion between the soil and the base of the footing prevent the lateral spreading. Therefore, the soil within the region *cfg* (triangular shape beneath the base) remains in an elastic state, and the ultimate bearing capacity is given by (K. Terzaghi and R.B. Peck [2.2]) the following equation:

$$q_u = 5.7 \times c \qquad (2.2)$$

Working on the similar approach, Hencky analyzed the problem of a uniformly loaded circular area on the surface and found that

$$q_u = 5.64 \times c \qquad (2.3)$$

Both the above derivatives were made for the loading at the ground surface. They are not applicable when the footing has been placed at a depth below the ground surface and applied a load. K. Terzaghi and R.B. Peck [2.2] investigated the problem using somewhat similar assumptions as to the mechanism of failure, and allowing for the friction and cohesion between the base of the footing and soil, arrived at the following expression for the bearing capacity of soil under a shallow strip footing which will cause the general shear failure:

$$q_u = c \times N_c + \gamma \times z \times N_q + 0.5 \times \gamma \times B \times N_y \qquad (2.4)$$

where N_c, N_q, and N_y are the bearing capacity factors and their values depend on the angle of shearing resistance of soil. These factors are indicated by the curves shown in Figure 2.5 prepared by Terzaghi [2.2].

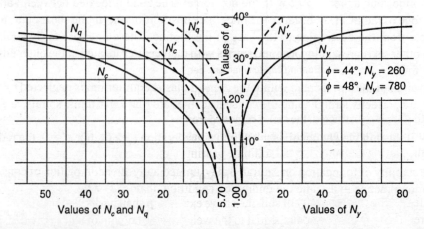

FIGURE 2.5 Terzaghi's bearing capacity factors. Charts showing relation between ϕ and the bearing capacity factors.

and

B = width of the base; z = depth of base of footing below ground level.

q_u = ultimate bearing capacity of soil; γ = density of soil.

When $\phi' = 0$, from Figure 2.5

$$N_c = 5.7,\ N_q = 1.0,\ N_y = 0$$

Therefore,

$$q_u = 5.7 \times c + \gamma \times z \tag{2.5}$$

The coefficient N_c is increased from 5.14 in Eq. (2.1) to 5.7 because the friction between underside of the footing and soil has been taken into account.

Meyerhop, G.G. [2.3] developed and expanded Terzaghi's method. Figure 2.6 shows the comparison between Terzaghi and Meyerhop. When the soil is purely cohesive clay and $\phi' = 0$, the two sets of values agree.

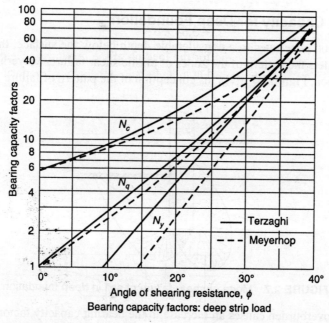

Bearing capacity factors: deep strip load

FIGURE 2.6 Comparison between Terzaghi and Meyerhop.

Before the footing is constructed, the soil is removed from the foundation. This soil has originally applied a pressure equal to the weight at the level of the base of the footing. If this soil is deducted from the ultimate bearing capacity, the net ultimate bearing capacity is given by

$$q_u = c \times N_c + \gamma \times z\,(N_q - 1) + 0.5 \times \gamma \times B \times N_y \tag{2.6}$$

To obtain the safe bearing (net) capacity of soil, the above expression shall be divided by a factor (F). A further soil pressure may then be added, equal to the weight of the column of soil excavated, and the total safe bearing capacity may be expressed as

$$q = \frac{c \times N_c + \gamma \times z \times (N_q + 1) + 0.5 \times \gamma \times B \times N_y}{F} + \gamma \times z \qquad (2.7)$$

2.3.3 Bearing Capacity of Circular and Square Footings

For computing the bearing capacity of spread footing with circular or square bases, no approximate theory is available. Based on experiments, the following semi-empirical equations have been derived:
For circular bases with radius r and resting on a fairly dense or soft soil

$$q_u = 1.3 \times c \times N_c + \gamma \times z \times N_q + 0.6 \times r \times \gamma \times N_y \qquad (2.8)$$

For square bases of sides $B \times B$ on dense or stiff soil

$$\dot{q}_u = 1.3 \times c \times N_c + \gamma \times z \times N_q + 0.4 \times \gamma \times B \times N_y \qquad (2.9)$$

If $c > 0$; $\phi' = 0$; $z = 0$, following the value of N from graph of Figure 2.5, $q_u = 7.4 \times c$, which is greater than $q_u = 5.7 \times c$ as shown in Eq. (2.2).

2.3.4 Bearing Capacity for Deep Foundation

When the foundation penetrates to a considerable depth below the surface, the weight of over-burden around it alters the pattern of the zones of plastic shear failure. Meyerhop [2.3] again has studied this condition. Figure 2.7 gives his conception of the pattern of failure.

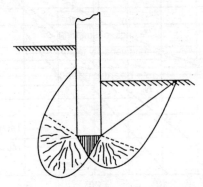

FIGURE 2.7 Mode of shear failure of soil in deep foundation.

The effect of overburden causes an increase in the bearing capacity factors and so in the net ultimate bearing capacity.

Figure 2.8 shows Meyerhop's estimate of the bearing capacity factors for ultimate bearing capacity for a deep strip foundation. The value of the pressure exerted by the soil may again be added to the figure obtained in order to determine the ultimate bearing capacity.

Skempton, A.A. [2.4] gives a comprehensive review of the various theories of bearing capacity together with experimental data from both laboratory and full-scale observations. He forms the general conclusion that, for cohesive soil, the factor N_c increases with the depth of the footing upto a maximum of about 7.5 for depth exceeding 2.5 times the width of the footing. His suggested curves are plotted on Figure 2.9.

It should be noted that the curve for strip footing starts at Prandtl's value of $5.14 \times c$ for surface loading.

Skempton, A.A. [2.4] suggested that the value of N_c for a rectangular footing of length L and width B may be found by linear interpolations, as given by the following expression:

$$N_c \text{ (for rectangle)} = \left(0.84 + 0.16 \times \frac{B}{L} \right) \times N_c \text{ (for square)}$$

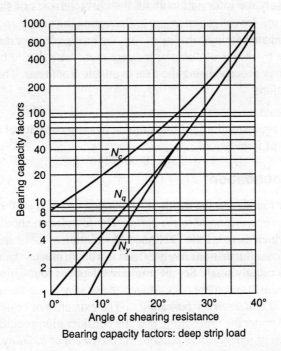

FIGURE 2.8 Meyerhop's bearing capacity factors in deep strip footing.

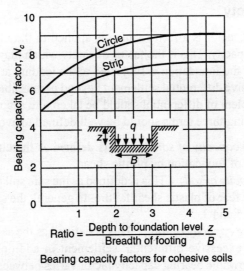

FIGURE 2.9 Skempton's bearing capacity factors in cohesive soils in deep foundation.

2.3.5   Stability of Foundations

The failure of foundation may take place either due to the collapse by general shear or by local shear failure. Also high differential settlement may result unacceptable condition, though the actual failure of foundation due to shear failure does not occur.

So, to know precisely the information about the characteristics of shear failure of soil is to carry out geotechnical soil investigation at site to determine the nature and properties of soil.

To estimate the ultimate bearing capacity of soil, the loading tests or measurement of cohesion and shearing resistance by means of direct or indirect shear tests should be carried out. Now, the design of foundation may proceed using the data available from tests. The following points may need careful considerations:

- The depth of foundation
- The load factor against failure for the ultimate bearing capacity of soil
- Area and shape of foundation.

2.3.6   Depth of Foundation

In clay soil for shallow foundation the depth of foundation depends on the following points:

1. *Variation of moisture content in the soil:*   The foundation should be carried down to a depth below which there is little likelihood of variation of moisture content. In the regions where the seasonal fluctuations rarely extend to a depth greater than 2.0 m and the variation below 1.0 m is usually small. So, the minimum depth of foundation should be 1.0 m. The variations of moisture content occur due to the nearby living trees and excavations.

2. *The existence of boilers in the basement:*   The existence of boilers in the basement may dry out the soil under the foundation, and due consideration should be given to this aspect.

3. *The installation of refrigeration plant in the basement of building:*   The soil may freeze out artificially affecting the bearing capacity of soil.

2.3.7   Factor of Safety

A factor of safety or load factor is a factor which is applied to the ultimate bearing capacity to arrive at a safe bearing capacity. This is the factor of safety which may be considered against the plastic shear failure when the foundation is subjected to the loading at the depth. The foundation may also fail due to excessive differential settlement beyond permissible value. So, when deciding a factor of safety, the problem of differential should be taken into account.

Therefore, the following three terms should be well defined to avoid any confusion:

1. *Ultimate bearing capacity of soil:*   This is defined as the ultimate soil pressure which brings the failure of foundation by plastic shear.

2. *Safe bearing capacity of soil:*   This is defined as the safe soil pressure which the soil can carry without any fear of plastic shear failure. In general, the safe bearing capacity factor varies between 2.5 and 3.

3. *Allowable bearing capacity of soil:*   This is defined as the safe soil pressure taking into consideration of excessive differential settlement in addition to plastic shear failure. Generally, the allowable bearing capacity factor varies between 3 and 3.5 when the soil is highly compressible to endanger the stability of structure.

Table 2.4 shows some approximate allowable bearing capacity of soil.

TABLE 2.4 Some approximate allowable bearing capacity of soil

Soil type	Allowable bearing capacity (in kN/m²)	
	Depth 1 m	Depth 2 m
Soft silt and mud	11–22	22–55
Slit wet but confined	110–220	165–220
Soft clay	110–165	110–165
Dense firm clay	220–275	275–330
Clay and sand mixed	220–330	275–385
Fine sand wet but confined	220	220–330
Coarse sand	330	330–440
Gravel and coarse sand	440–550	550–660
Cemented gravel and coarse sand	550–660	660–880
Poor rock	770–1100	770–1100
Sound bedrock	2200–4400	2200–4400

2.4 SETTLEMENT

The term settlement is defined as the vertical displacement of the base of a structure, or of the surface of a road or embankment due to the compression and deformation of the underlying soil. When the weight of every structure compresses and deforms the underlying soil, the settlement is irrelevant because the stresses in the framework of structure are not altered. On the other hand, if the weight of structure causes differential settlements, the entire structural framework is subjected to unacceptable increase in stresses distorting the framing system, eventually, resulting the collapse of the structure.

Because of the complexity of the geotechnical properties of soil and the disturbing influence of stratification, the settlement of buildings can be accurately predicted only under exceptional conditions. Nevertheless a theoretical analysis of settlement phenomena is indispensable because the results permit the engineer at least to recognize the factors that determine the magnitude and distribution of the settlement. Knowledge of these factors constitutes the prerequisite for converting construction experience into semi-empirical rules for the design of foundations.

2.4.1 Causes for Settlement

The settlement may be caused due to the following facts:

1. Static loads such as those imposed by the weight of a structure or an embankment.
2. Moving loads such as heavy traffic vehicles are transmitted through a road or airfield pavement.
3. Changes in moisture content, which may arise from natural causes such as seasonal fluctuation in water table or the abstraction of water by roots of large trees. Nearby excavation, pile driving, pumping or drainage may also have an important effect in the settlement of foundation.
4. Undermining due to mining operations, tunnelling or underground erosion.

2.4.2   General Principles when Studying the Problems of Settlement of Foundations

1. Granular soils like gravel, coarse sand, and medium sand generally attain their maximum settlement under load as soon as the load is applied, and they retain that settlement. They do not cause the subsidence to continue to increase over a long period of time. Furthermore, the settlement is usually slight and unimportant.

2. Slit and fine sandy soil attain a large part of their compaction when the load is applied, but the subsidence may increase somewhat over a long period of time because of a decrease of the water content. If the soil is free to move laterally, saturation may expedite its movement under the action of pressure so that a serious settlement may eventuate in quick sand condition. The resultant settlement may be disastrous.

3. Clay soils attain a part of their compaction as the load is applied, but being plastic, they generally continue to consolidate slowly and at a decreasing rate for a long period of time. Most of this is due to slow squeezing out of the water.

4. Muck and mud are so dangerous for supporting loads that a prediction of the settlement of a foundation placed on them is largely a guesswork.

5. Temporary loads such as wind, live loads, and traction generally act so briefly that their effect upon the cumulative settlements is negligible. In this sense, a week is a brief time. However, a large warehouse for 'permanent' storage is an exception for which it may be desirable to assume a long-term live load of 50% of design live load when settlement is estimated.

6. It is generally the differential settlement rather than the absolute magnitude of a settlement that causes trouble with a structure.

7. Frost action may cause local heaving, subsequent softening of soil, and localized settlement. Therefore, the bottom of foundations should be placed below the probable frost line.

    *   The depth of foundation in cold region should not be less than 2.0 m.
    *   In warmer regions the depth of foundations should not be less than 1.0 m.
    *   Because of the desirability of proper embedment and the removal of top soil, no important foundation depth should be less than approximately 1.0 m to 1.5 m below the ground surface, even in warm climate.

8. A compressible stratum below a much firmer one may still constitute a hazard and cause serious long-term settlement. An estimate of probable settlement should take into account of soil strata that are within some reasonable distance of the bottom of the substructure. The suggestions in Table 2.5 may be helpful in determining the depth below which the settlement caused by the weight of the structure may be assumed to be unimportant.

In Table 2.5, p denotes the average unit pressure caused by the structure, assuming a 2:1 distribution. The higher unit pressures for thin strata of 3.0 m or less when trapped between firm impervious strata, are suggested because the water in the plastic layer cannot escape easily when the pressure is applied. On the other hand, a porous soil will not greatly retard the movement of the water that is squeezed out of the neighbouring stratum.

TABLE 2.5 Showing minimum average unit pressure to consider when estimating probable settlement

Type of soil	Average minimum applied pressure by the structure p (in kN/m²)
Deep soft clay	15.0
Thin stratum of soft clay between firm impervious strata	25.0
Deep stiff clay	25.0
Thin stratum of stiff clay between firm impervious strata	35.0
Deep slit and very fine sand	25.0

2.4.3 Types of Settlement

The settlement caused by the compressive loading of foundation base on the supporting soil may be divided into two kinds described as follows:

1. *Immediate settlement:*   The immediate settlement is a combination of elastic compression and plastic deformation, without change in volume or water content, as shown in Figure 2.10. This type of settlement develops as the construction proceeds.

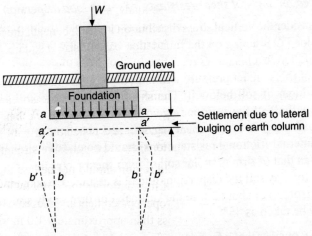

FIGURE 2.10 Immediate settlement showing shape of lateral bulging of earth column.

2. *Settlement due to consolidation:* This is the result of the decrease in the volume of loaded soil caused by the gradual expulsion of water from the voids. In clay soils such settlement develops very slowly, but may attain considerable magnitude in course of settlement. Settlement is seldom uniform over the area occupied by the foundation of a large building, because of non-uniformity of pressure distribution in the soil as well as variations in the compressibility at different parts of the area occupied by the foundations. Consolidation sometimes takes place in a compressible stratum situated at a considerable depth, although the soil immediately below the foundation is relatively firm and may result in settlement of the foundation. In cohesionless soil consolidation or compaction takes place relatively quickly, and cannot be easily separated from the 'immediate' settlement as defined before.

2.4.4 Methods of Predicting Settlement

1. *For immediate settlement of structures:* The elastic theory may be used. Loading tests to provide useful information regarding immediate settlement.
2. *For long-term consolidation settlement:* On clay soils the most reliable method is that based on compressive tests on undisturbed samples and application of the theory of consolidation.

2.4.5 Pressure Distribution beneath Foundations

Before we calculate the settlement of foundation, we should study the mode of pressure distribution in soil beneath the foundation. The mode of contact pressure distribution beneath the foundation base is dependent on the rigidity of foundation base and the type of soil, as shown in Figure 1.1. For a rigid foundation base placed on soft clay, the contact pressure distribution varies with maximum intensity at edges and reducing the intensity at mid and on sandy soil, maximum pressure being at mid and reducing to almost zero at edges.

2.4.6 Vertical Stress Distribution in Depth beneath the Foundation Base

Method 1: *Based on angle of shear resistance of soil in load dispersion in settlement estimation:*

We shall consider the vertical stress distribution in depth beneath the foundation base. Consider a concentrated load Q is acting on the foundation base of size a square. The contact pressure just below the foundation level is $q = Q/a^2$.

The effect of this contact pressure will not only confine itself within the soil underneath the base and the column of soil below it. The shear stresses in the soil around the surface of this column of soil will affect the surrounding soil and will spread the load around it. The angle of dispersion of load depends on the shear strength and cohesion of soil. For weak clay soils with small angle of internal frictional resistance (α) and low cohesive strength, the dispersion of load will be lower than that of firm granular soil of high shear strength.

In practice, for clay soil the dispersion of load is assumed to take place at a slope of 2:1 (i.e. 2 vertical to 1 horizontal) or about 26° to the vertical. For firm sandy soil, the angle of dispersion to the vertical may be taken as 45°.

Example 2.8: Consider that a foundation base is placed on soil of medium to stiff fine sand at a depth 2 m below ground level.

The angle of shear resistance of soil = ϕ = 30; and the depth of stratum = 0.8 m
The foundation is loaded with a concentrated load Q = 900 kN
The size of base = 3 m^2
To calculate the vertical stress distribution at 8 m depth
The contact pressure at foundation level = q = 900/9 = 100 kN/m^2
The depth of stratum below foundation level = 8 – 2 = 6 m
The width of dispersion at 6 m below foundation level = 3 + 6 × tan 30° × 2 = 9.92 m (say 10 m)
Therefore, vertical stress distribution at 6 m beneath the foundation base = σ_z = 900/(10 × 10)
= 9 kN/m^2

This method of approach is also illustrated in Figure 1.2 (in previous chapter).

For rough estimation of settlement of foundation, this method of load dispersion is adequate.

Method 2: *Based on Boussinesq's equation:*

Consider that a concentrated vertical load Q is applied.

Then, the vertical stress (σ_z) at a depth z below the base and any point N is given by Boussinesq's equation:

$$\sigma_z = \frac{3Q}{2\pi \times z^2} \times \left[\frac{1}{1+\left(\frac{r}{z}\right)^2}\right]^{1/2} \tag{2.10}$$

where,

Q = concentrated vertical load at the foundation base

z = vertical distance between N and the underside of base

r = horizontal distance from line of action of load to N

Boussinesq's equation is based on the assumption that the soil is elastic, homogeneous and isotropic. The above characteristics in natural soil are not true. But for practical purposes we may assume that the stress distribution is justified. The stress distribution is bell-shaped, as shown in Figure 2.11.

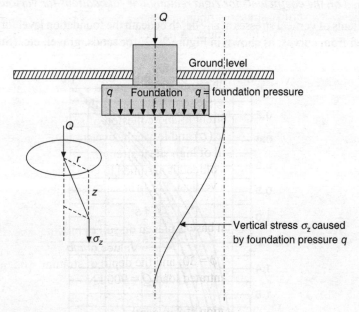

FIGURE 2.11 Vertical stress distribution in soil beneath the loaded area calculated by Boussinesq's equation.

Table 2.6 shows the value of influence factors for circular foundation in determining the vertical stresses for various ratios of diameter and the depth of soil as calculated by L. Jurgenson [2.5].

TABLE 2.6   Showing influence factors for various ratios of diameter (D) to vertical depth (z)

D/z	Influence factors	D/z	Influence factors	D/z	Influence factors
0.00	0.00	2.0	0.6465	4.0	0.9106
0.2	0.0148	2.2	0.6956	6.0	0.9684
0.4	0.0571	2.4	0.7376	8.0	0.9857
0.6	0.1213	2.6	0.7733	10.0	0.9925
0.8	0.1966	2.8	0.8036	12.0	0.9956
1.0	0.2845	3.0	0.8293	14.0	0.9972
1.2	0.3695	3.2	0.8511	16.0	0.9981
1.4	0.4502	3.4	0.8697	20.0	0.9990
1.6	0.5239	3.6	0.8855	40.0	0.9999
1.8	0.5893	3.8	0.8990	200.0	1.0

Note: σ_z = Influence factor × contact pressure q

Example 2.9:   Diameter $D = 3$ m; depth beneath foundation, $z = 6$ m; $Q = 900$ kN; $q = 900/\pi r^2 = 127$ kN/m^2; $D/z = 3/6 = 0.5$ (from Table 2.6). Influence factor = 0.0892 (average). $\sigma_z = 0.0892 \times 127 = 11.4$ kN/m^2.

Method 3: *Based on the coefficients for rigid rectangular foundations for various depths:*

The coefficients of vertical stresses at any depth beneath the foundation level for rigid foundation may be obtained from curves, as shown in Figure 2.12, for sands, gravel, etc. (Sutherland [2.6]).

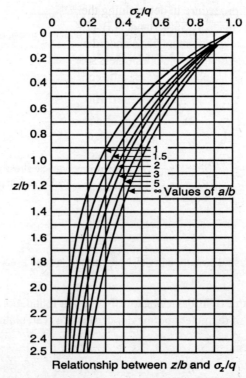

Relationship between z/b and σ_z/q

FIGURE 2.12   Vertical stresses beneath foundation.

Example 2.10: Let us consider a foundation of square base subjected to same contact pressure, as shown in previous example.

The foundation base $= b \times b = 3 \text{ m} \times 3 \text{ m}$
Foundation load $= Q = 900 \text{ kN}$
Contact pressure $= q = 900/9 = 100 \text{ kN/m}^2$

To calculate vertical stress σ_z at 6 m depth beneath foundation, refer to Figure 2.12.
Referring to Figure 2.12, $z/b = 6/3 = 2$
Following the curve

$$\frac{a}{b} = \frac{b}{b} = 1$$

$$\sigma_z/q = 0.09$$

Therefore,

$$\sigma_z = 0.09 \times 100 = 9 \text{ kN/m}^2, \quad \text{same as found in method 1.}$$

Method 4: Newmark's method in vertical stress calculations for rectangular flexible foundations (thin plates such as flexible rafts, water or oil tank foundations, etc.). This method is applied to flexible foundations.

2.4.7 Estimation of Settlements of Foundations of Cohesionless Soils

The settlements on cohesionless soils such as sands, gravels, and granular-fill materials take place almost immediately as the foundation loading is applied. As it is difficult to obtain field test samples, there is no laboratory test procedure in determining their consolidation characteristics.

From the observations made by Sutherland, H.B. [2.6], it was concluded that there is no reliable method of correlating the field settlement of a standard plate to the settlement of actual foundation at the same location. So, the settlements of cohesionless soils are estimated by semi-empirical methods based on the results of standard penetration or static cone penetration tests described as follows:

Estimation of settlements from standard penetration tests

Menzenbach, E. [2.7] arrived at the conclusion of a relationship between the results of standard penetration tests to the deformation modulus of the soil. This relationship is shown in Figure 2.13.

This relationship is shown for different values of the effective overburden pressure (p_0) at the level of test. The values of deformation modulus are then used to calculate the immediate settlement. The Poisson's ratio (m) should be taken as 0.15 for coarse-grained soils and 0.25 for fine-grained soils.

The calculations of net immediate settlement Δl (elastic settlement) beneath the corner of a flexible loaded area is calculated from the following equation:

$$\Delta l = q_n \times B \times (I - m^2)/(E_d \times I_p) \tag{2.11}$$

where

$B =$ width of foundation
$E_d =$ deformation modulus
$m =$ Poisson's ratio
$q_n =$ net foundation pressure
$I_p =$ influence factor.

Value of E_d to be taken from Figure 2.13.

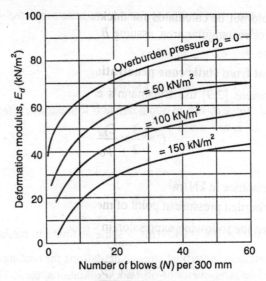

FIGURE 2.13 Curves showing the relationship between deformation modulus and standard penetration resistance (prepared by Menzenbach).

Value of I_p: I_p is a function of the length-to-breadth ratio of the foundation and the thickness (H) of the compressible layer. Terzaghi has given a method of calculating I_p from curves derived by Steinbrenner W. [2.8].

For Poisson's ratio of 0.5, $\qquad I_p = F_1$

For Poisson's ratio of zero, $\qquad I_p = F_1 + F_2$

The values of F_1 and F_2 for various ratios of H/B and L/B as given in Figure 2.14.

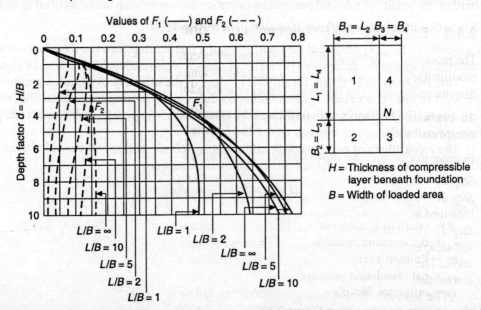

FIGURE 2.14 Curves showing the values of F_1 and F_2 corresponding to ratios of H/B and L/B.

Elastic settlements should not be calculated for thickness (H) greater than $4B$. To calculate the settlement at the centre of rectangular area, assume B = half the foundation width to obtain H/B and L/B.

Estimation of settlement from static cone penetration tests

De Beer, E. and A. Martens [2.9] use Buismann's empirical formula as follows: Constant of compressibility

$$C = \frac{3}{2} \times \frac{C_{kd}}{p_0}$$

where

C_{kd} = static cone resistance in kN/m^2

p_o = effective overburden pressure at point of measurement in kN/m^2

Then, Terzaghi has given the following expression in calculating the settlement:

$$\Delta i = \frac{H}{\dfrac{C \times \log e\,(p_o + \sigma_z)}{p_0}} \tag{2.12}$$

where

Δi = final settlement in m in layer of soil of thickness H in metre.

p_0 = mean initial effective overburden pressure of layer before applying foundation loading in kN/m^2.

σ_z = vertical stress in kN/m^2 induced at centre of layer by the net foundation pressure (q_n).

Where the cone resistance is uniform for a considerable depth within the stressed zone, it may be necessary to subdivide the layer, because the values of σ_z decrease rapidly with increasing depth below foundation level.

2.4.8 Estimation of Settlements on Cohesive Soils

The procedure of estimating the consolidation settlements is based on Skempton and Bjerrum's [2.11] modification of Terzaghi's theory of consolidation. It is assumed that consolidation is a one-dimensional strain. The following procedures are adopted in the analysis of settlement:

To evaluate the values of coefficient of consolidation (C_v) and coefficient of volume of compressibility (m_v) of clay soil under the foundation level

In order to compute the above values, the following steps are taken:

Step 1: Divide the whole clay stratum into several equal layers.

Step 2: Carry out soil investigations at site. Take undisturbed borehole logs (samples) at various locations as selected on site plan.

Step 3: In the laboratory, consolidation tests were carried out by means of apparatus oedometer in soil samples to calculate the magnitude and rate of consolidation of the clay soil below the foundation level. The tests were one-dimensional consolidation test. From the results the *coefficient of consolidation (C_v)* was calculated.

The load-settlement data obtained from full cycle of loading and unloading are used to draw a pressure-voids ratio curve from which the *coefficient of volume of compressibility (m_v)*

was derived. This is used to compute the magnitude of consolidation settlement under any given loading.

Assessment of loading causing settlement

When considering long-term consolidation settlement, it is essential that the foundation loading used in the analysis should be realistic and representative of the sustained loading over the time period under consideration.

The live loading used in a settlement analysis is an average value representing the continuous live load over the time period considered. The wind load is only considered in settlement analyses for high structures where it represents a considerable proportion of the total loads, and then only the wind loads representing the average of continuous winds over the full period are allowed for. The calculation of consolidation settlement is based on the increases in effective vertical stress induced by the loads from the structure.

Before we calculate the effective vertical stress, the following points should be explained:

Total overburden pressure (p): Total overburden pressure (p) is defined as the intensity of total pressure due to the weights of both soil and soil water on any horizontal plane, at and below foundation level, before the construction of structure starts.

If

the depth of foundation from ground level $= z$
water table from foundation level $= h$
density of dry soil $= \gamma$
submersed density of soil $= \gamma_{sat}$

then,

total overburden pressure at $(z - h)$ m depth $= p_1 = \gamma (z - h)$
and total overburden pressure at z m depth

$$p = p_1 + \gamma_{sat} \times h = \gamma \times (z - h) + \gamma_{sat} \times h \qquad (2.13)$$

Example 2.11: Consider that a foundation is placed in the sandy soil.

Depth of foundation below ground level, $z = 2.0$ m
Water table from foundation level, $h = 1.4$ m
Density of dry soil, $\gamma = 17.5$ kN/m^3
Submersed density of soil, $\gamma_{sat} = 20.0$ kN/m^3

Therefore, total overburden pressure at 0.6 m depth

$$p_1 = \gamma \times (z - h) = 17.5 \times 0.6 = 10.5 \text{ kN/m}^2$$

and total overburden pressure at 2.0 m depth

$$p = p_1 + \gamma_{sat} \times h = 10.5 + 20 \times 1.4 = 38.5 \text{ kN/m}^2$$

Effective overburden pressure (p$_o$): Effective overburden pressure is defined as the intensity of intergranular pressure on any horizontal plane at and below the foundation level before the construction operations are commenced. It is the total overburden pressure (p) minus the pore-water pressure which is, in general, equal to the head of water above the horizontal plane considered below foundation level.

If,

the depth of foundation below ground level = z
water table from foundation level   = h
dry density of soil   = γ
submersed density of soil   = γ_{sat}

Then, effective overburden pressure

$$p_0 = p - \gamma_w \times h \tag{2.14}$$

where
   γ_w = weight of water.

Example 2.12: If the depth of foundation below ground level, $z = 2.0$ m and water table from foundation level, $h = 1.4$ m, then effective overburden pressure

$$(p_o) = p - \gamma_w \times h = 38.5 - 10 \times 1.4 = 24.5 \text{ kN/m}^2$$

(assume weight of water = 10 kN/m^3)

Total foundation pressure (q): Total foundation pressure is defined as the intensity of total pressure below the foundation level after the construction of the structure is complete and fully loaded. It includes the weight of foundation substructure and the loadings from the superstructure, plus the gross loading from any back-filled soil and soil water supported by the substructure.

Net foundation pressure (q_n): Net foundation pressure is defined as the net increase on the ground beneath the foundation level due to dead and live load from the superstructure and the substructure. Thus,

$$q_n = q - p \tag{2.15}$$

Calculation of pressure and stress distribution: The distribution of effective vertical pressure of the overburden (p_o) and the vertical stress (σ_z) resulting from net foundation pressure (q_n) is shown in Figure 2.15.

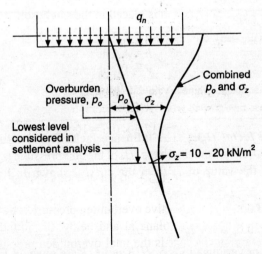

FIGURE 2.15 Graphs showing increase in overburden pressure (p_o) and decrease in vertical stress (σ_z) due to foundation loading deep beneath foundation base.

Values of σ_z at various depths below foundation level are obtained by the method of Boussinesq's or by Newmark. In the case of deep compressible soils the lowest level considered in the settlement analyses is the point where the vertical stress σ_z is relatively small, say, in the order of 10–20 kN/m^2.

Calculation of net immediate settlement in cohesive (clay) soil (Δi):   The net immediate settlement (Δi), i.e. the elastic settlement beneath the corner of a loaded area, is calculated from the following equation:

$$\Delta i = q_n \times B \left(\frac{1 - m^2}{E_d \times I_p} \right) \tag{2.16}$$

where

B = width of foundation

E_d = deformation modulus

m = Poisson's ratio

q_n = net foundation pressure

I_p = influence factor.

The values of E_d: Because of sample disturbance, the values of E_d obtained from laboratory compression test are unreliable and it is preferable to obtain E_d values from the plate bearing tests done in the field or from established empirical ratios of the E_d value to the undrained cohesion of clay. Butler gives an E_d/c ratio of 400 for London clay.

Bjerrum quotes ratios in the range of 500–1500 for normally consolidated clays. The lowest value is for clays of high plasticity and the higher for clays of low plasticity. Bjerrum's ratios were based on the measurements of undrained cohesion by the vane tests.

The values of Poisson's ratio (m):   Bowles has listed the values of m given as follows (see Table 2.7):

TABLE 2.7   Showing values of Poisson's ratio (m) for different types of soil

Soil type	m
Clay, saturated	0.4–0.5
Clay, unsaturated	0.1–0.3
Sandy clay	0.2–0.3
Silt	0.3–0.35
Sand dense coarse-grained (void ratio 0.4–0.7)	0.15
Sand dense fine-grained (void ratio 0.4–0.7)	0.15

The values of influence factor (I_p):   The influence factor (I_p) is a function of the length-to-breadth ratio of the foundation and the thickness (H) of the compressible layer. Terzaghi has derived a method of calculating the value of I_p from the curves, shown in Figure 2.14, prepared by Steinbrenner [2.8].

For Poisson's ratio of 0.5; $I_p = F_1$

For Poisson's ratio of 0.0; $I_p = F_1 + F_2$

Values of F_1 and F_2 for various ratios of H/B and L/B are given in Figure 2.14.

Elastic settlements should not be calculated for thickness (H) greater than $4B$.

Referring to Figure 2.14, the immediate settlement at any point N can be calculated:

Thus, immediate settlement at any point N

$$\Delta i = q_n / [E_d \times (1 - m^2)] \times [I_{p1} \times B_1 + I_{p2} \times B_2 + I_{p3} \times B_3 + I_{p4} \times B_4] \qquad (2.17)$$

To calculate settlement at the centre of rectangular foundation, assume B = half the foundation width to obtain H/B and L/B.

Janbu, N., Bjerrum L. and Kjaernsli B. [2.10] derived a more convenient method to calculate the average settlement of foundation assuming a constant value of E_d given as follows:

$$\text{Average settlement, } \Delta i = (\mu_1 \times \mu_0 \times q_n \times B)/E_d \qquad (2.18)$$

In the above equation, the value of Poisson's ratio is assumed constant equal to 0.5. The values of μ_1 and μ_0 are obtained from the curves in Figure 2.16 relating to the depth of foundation D, the thickness of compressible layer H and the length and width (L/B) ratio of foundation.

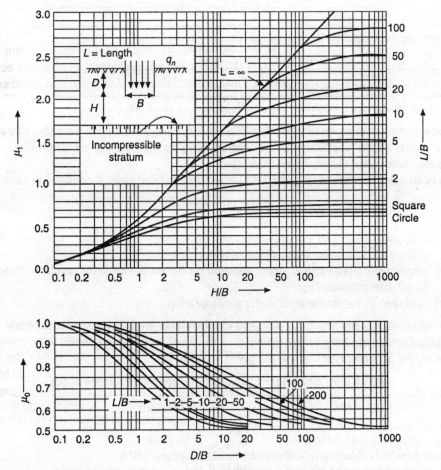

FIGURE 2.16 Curves showing factors μ_0 and μ_1 in calculating average settlement (by Jambu, Bjerrum and Kjaernsli).

Calculation of consolidation settlement (Δc)

Consolidation settlement (Δc) is calculated preferably from the values of the coefficient of volume compressibility (m_v) as determined from a number of oedometer test results. Skempton and Bjerrum [2.11] derived a formula for the calculation of consolidation settlement as follows:

$$\Delta c = \mu_g \times \rho_{oed} \tag{2.19}$$

where

μ_g = Coefficient depending on the type of soil

ρ_{oed} = Settlement as calculated from oedometer tests.

Values of μ_g: Skempton and Bjerrum [2.11] have related μ_g to the pore pressure coefficient of the soils as determined from triaxial compression tests and to the dimensions of the loaded area. Generally, for all practical purposes the values, given in Table 2.8, are sufficiently accurate in calculating the consolidation settlement.

TABLE 2.8 Showing the values of μ_g relating to the types of soil

Types of soil	μ_g
Very sensitive clays (soft alluvial, estuarine and marine clays)	1.0–1.2
Normally-consolidated clays	0.7–1.0
Overconsolidated clays (London clay, Weald, Kimmeridge, Oxford and Lias clays)	0.5–0.7
Heavily overconsolidated clays (glacial, till, Keuper marl)	0.2–0.5

Note: The values of μ_g for London clay is generally taken to be equal to 0.5.

When the variation in compressibility of a soil is known from the results of a number of oedometer tests, the values of the coefficient of volume of compressibility (m_v) are determined, and the consolidation settlement can easily be calculated.

The oedometer settlement (ρ_{oed}) of a soil layer is calculated from the following formula:

$$\rho_{oed} = m_v \times \sigma_z \times H \tag{2.20}$$

where

m_v = average coefficient of volume compressibility obtained for the effective pressure increment in the particular layer under consideration.

σ_z = average effective vertical stress imposed on the particular layer resulting from the net foundation pressure (q_n)

H = thickness of particular layer under consideration.

The values of ρ_{oed} and hence Δc, obtained for each layer are added together to obtain the total consolidation settlement beneath the loaded area. In the absence of oedometer tests, some typical values of m_v for different types of soil are given in Table 2.9.

TABLE 2.9 Showing the values of (m_v) for different types of soil

Types of soil	*Qualitative description*	*Coefficient of volume compressibility (m_v) (in m²/MN)*
Heavily overconsolidated boulder clays (e.g. many Scottish boulder clays), stiff weathered rocks (e.g. weather siltstone), hard London clay, Gault clay, and Oxford clay (at depth)	Very low compressibility	Below 0.05

(Contd.)

TABLE 2.9 Showing the values of (m_v) for different types of soil (*Contd.*)

Types of soil	Qualitative description	Coefficient of volume compressibility (m_v) (in m²/MN)
Boulder clay (e.g. Teeside Cheshire), very stiff 'blue' London clay, and Keuper marl	Low compressibility	0.05–0.1
Upper 'blue' London clay, weather brown London clay, fluvio-glacial clay, Lake clay, weathered Oxford clay, weathered Boulder clay, weathered Keuper marl and normally-consolidated clay (at depth)	Medium compressibility	0.1–0.3
Normally-consolidated alluvial clays (e.g. estuarine clays of Thames, Firth of Forth, Bristol Channel, Shatt-al-Arab, Niger Delta, Chicago clay), and Norwegian 'Quick' clay	High compressibility	0.3–1.5
Very organic alluvial clays and peats	Very high compressibility	Above 1.5

If only one or two oedometer test results are available for a given loaded area, it is more convenient to calculate ρ_{oed} directly from the *pressure-voids ratio curves* (Figure 2.17) obtained in the tests.

Then, the following procedure should be followed:

- For normally-consolidated clays (such as estuaries or marine clays). The virgin compression curve (Figure 2.17) should be used for the settlement calculations.
- For pre-consolidated or overconsolidated clays (such as boulder clays, the London, Woolwich and Reading, Gault, Weald, Kimmeridge, Oxford, and Lias clays), the actual pressure-voids ratio curves (Figure 2.17) should be used.
- For the initial (unloaded condition, the initial voids ratio (e_1) is read off the p–e curve (Figure 2.17) corresponding to the initial overburden pressure (p_o) at the centre of the layer.

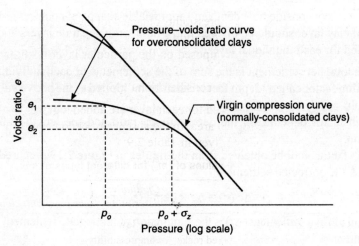

FIGURE 2.17 Curves showing pressure–void ratio in settlement analysis.

- After foundation loading is applied, the vertical stress is increased by σ_z due to net foundation pressure (q_n) (see Figure 2.18).

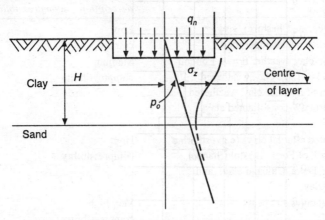

FIGURE 2.18   Curves showing distribution of initial vertical pressure p_o and increased vertical stress σ_z by net foundation pressure q_n.

- Thus, corresponding to total increased pressure ($p_o + \sigma_z$), the final voids ratio (e_2) is read off the p–e curve.
- The decrease in thickness of the layer, i.e. the oedometer settlement ρ_{oed}, after full consolidation is given by the equation:

$$\rho_{oed} = \frac{H(e_1 - e_2)}{1 + e_1} \tag{2.21}$$

- Consolidation settlement,

$$\Delta c = \mu_g \times \rho_{oed}$$

If the clay layer is of considerable depth and appreciable change of compressibility with depth, the total depth of clay layer should be divided into a number of separate layers and the settlement shall be calculated for each individual layer.

- Then, the total net settlement is the sum of the settlements of each individual layer.
- A correction factor called 'depth factor' shall be multiplied to the above value to obtain the final result.
- The depth factor depends on the depth-to-area ratio and the length-to-breadth ratio of foundation.
- The depth factor shall be obtained from the figures in Figure 2.19 prepared by Fox [2.12].
- Therefore, the corrected settlement,

$$\Delta c\,(c) = \Delta c \times \text{depth factor}$$

- Estimation of final settlement (Δf) is the summation of immediate settlement + consolidation settlement.

Hence,

$$\Delta f = \text{Final settlement} = \Delta i + \Delta c\,(c)$$

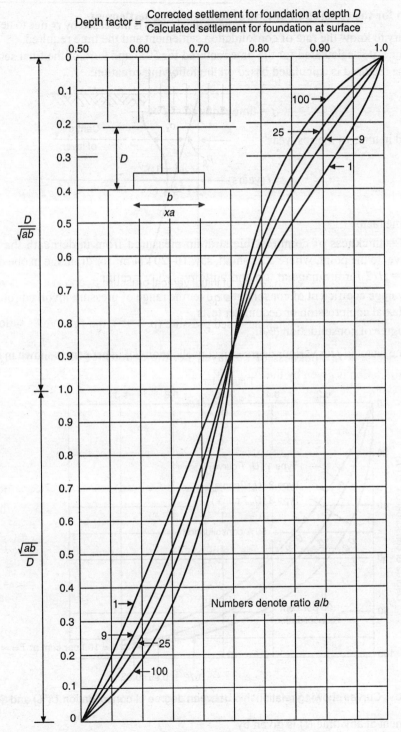

FIGURE 2.19 Fox's correction curves showing depth factors depending on foundation depth and size ratio.

Calculation for the estimation of rate of consolidation settlement

It is necessary to know the rate of consolidation settlement and the time required.

In practice, it is calculated for the time required for 50% and 90% of the final settlement. The time required is calculated based on the following equation:

$$t = \text{time required} = T \times \frac{d^2}{C_v} \tag{2.22}$$

or expressed in units of metres/year

$$t(\text{years}) = \frac{T \times d^2 \times 10^{-7}}{3.154 \times C_v} \tag{2.23}$$

where

T = time factor

$d = H$ = thickness of compressible stratum measured from underneath the foundation level to the point, where σ_z is small, say, 10–20 kN/m² for drainage in one direction, or $d = H/2$ for drainage at top and bottom of clay stratum

C_v = average coefficient of consolidation over the range of pressure involved (obtained from triaxial compression or oedometer tests

U = degree of consolidation (%).

Values of time factor (T) for various degrees of consolidation (U) in per cent is shown in Figure 2.20.

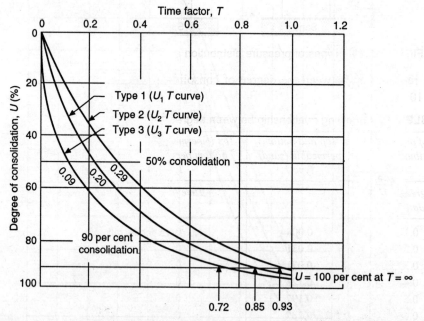

FIGURE 2.20   Curves showing relationship between degree of consolidation U(%) and time factor T.

Total settlement at any time (t) is given by

$$\Delta t = \Delta i + U \times \Delta c \tag{2.24}$$

Referring to Figure 2.20, the type of curve to be used depends on the ways of pressure distribution stated as follows:

1. When there is a two-way drainage, i.e. when there is a permeable layer above and below the compressible (clay) layer, there is only one type of curve for all types of pressure distribution, i.e. Type 1 (U_1 T curve).
2. When there is a one-way drainage, i.e. when there is an impermeable layer (clay) above the compressible layer and permeable layer (sand) below the compressible layer, Type 2 (U_2 T curve) is to be followed.
3. When there is a one-way drainage, i.e. when there is a permeable layer (sand or concrete) above the compressible layer and an impermeable layer (clay) below the compressible layer, Type 3 (U_3 T curve) is to be followed (concrete is assumed to be pervious than most clays. That is the reason concrete is considered permeable).

The standard cases of pressure distribution is shown in Figure 2.21.

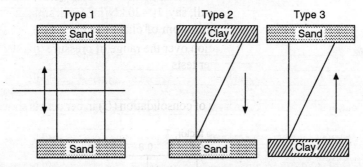

FIGURE 2.21 Types of pressure distribution arrows showing direction of drainage.

The relationship between the degree of consolidation (U) and time factor (T) is shown in Table 2.10.

TABLE 2.10 Showing relationship between degree of consolidation (U) and time factor (T)

Types of pressure distribution	Top and bottom permeable (sand) Type 1	Top impermeable (clay) and bottom permeable (sand) Type 2	Top permeable (sand) and bottom impermeable (clay) Type 3
Degree of consolidation (U)		Time factor (T)	
0.1	0.008	0.047	0.003
0.2	0.031	0.100	0.009
0.3	0.071	0.158	0.024
0.4	0.126	0.221	0.048
0.5	0.197	0.294	0.092
0.6	0.287	0.383	0.160
0.7	0.403	0.500	0.271
0.8	0.567	0.665	0.440
0.9	0.848	0.940	0.720

2.5 EXAMPLE 1—ESTIMATION OF SETTLEMENT OF FOUNDATION OF BUILDING

A four-storied office building with basement was founded on London clay at a depth of 8.0 m from ground level. The basement structure consists of two floors with raft foundation. The columns rest on raft and the exterior columns are integrated with the basement retaining wall. Estimate the settlements at the central column and centre of foundation raft (see Figure 2.22).

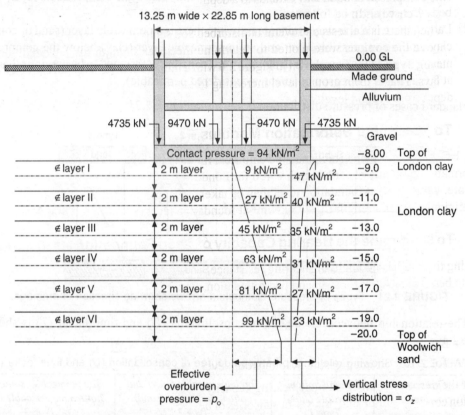

FIGURE 2.22 Shows effective overburden pressure and vertical stress distribution underneath foundation raft.

Design data

1. *Dead loads:* Dead load on the central columns at basement level

$$651.39 + 137.75 = 789.14 \text{ kN}$$

Dead load of basement slab (600 mm thick)

$$\frac{2.3 + 5.3}{2} \times 4.5 \times 0.6 \times 24 = 246.24 \text{ kN}$$

(assumed basement slab area supported by column = 3.8 m × 4.5 m)

$$\Sigma \text{DL} = 1035.38 \text{ kN}$$

2. *Live load:* (full live load as for office building)

$$367.65 + 85.5 = 453.15 \text{ kN}$$

$$P = \Sigma DL + LL = 1489 \text{ kN, say}$$

Geotechnical data

1. Several field borehole logs data showed London clay at a depth 8 m below topsoil, alluvium and gravel. The London clay extends to a depth 12 m underlain by Woolwich and Reading beds (dense sand).

2. Laboratory triaxial tests on several undisturbed soil samples were carried out for London clay and the values were plotted to determine the shear strength of clay/depth and the mean line was drawn as shown in Figure 2.1 with a minimum shear strength $C_u = 75$ kN/m^2 at 8.0 m depth from ground level increasing to a maximum value of 220 kN/m^2 at 20 m depth from ground level.

2.5.1 To Determine Deformation Modulus (E_d)

Butler, F.G. [2.16] gives an established the empirical ratio of E_d/C_u
= Deformation modulus/shear strength = 400 for London clay.
Therefore, value of E_d at foundation level may be taken equal to = 400 × 75 = 30000 kN/m^2
[with minimum shear strength $C_u = 75$ kN/m^2 at foundation level (8.0 m from ground level)].

2.5.2 To Determine the Bearing Capacity of Deep Foundation at 8.0 m Depth

Assuming the soil has no angle of shearing resistance,
Ultimate bearing capacity for strip and pad foundation,

$$q_u = C_u \times N_c + p$$

where

N_c = Bearing capacity factor

p = Total overburden pressure at foundation level.

For the determination of ultimate bearing capacity of soil for deep strip and pad foundation, Skempton concluded after studying various theories of bearing capacity together with experimental data that for cohesive soil, the bearing capacity factor N_c increases with the depth of footing, and prepared the graph, as shown in Figure 2.9.

Assumed depth of foundation, $z = 8$ m

Breadth of base, $B = 2.3$ m (average);

Length of base, $L = 4.5$ m (centre to centre of column)

Ratio $z/B = 8/2.3 = 3.48$

With $\phi' = 0$; referring to Figure 2.9, $N_c = 7.5$
Ultimate bearing capacity of soil,

$$q_u = C_u \times N_c$$

$$75 \times 7.5 = 563 \text{ kN/m}^2$$

The basic equation $q_u = C_u \times N_c$ for ultimate bearing capacity of soil is based on the consideration that the foundation is a strip footing. If the foundation is not a strip footing but is square, rectangle, or circular, the support given by the soil is a three-dimensional bulb of pressure. The bearing capacity may be expected to be greater than for a strip footing.

For square base, Terzaghi suggests the following equation with $\phi' = 0$; $q_u = 1.3 \times C_u \times N_c$

For rectangular foundation. Skempton suggests the following:

If L = length of base and B = breadth of base, then N_c for rectangle

$$0.84 + \frac{0.16 \times B}{L} \times N_c \text{ (for square)}$$

Therefore, for rectangle,

$$N_c = \frac{0.84 + 0.16 \times 2.3}{4.5} N_c = 0.92 \times N_c \text{ (for square)}$$

So, ultimate bearing capacity of soil

$$q_u = 1.3 \times C_u \times 0.92 \times N_c = 1.3 \times 75 \times 0.92 \times 7.5 = 673 \text{ kN/m}^2$$

Overburden pressure = Weight of soil at the level of the base of slab

$$p = \gamma_{sat} \times z = 19 \times 8 = 152 \text{ kN/m}^2$$

(considering that the water table is only 1 m below ground level, the weight of soil is taken as saturated soil).

This weight of soil shall be deducted from the ultimate bearing capacity of soil to obtain the net ultimate bearing capacity of soil.

Hence, net ultimate bearing capacity,

$$q_u \text{ (net)} = 1.3 \times C_u \times N_c - p = 683 - 152 = 531 \text{ kN/m}^2$$

Assuming a safety factor = 2.5 and adding the weight of column of soil excavated, safe bearing capacity of soil,

$$q_s = \frac{q_u}{2.5 + p} = \frac{531}{2.5 + 152} = 364 \text{ kN/m}^2$$

Actual foundation pressure under the column base of (2.3 m × 4.5 m) assumed,

$$q_n = \frac{P}{B \times L} = \frac{1489}{2.3 \times 4.5} = 144 \text{ kN/m}^2 \ll q_s, \qquad \textbf{(OK)}$$

2.5.3 To Calculate the Net Immediate Settlement (Δi) at the Centre of Column Base

Net foundation pressure,

$$q_n = 144 \text{ kN/m}^2 \qquad \text{(see Figure 2.22)}$$

Referring to Eq. (2.18): as derived by Jambu, Bjerrum and Kjaernsli, Average immediate settlement

$$\Delta i = \mu_1 \times \mu_0 \times q_n \times B/E_d$$

The factors μ_1, μ_0 are related to the depth of foundation D, thickness of compressible layer H, and the length/width (L/B) ratio of the foundation slab.

$$D = 8 \text{ m}; \ H = 20 \text{ m}; \ L/B = 4.5/2.3 = 1.95$$

Referring to Figure 2.16 (showing factors):

With $L/B = 1.95$ and $H/B = 20/2.3 = 8.7$; $\mu_1 = 0.9$

With $L/B = 1.95$ and $D/B = 8/2.3 = 3.47$; $\mu_0 = 0.6$

E_d = deformation modulus = 30000 kN/m^2 as already calculated.

Therefore, immediate settlement under column base

$$\Delta i = 0.9 \times 0.6 \times \frac{144 \times 2.3}{30000} \times 1000 \text{ mm} = 6 \text{ mm}$$

2.5.4 To Calculate the Net Immediate Settlement (Δi) at the Centre of Foundation Raft

The calculation of the net immediate settlement (Δi) at the centre of foundation raft is based on the following consideration (see Figure 2.22):

Consider the basement slab of the substructure as a raft founded on the London clay. Assume that the raft is stiff enough to distribute the whole load of the superstructure and substructure evenly on the soil to create an uniform contact pressure.

1. *Load at the foundation level:*

	Interior column		Exterior column	
	DL (kN)	LL (kN)	DL (kN)	LL (kN)
Upto GF level	513.64	282.15	408.26	195.85
Upto inter level	137.75	85.50	112.20	59.65
Upto basement	137.75	85.50	112.20	59.65
Total	789.14	453.15	632.66	316.15

Total (DL + LL) = (789.14 + 453.15) = 1242.29 kN   (632.66 + 316.15) kN = 948.8 kN

(Note: Full live load is considered as the building is for commercial high-tech use)

Total number of internal columns = 8 + 4/2 = 10

Total number of exterior columns = 8 + 4/2 = 10

Therefore,

Total load at basement level = 10 × (1242.29 + 948.8)   = 21911 kN

Weight of basement wall = 2 × (12.85 + 22.45) × 0.4 × 24 =   678 kN

Weight of basement slab = (13.25 × 22.85) × 0.8 × 24   = 5813 kN

Total = 28402 kN

Area of basement in contact with soil = 13.25 × 22.85 = 302.76 m^2

Therefore, contact pressure at foundation level

$$q = \frac{28402}{302.76} = 93.8 \text{ kN/m}^2 \text{ (say 94 kN/m}^2)$$

2. *To calculate net immediate settlement:* Net foundation pressure

$$q_n = q - p_0 = 94 - 0 = 94.0 \text{ kN/m}^2$$

(since there is no soil above the base slab (basement), the effective overburden pressure, $p_0 = 0$)
Referring to Eq. (2.18), immediate settlement

$$\Delta i = \mu_1 \times \mu_0 \times q_n \times \frac{B}{E_d} \quad \text{(by Jambu, Bjerrum and Kjaernsli)}$$

and referring to Figure 2.16

$$\frac{L}{B} = \frac{22.85}{13.25} = 1.73; \quad \frac{H}{B} = \frac{12}{13.25} = 0.9; \quad \mu_1 = 0.5$$

$$\frac{D}{B} = \frac{8}{13.25} = 0.6; \quad \frac{L}{B} = 1.73; \quad \mu_0 = 0.8$$

(where, H = depth of clay stratum; D = depth of base below ground level)
Hence, immediate settlement at the centre of raft

$$\Delta i = 0.5 \times 0.8 \times 95 \times 13.25 \times \frac{1000}{30000} = 16.6 \text{ mm}$$

2.5.5 To Calculate the Consolidation Settlement (Δc)

Net foundation pressure, $q_n = 94 \text{ kN/m}^2$
We shall now calculate the distribution of effective overburden pressure (p_0) and the induced
vertical stress (σ_z) throughout the full depth of clay stratum. Since we have only one consolidation
test result, we shall base our calculation for settlement on the $p_0 - e$ curve shown in Figure 2.23.

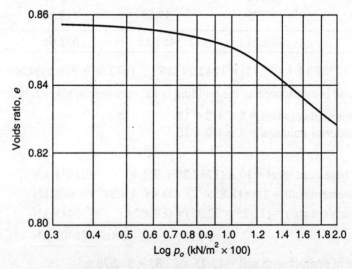

FIGURE 2.23 Pressure–void ratio curve.

Because the clay stratum is quite thick, we must divide it into 2.0 m thick horizontal layers, and calculate separately the settlement for each layer and add up to give the total consolidation settlement (see Figure 2.22).

1. *To calculate the effective overburden pressure* $= p_o$:   Since there is no soil over the raft due to basement, the initial net overburden pressure just beneath the base raft level is zero. So,

   A centre of layer I, 9.0 m depth, $p_{o1} = 1 \times (19 - 10) = 9$ kN/m^2

   A centre of layer II, 11.0 m depth, $p_{o2} = 3 \times 9 = 27$ kN/m^2

   A centre of layer III, 13.0 m depth, $p_{o3} = 5 \times 9 = 45$ kN/m^2

   A centre of layer IV, 15.0 m depth, $p_{o4} = 7 \times 9 = 63$ kN/m^2

   A centre of layer V, 17.0 m depth, $p_{o5} = 9 \times 9 = 81$ kN/m^2

   A centre of layer VI, 19.0 m depth, $p_{o6} = 11 \times 9 = 99$ kN/m^2

2. *To calculate the vertical stress* σ_z *due to net foundation pressure* q_n; Referring to Figure 2.12 (relationship between z/b and σ_z/q_n):

   For layer I: at 9 m depth,

   $$\frac{a}{b} = \frac{22.85}{13.25} = 1.72; \frac{z}{b} = \frac{9}{13.25} = 0.68; \frac{\sigma_{z1}}{q_n} = 0.5; \qquad \sigma_{z1} = 94 \times 0.5 = 47 \text{ kN/m}^2$$

   For layer II: at 11 m depth,

   $$\frac{a}{b} = 1.72; \frac{z}{b} = \frac{11}{13.25} = 0.83; \frac{\sigma_{z2}}{q_n} = 0.43; \qquad \sigma_{z2} = 94 \times 0.43 = 40 \text{ kN/m}^2$$

   For layer III: at 13 m depth,

   $$\frac{a}{b} = 1.72; \frac{z}{b} = \frac{13}{13.25} = 1; \frac{\sigma_{z3}}{q_n} = 0.37; \qquad \sigma_{z3} = 94 \times 0.37 = 35 \text{ kN/m}^2$$

   For layer IV: at 15 m depth,

   $$\frac{a}{b} = 1.72; \frac{z}{b} = \frac{15}{13.25} = 1.13; \frac{\sigma_{z4}}{q_n} = 0.33; \qquad \sigma_{z4} = 94 \times 0.33 = 31 \text{ kN/m}^2$$

   For layer V: at 17 m depth,

   $$\frac{a}{b} = 1.72; \frac{z}{b} = \frac{17}{13.25} = 1.28; \frac{\sigma_{z5}}{q_n} = 0.29; \qquad \sigma_{z5} = 94 \times 0.29 = 27 \text{ kN/m}^2$$

   For layer VI: at 19 m depth,

   $$\frac{a}{b} = 1.72; \frac{z}{b} = \frac{19}{13.25} = 1.43; \frac{\sigma_{z6}}{q_n} = 0.25; \qquad \sigma_{z6} = 94 \times 0.25 = 23 \text{ kN/m}^2$$

   (where a = length of raft; b = width of raft; z = depth below raft)

3. *Resultant pressure at the centre of each layer* $(p_o + \sigma_z)$:

In layer I: $(p_o + \sigma_z) = (9 + 47) = 56 \text{ kN/m}^2$

In layer II: $(p_o + \sigma_z) = (27 + 40) = 67 \text{ kN/m}^2$

In layer III: $(p_o + \sigma_z) = (45 + 35) = 80 \text{ kN/m}^2$

In layer IV: $(p_o + \sigma_z) = (63 + 31) = 94 \text{ kN/m}^2$

In layer V: $(p_o + \sigma_z) = (81 + 27) = 108 \text{ kN/m}^2$

In layer VI: $(p_o + \sigma_z) = (99 + 23) = 122 \text{ kN/m}^2$

4. *Void ratio* e_1 *due to* p_o: Referring to Figure 2.23 (pressure–void ratio curve)

In layer I: for p_o = 9 kN/m^2; $e_1 = 0.86$

In layer II: for p_o = 27 kN/m^2; $e_1 = 0.858$

In layer III: for p_o = 45 kN/m^2; $e_1 = 0.856$

In layer IV: for p_o = 63 kN/m^2; $e_1 = 0.854$

In layer V: for p_o = 81 kN/m^2; $e_1 = 0.852$

In layer VI: for p_o = 99 kN/m^2; $e_1 = 0.850$

5. *Void ratio* e_2 *due to* $(p_o + \sigma_z)$:

In layer I: for $(p_o + \sigma_z)$ = 56 kN/m^2; $e_2 = 0.857$

In layer II: for $(p_o + \sigma_z)$ = 67 kN/m^2; $e_2 = 0.855$

In layer III: for $(p_o + \sigma_z)$ = 80 kN/m^2; $e_2 = 0.853$

In layer IV: for $(p_o + \sigma_z)$ = 94 kN/m^2; $e_2 = 0.851$

In layer V: for $(p_o + \sigma_z)$ = 108 kN/m^2; $e_2 = 0.849$

In layer VI: for $(p_o + \sigma_z)$ = 122 kN/m^2; $e_2 = 0.847$

6. *Ratio* $(e_1 - e_2)/(1 + e_1)$:

For layer I: r_1 = ratio $(e_1 - e_2)/(1 + e_1) = (0.86 - 0.857)/(1 + 0.86) = 0.00162$

For layer II: r_2 = ratio $(e_1 - e_2)/(1 + e_1) = (0.858 - 0.855)/(1 + 0.858) = 0.00162$
For layer III: r_3 = ratio $(e_1 - e_2)/(1 + e_1) = (0.856 - 0.853)/(1 + 0.856) = 0.00161$

For layer IV: r_4 = ratio $(e_1 - e_2)/(1 + e_1) = (0.854 - 0.851)/(1 + 0.854) = 0.00161$

For layer V: r_5 = ratio $(e_1 - e_2)/(1 + e_1) = (0.852 - 0.849)/(1 + 0.852) = 0.00161$

For layer VI: r_6 = ratio $(e_1 - e_2)/(1 + e_1) = (0.85 - 0.847)/(1 + 0.85) = 0.00161$

7. *Consolidation settlement:*

In layer I: Δc_1 = $r_1 \times H \times 1000 = 0.0016 \times 2 \times 1000 = 3.24 \text{ mm}$

In layer II: Δc_2 = $r_2 \times H \times 1000 = 0.00162 \times 2 \times 1000 = 3.24 \text{ mm}$

In layer III: Δc_3 = $r_3 \times H \times 1000 = 0.00161 \times 2 \times 1000 = 3.22 \text{ mm}$

In layer IV: Δc_4 = $r_4 \times H \times 1000 = 0.00161 \times 2 \times 1000 = 3.22 \text{ mm}$

In layer V: $\qquad \Delta c_5 = r_5 \times H \times 1000 = 0.00161 \times 2 \times 1000 = 3.22$ mm

In layer VI: $\qquad \Delta c_6 = r_6 \times H \times 1000 = 0.00161 \times 2 \times 1000 = 3.22$ mm

$\therefore \qquad \Sigma \Delta c = 3.24 + 3.24 + 3.22 + 3.22 + 3.22 + 3.22 = 19.36$ mm

8. *Corrected consolidated settlement:* The value of consolidation settlement calculated shall be reduced by a correction factor to arrive at net consolidation settlement.

   This correction factor is dependent on the depth/area ratio and the length and breadth ratio of foundation size.

   $$\text{The ratio} = \frac{\text{Length}}{\text{Breadth of foundation dimensions}} = \frac{22.85}{13.25} = 1.73$$

   and

   $$\text{the ratio} = \frac{\text{Depth of foundation below ground}}{(\text{Area of foundation size})^{0.5}} = \frac{D}{(a \times b)^{0.5}}$$

   $$= \frac{8}{(13.25 \times 22.85)^{0.5}} = \frac{8}{17.4} = 0.46$$

   Referring to Figure 2.19: depth factor = 0.85

   $$\text{Depth factor} = \frac{\text{Corrected settlement for foundation depth } D}{\text{Calculated settlement}}$$

   Therefore, corrected settlement at foundation depth

   $$\Delta cc = \Delta c \times \text{depth factor} = 19.36 \times 0.85 = 16.5 \text{ mm}$$

9. Final settlement at foundation depth

   $$\Delta \text{ final} = \Delta i + \Delta cc$$

   $$= 16.6 + 16.5 = 33.1 \text{ (say 33 mm)}.$$

2.5.6 To Calculate the Rate of Consolidation Settlement

From laboratory test results, the coefficient of consolidation, $C_v = 0.0139 \times 10^{-6}$ m^2/sec.

The Woolwich sand bed underlying the London clay acts as a drainage layer and the reinforced concrete raft of high density with 800 mm thick is considered impervious.

Thus, the drainage is in one-direction, the process of consolidation will travel downwards to the sand layer.

For one-way drainage, the time factors, U, in T_{50} and T_{90} (as in Figure 2.21) are for 50% and 90% consolidation. Therefore, by equation:

$$t \text{ (in years)} = \frac{T \times d^2 \times 10^{-7} \text{ m}}{3.154 \times C_v \text{ m}^2/\text{sec}}, \qquad \text{(refer to Eq. 2.23)}$$

where

$d(H)$ = depth of consolidation layer.

The time factor T depends on the degree of consolidation (U) in %, as shown in Figure 2.20 with one-way pressure distribution (U_2 T curve) Type 2

With 50% degree of consolidation: $T_{50} = 0.2$

$$t = \frac{0.2 \times 12 \times 10^{-7}}{3.15 \times 0.0139 \times 10^{-6}} = 5.5 \text{ years}$$

With 90% degree of consolidation, $T_{90} = 0.85$

$$t = \frac{0.85 \times 12 \times 10^{-7}}{3.154 \times 0.0139 \times 10^{-6}} = 23 \text{ years}$$

Hence, net total settlement after 5.5 years with 50% consolidation

$$\Delta 5.5 = \Delta i + \Delta cc = 16.6 + \frac{16.5}{2} = 24.85 \text{ (say 25 mm)}$$

Therefore, net total settlement after 23 years with 90% consolidation

$$\Delta 23 = \Delta i + \Delta cc = 16.6 + 0.9 \times 16.5 = 31.45 \text{ (say 32 mm)}.$$

2.6 EXAMPLE 2—ESTIMATION OF SETTLEMENTS OF BRIDGE PIER

A bridge pier with its base 8.5 m long and 7.5 m wide is founded on soil of dense sand and gravel. The pressures due to dead load and live load at base are 220 kN/m² and 360 kN/m²

$$q_n = 220 \text{ kN/m}^2$$

[B = 7.5 m; L = 8.5 m; depth of base below ground, D = 3.0 m]

A schematic dipiction of pier with soil profile is presented in Figure 2.24.

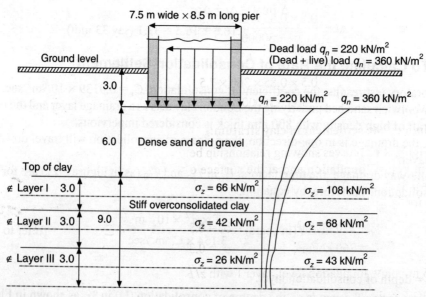

FIGURE 2.24 Vertical stress distribution at different depths below pier foundation level.

Geotechnical data:

1. The borehole logs showed dense sand and gravel up to a depth of 9 m underlain by very deep stiff overconsolidated clay to a depth 25 m below ground level.
   Depth of sand and gravel stratum, $H = 6$ m
2. Standard penetration tests gave an average value of $N = 40$ per 300 mm in the sand and gravel stratum.
3. A number of oedometer tests were carried out on samples of the stiff clay.

Triaxial tests on undisturbed samples of the clay gave a minimum shear strength $C_u = 120$ kN/m^2 and a modulus of deformation $E_d = 40000$ kN/m^2
Calculate the immediate and long-term settlement of bridge pier.

2.6.1   To Calculate Immediate Settlements

To calculate immediate settlements in sand and gravel strata: Referring to Figure 2.24 and Referring to Figure 2.13 (curve showing relationship between deformation modulus and standard penetration resistance)
with $p_o = 120$ kN/m^2, and $N = 40$
Deformation modulus, $E_d = 50$ MN/m^2

Referring to Eq. (2.18), immediate settlement

$$\Delta i = (\mu_1 \times \mu_0 \times q_n \times B)/E_d$$

Referring to Figure 2.16

with $L/B = 8.5/7.5 = 1.13$; $H/B = 6/7.5 = 0.8$; $D/B = 3/7.5 = 0.4$; $\mu_1 = 0.5$; $\mu_0 = 0.85$

For dead load $q_n = 220$ kN/m^2. Therefore,

$$\Delta i = \frac{0.5 \times 0.85 \times 220 \times 7.5}{50000} \times 1000 = 14 \text{ mm}$$

For DL + LL = 360 kN/m^2

$$\Delta i = \frac{0.5 \times 0.85 \times 360 \times 7.5}{50000} \times 1000 = 23 \text{ mm}$$

To calculate immediate settlement in clay stratum:

Referring to Figure 2.12 (curves showing relationship between z/b and σ_z/q):
At a depth 6 m below foundation and at the surface of clay with $L/B = 8.5/7.5 = 1.13$; and $z/B = 6/7.5 = 0.8$; $\sigma_z/q_n = 0.37$
vertical stress for

$$q_n = 220 \text{ kN/m}^2; \qquad \sigma_z = 0.37 \times 220 = 81 \text{ kN/m}^2$$
$$q_n = 360 \text{ kN/m}^2; \qquad \sigma_z = 0.37 \times 360 = 133 \text{ kN/m}^2$$

At a depth 7.5 m below foundation level, layer I with $z/B = 7.5/7.5 = 1$; $\sigma_z/q_n = 0.3$

vertical stress for

$$q_n = 220 \text{ kN/m}^2; \qquad\qquad \sigma_z = 0.3 \times 220 = 66 \text{ kN/m}^2$$
$$q_n = 360 \text{ kN/m}^2; \qquad\qquad \sigma_z = 0.3 \times 360 = 108 \text{ kN/m}^2$$

At a depth 10.5 m below foundation level, layer II: $z/B = 10.5/7.5 = 1.4$; $\sigma_z/q_n = 0.19$;

vertical stress for

$$q_n = 220 \text{ kN/m}^2; \qquad\qquad \sigma_z = 0.19 \times 220 = 42 \text{ kN/m}^2$$
$$q_n = 360 \text{ kN/m}^2; \qquad\qquad \sigma_z = 0.19 \times 360 = 68 \text{ kN/m}^2$$

At a depth 13.5 m below foundation level, layer III: $z/B = 13.5/7.5 = 1.8$; $\sigma_z/q_n = 0.12$;

vertical stress for

$$q_n = 220 \text{ kN/m}^2; \qquad\qquad \sigma_z = 0.12 \times 220 = 26 \text{ kN/m}^2$$
$$q_n = 360 \text{ kN/m}^2; \qquad\qquad \sigma_z = 0.12 \times 360 = 43 \text{ kN/m}^2$$

Consider at a depth 6 m below foundation:

Vertical stress σ_z for ($q_n = 220 \text{ kN/m}^2$) = 81 kN/m^2

Let the loaded area at 6 m below foundation level

$$A = 220 \times 7.5 \times \frac{8.5}{81} = 173 \text{ m}^2$$

Assume, width of dispersion is a. Therefore,

$$(2a + 7.5)\,(2a + 8.5) = A = 173$$

Solving the equation $a = 2.5$ m. So, the vertical stress 26 kN/m^2 is distributed over an area

$$(7.5 + 2.5 \times 2) = 12.5 \text{ m by } (8.5 + 2.5 \times 2) = 13.5 \text{ m}$$

The loaded area 12.5 × 13.5 is divided into 4 rectangles of $B = 6.25$ m and $L = 6.75$ m.
Referring to Figure 2.14 (curves showing the values of F_1 and F_2 corresponding to ratios of H/B and L/B), where H = thickness of clay layer with

$$\frac{H}{B} = \frac{(18 - 9)}{6.25} = \frac{9}{6.25} = 1.44$$

$$\frac{L}{B} = \frac{6.75}{6.25} = 1.08$$

$$F_1 = 0.15 = i_p$$

for $q_n = 220 \text{ kN/m}^2$ and $m = 0.5$
Immediate settlement at the corner of rectangle (from Eq. 2.16)

$$\Delta i = q_n \times B \times \frac{(1 - m^2) + i_p}{E_d}$$

$$= 81 \times 6.25 \times \frac{(1 - 0.5)^2 \times 0.15}{40000}$$

$$= 1.4 \text{ mm}$$

This value is reduced by a factor given by Figure 2.19.

Referring to Figure 2.19 (showing depth factors depending on foundation depth and size ratio) with

$$\frac{D}{(A \times B)^{0.5}} = \frac{3}{(7.5 \times 8.5)^{0.5}} = 0.38$$

$$\frac{A}{B} = \frac{8.5}{7.5} = 1.13$$

Depth factor = 0.90

Therefore, reduced immediate settlement

$$0.9 \times 1.4 = 1.3 \text{ mm}$$

and immediate settlement at the centre

$$\Delta i = 4 \times 1.3 = 5.2 \text{ mm}$$

For $q_n = 360 \text{ kN/m}^2$

Immediate settlement at the centre

$$\Delta i = \frac{5.2 \times 133}{81} = 8.5 \text{ mm}$$

2.6.2 To Calculate Net Consolidation Settlement of Clay Stratum

As a number of consolidation tests were carried out, we can calculate the value of coefficient of compressibility (m_v) in calculating the oedometer settlement (ρ_{oed}). 9 m thick layer of clay is divided into 3 layers of 3 m thick each layer. The oedometer settlement is calculated by following Eq. (2.20):

$$\rho_{oed} = m_v \times \sigma_z \times H$$

Net consolidation settlement is calculated

$$\Delta c = \mu_g \times \rho_{oed}$$

where, μ_g is a factor depending on the type of clay. For overconsolidated clay the value of μ_g is taken equal to 0.50.

Correction factor from Figures 2.19 (Fox's correction curves) showing depth factors depending on foundation depth and size ratio. Now, referring to Figure 2.19

$$D = 3 \text{ m}$$

$$\text{ratio} = \frac{D}{(A \times B)^{0.5}} = \frac{3}{(8.5 \times 7.5)^{0.5}} = 0.38$$

Depth factor = 0.9

Corrected settlement = depth factor × calculated settlement

Table 2.11 shows the oedometer settlement values.

TABLE 2.11 Showing oedometer settlements at various depths

Net foundation pressures q_n (kN/m²)	Depth of layer below foundation level (m)	Thickness of layer (m)	Coefficient of compressibility m_v (m²/kN)	Average vertical stress on layer σ_z (kN/m²)	Oedometer settlement ρ_{oed} (mm)
220	6–9	3	0.00011	66	22
	9–12	3	0.00007	42	9
	12–15	3	0.00003	26	2
360	6–9	3	0.00020	108	65
	9–12	3	0.00012	68	25
	12–15	3	0.00004	43	5

From Table 2.11, for net foundation pressure of 220 kN/m²:
Total consolidation settlement

$$\Delta c = 22 + 9 + 2 = 33 \text{ mm}$$

Therefore, net consolidation settlement

$$\Delta c \text{ (net)} = \mu_g \times \text{correction factor} \times \Delta c = 0.5 \times 0.9 \times 33 = 15 \text{ mm}$$

For net foundation pressure of 360 kN/m², total consolidation settlement

$$\Delta c = 65 + 25 + 5 = 95 \text{ mm}$$

Therefore, net consolidation settlement

$$\Delta c \text{ (net)} = \mu_g \times \text{correction factor} \times \Delta c = 0.5 \times 0.9 \times 95 = 45 \text{ mm}$$

To summarize the total settlement:

Total settlement = Δ = immediate settlement in sand and gravel + immediate settlement in clay + consolidation settlement in clay.

Thus, for dead load of 220 kN/m² at foundation level, total settlement

$$\Delta c \text{ (220)} = (14 + 5.2 + 15) \text{ mm} = 34.2, \qquad \text{say 34 mm}$$

And for (dead + live) load of 360 kN/m² at foundation level, total settlement

$$\Delta c \text{ (360)} = (23 + 8.5 + 45) \text{ mm} = 76.5, \qquad \text{say 77 mm}$$

2.6.3 To Calculate the Rate of Settlement

From laboratory test results, the coefficient of consolidation

$$C_v = 0.0139 \times 10^{-6} \text{ m}^2/\text{sec}$$

The sand overlying clay stratum acts as a drainage layer. So, the process of consolidation will travel upwards to the sand layer, and in calculating the rate of settlement, the drainage is acting only in one direction.

For one-way drainage system, the time factors T_{50} and T_{90} for 50% and 90% consolidation from the Type 3 (U_3 T) curve in Figure 2.20 are:

$$T_{50} = 0.1 \text{ and } T_{90} = 0.7$$

and for drainage in one direction,

$$d = H \text{ (depth of clay layer)} = 9 \text{ m}$$

So, referring to Eq. (2.23)

$$t\text{(years)} = \frac{T \times d \times 10^{-7}}{(3.154 \times C_v)}$$

Hence, time required in years for 50% consolidation

$$t_{50} = \frac{0.1 \times 9^2 \times 10^{-7}}{(3.154 \times 0.0139 \times 10^{-6})} = 18 \text{ years}$$

and the time required in years for 90% consolidation

$$t_{90} = \frac{0.7 \times 9^2 \times 10^{-7}}{3.154 \times 0.0139 \times 10^{-6}} = 129 \text{ years.}$$

REFERENCES

[2.1]   Peck, R.B., W.E. Hanson and T.H. Thornburn, Foundation Engineering, Asia Publishing House, New Delhi, 1962.

[2.1a] Prandtl, L., Uber die Harte plastischer Korper. Nach. Kgl.Ges. Wiss. Gottingen Math.Phys. Kl (1920).

[2.2]   Terzaghi, K. and R.B. Peck, Soil Mechanics in Engineering Practice, Wiley, USA, 1962.

[2.2a] Stroud, M.A. and F.G. Butler, The SPT and the Engineering Properties of Glacial Materials, Pro. Symposium on Engineering Behaviour of Glacial Materials, Birmingham, pp. 124–135, 1975.

[2.3]   Meyerhop, G.G., The Ultimate Bearing Capacity of Foundations,*Geotechnique*, **2**:301, 1950.

[2.4]   Skempton, A.W., The Bearing Capacity of Clays, Building Research Congress, division I 180, 1951.

[2.5]   Jurgenson, L., The Application of Theories of Elasticity and Plasticity to Foundation Problems, *Journal of the Boston Society of Civil Engineers*, Vol. 21, pp. 206–211, 1934.

[2.6]   Sutherland, H.B., Review of Paper: Granular Materials,in *Proceedings of the Conference on Settlement of Structures*, pp. 473–499, Pentech press, Cambridge, 1974.

[2.7]   Menzenbach, E., Le capacidad soportante de pilotes y grupos pilotes, *Technologia* (Ingeneria Civil) Series 2, No.1, pp. 20–21, Havana University, Cuba, 1967.

[2.8]   Steinbrenner, W., Taflen zur setzungs berechnung, *Die Strasse*, **1**: 121–124, 1934.

[2.9]   De Beer, E. and A. Martens, Method of Computation of an Upper Limit for the Influence of the Heterogeneity of Sand Layers in the Settlement of Bridges, in *Proceedings of the 4th International Conference on Soil Mechanics*, Vol.1, pp. 275–282, London, 1957.

[2.10]   Janbu, N., L. Bjeerum and B. Kjaernli, Veiledning vedl ϕ sning avfundamenterings oppgarer, Publication no.16, Norwegian Geotechnical Institute, 1956.

[2.11]   Skempton, A. and L. Bjerrum, A Contribution to the Settlement Analysis of Foundation in Clay, *Geotechnique* **7**: 168–178, 1957.

[2.12]   Fox, E.N., The Mean Elastic Settlement of a Uniformly Loaded Area at a Depth below the Ground Surface, in *Proceedings of the 2nd International Conference on Soil Mechanics*, Vol.1, pp. 129–132, Rotterdam, 1948.

[2.13]   BS 8004: 1986: British Standard Code of Practice for Foundations.

[2.14]   Eurocode 7: 2004: Geotechnical Design. Part I: General Rules.

[2.15]   CIRIA Report 104, Design of Retaining Walls Embedded in Stiff Clays, London, Construction Industry Research and Information Association, 1984.

[2.16]   Butler, F.G., Review Paper: Heavily Overconsolidated Clays, in proceedings of the conference on settlement of structures, pp. 531–578, Pentech Press, Cambridge, 1974.

Chapter 3

Isolated Footing Foundations

3.0 DEFINITION AND DESCRIPTION

The isolated footing foundation may be defined as spread footing which supports the column load individually and independently, and spreads the point load of column to the soil by its spread footing so that the contact pressure under the base does not exceed the allowable bearing capacity of soil (Terzaghi and Peck [3.1]).

The depth of the isolated footing below ground level is generally kept shallow, but should be kept below the level to avoid any weathering action, say frost.

The foundation may be defined as shallow if the depth of the footing (z) does not exceed the width of footing (B).

The shape of the footing may be square or rectangular, depending on the space (area) provided for the placement of base on the soil.

3.1 BEHAVIOUR OF FOOTING UNDER THE ACTION OF CONTACT PRESSURE

3.1.1 Behaviour of Circular Footing under the Action of Contact Pressure

Consider a circular spread footing with circular column subjected to upward contact pressure due to the action of vertical downward point load on the column. The contact pressure under the entire footing tries to bend the slab into curved shape upward so as to form a saucer that is concave on top, as shown in Figure 3.1(a) (Dunham [3.2]). The qualitative contour plan is shown in Figure 3.1(b). The footing, therefore, elongates radially near the bottom whereas shortens radially near the top. The footing acts like a cantilevered member that bends in radial directions about a centrally located column base as shown in Figure 3.1(c). Due to the elongation of concrete near the bottom, there will be the development of tension and cracks in the concrete. Furthermore, the radial elongation of the bottom must be accompanied by a circumferential elongation of the same region.

Reinforcements are used radially and circumferentially to resist the tension and to minimize the extent of cracks, as shown in Figure 3.1(d).

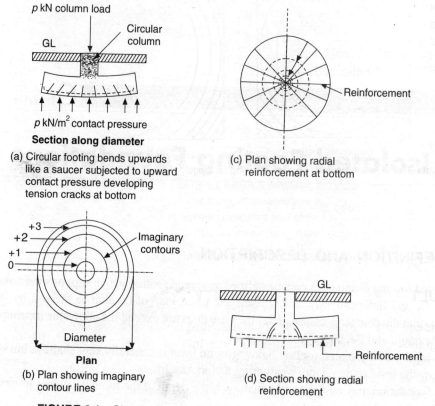

Section along diameter

(a) Circular footing bends upwards like a saucer subjected to upward contact pressure developing tension cracks at bottom

(b) Plan showing imaginary contour lines

(c) Plan showing radial reinforcement at bottom

(d) Section showing radial reinforcement

FIGURE 3.1 Circular footing under the action of contact pressure.

3.1.2 Behaviour of Square or Rectangular Footing under the Action of Contact Pressure

It is not possible under normal circumstances to adopt circular footing as it is difficult and time consuming to place reinforcement radially and circumferentially with circular framework and the construction work becomes costly.

So, square or rectangular footing is generally used. The square or rectangular footing deforms the same way as that of circular footing, as shown in Figures 3.2(a) and 3.2(b) Dunham [3.2].

Referring to Figure 3.2 (a) for square footing, we may assume that the corners of the column is likely to control the base due to high stiffness and are the points of high pressure. It also seems likely that contours near the column will be squares with rounded corners, whereas those further away become nearly circular. The corners of the footing obviously curve upwards the most. For rectangular footing, as shown in Figure 3.2(b), the deformation contour is the same as that of square footing, with one exception that the ends of footing must deflect more than the sides.

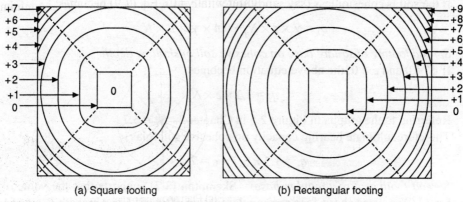

(a) Square footing   (b) Rectangular footing

Note: The mode of deformation of square and rectangular footing due to upward
contact soil pressure, as shown in Figure 3.2 (a) and 3.2 (b) is somewhat the
same as for a circular one shown in Figure 3.1.
The contours of curvature near the column are rounded squares, whereas
those further away become very nearly circular.

FIGURE 3.2   Imaginary contours to show curvature of the top of square and rectangular footings.

3.2   ULTIMATE BEARING CAPACITY

The basic equations for bearing capacity, as described in Chapter 2, are based on the consideration of a strip footing, i.e. the two-dimensional case. In cases of footings of square, rectangular, or circular bases, the support given by soil is by a three-dimensional bulb of pressure. The bearing capacity of such footings may be expected to be greater than that for a strip footing. The ultimate bearing capacity of footings of square and rectangular bases are given by the following expressions:

3.2.1   For Spread Footing of Shallow Depth

When the depth of foundation does not exceed the breadth of footing, the ultimate bearing capacity is expressed as follows:

To determine allowable bearing capacity of soil using BS 8004:1986 (foundations) [3.3]

1. *Spread footing of square base on cohesionless soil of shallow depth:*   The ultimate bearing capacity of spread footing with square bases ($B \times B$) on dense or stiff soil is given by Eq. (2.9) based on experiments as stated in Chapter 2.

$$q_u = 1.3 \times c \times N_c + \gamma \times z \times N_q + 0.4 \times \gamma \times B \times N_y$$

where, N_c, N_q, and N_y are the bearing capacity factors.
The values of these factors may be obtained from the graphs (in Figure 2.5 in Chapter 2) prepared by Terzaghi, and are dependent on the angle of internal friction (ϕ') of soil; c = cohesion of soil; γ = density of soil; and B = width of base.

If the soil is cohesionless (say sandy soil with $c = 0$), Eq. (2.9) becomes

$$q_u = \gamma \times z \times N_q + 0.4 \times \gamma \times B \times N_y$$

2. *Spread footing of square base on cohesive soil of shallow depth:*
   If $\phi' = 0$ and $c > 0$, the above equation becomes

$$q_u = 1.3 \times c \times N_c$$

Referring to the graphs in Figure 2.5 in Chapter 2, $N_c = 5.7$
Therefore, ultimate bearing capacity on cohesive soil (clay)

$$q_u = 1.3 \times 5.7 \times c = 7.4 \times c$$

3. *Spread footing of rectangular base:*   Skempton [3.7] suggests that the value of N_c in Eq. (2.9) as stated above for a rectangular footing of length L and breadth B, may be found by linear interpolation as given by the expression:

$$N_c \text{ for rectangle} = \left(0.84 + 0.16 \times \frac{B}{L}\right) N_c \text{ for square}$$

To determine the allowable bearing capacity of soil using of Eurocode 7:2004 (Geotechnical design) by analytical method (see Annex D of Eurocode 7) [3.4]

1. *Undrained conditions:*   The design (allowable) bearing pressure may be calculated in the following expression:

$$\frac{R}{A'} = q_d = (\pi + 2) \times \frac{C_u}{\gamma_{C_u}} \times b_c \times s_c \times i_c + q \qquad (3.1)$$

(based on Eq. (D.1) of Annex D of Eurocode 7)

where

R = design bearing resistance

q_d = design (allowable) bearing pressure; q_d = design bearing pressure

$A' = B' \times L'$ = design effective foundation base area (see Figure (D.1) of Annex D of Eurocode 7)

C_u = undrained shear strength of soil

γ_{C_u} = partial factor for soil parameter; γ_{C_u} = partial safety factor

q = surcharge pressure at the level of the foundation base

with the following dimensionless factors:

b_c = dimensionless factor for base inclination

$$b_c = 1 - \left[\frac{2\alpha}{(\pi + 2)}\right] \text{(see Annex D)}$$

where

α = inclination of base with the horizontal

i_c = inclination factor of the load

$s_c = 1 + 0.2 \times (B'/L')$ for a rectangular shape; $s_c = 1.2$ for square or circular base

The inclination of load caused by a horizontal load at base

$$i_c = \frac{1}{2}\left(1 + \sqrt{1 - \frac{H}{A' \times C_u}}\right)$$

where

H = horizontal thrust with $H \leq A' \times C_u$

2. *Drained conditions:* Based on Eq. (D.2) of Annex D of Eurocode 7, we find:

$$\frac{R}{A'} = q_d = \frac{c'}{\gamma_{c'}} \times N_c \times b_c \times s_c \times i_c + q' \times N_q \times b_q \times s_q \times i_q$$

$$+ 0.5 \times \gamma' \times B' \times N_\gamma \times b_\gamma \times s_\gamma \times i_\gamma \tag{3.2}$$

where

c' = ultimate effective cohesion

$\gamma_{c'}$ = partial factor for soil parameter

With the following design values of dimensionless factors for the bearing resistance:

$$N_q = e^{\left[\pi \times \tan\left(\frac{\phi'}{\gamma_{\phi'}}\right)\right]} \times \tan^2 \times \left[45 + \left(\frac{\phi'}{\gamma_{\phi'} \times 2}\right)\right]$$

Where $\gamma_{\phi'}$ = partial factor for the angle of shearing resistance (tan ϕ')

$$N_c = (N_q - 1)\cot\left(\frac{\phi'}{\gamma_{\phi'}}\right)$$

$$N_\gamma = 2 \times (N_q - 1)\tan\left(\frac{\phi'}{\gamma_{\phi'}}\right),$$

where structure–ground interface friction angle, $\delta \geq \dfrac{\phi'}{2}$ (rough base)

For inclination of the foundation base:

$$b_c = b_q - \frac{(1 - b_q)}{\left[N_c \times \tan\left(\frac{\phi'}{\gamma_{\phi'}}\right)\right]} \quad \text{(see Annex D)}$$

$$b_q = b_\gamma = 1 - \alpha \times \tan\left(\frac{\phi'}{\gamma_{\phi'}}\right)^2$$

For shape of foundation base:

$$s_q = 1 + \left(\frac{B'}{L'}\right) \times \sin\left(\frac{\phi'}{\gamma_{\phi'}}\right) \qquad \text{for a rectangular shape}$$

$$s_q = 1 + \sin\left(\frac{\phi'}{\gamma_{\phi'}}\right) \qquad \text{for a circular shape}$$

$$s_\gamma = 1 - 0.3 \times \left(\frac{B'}{L'}\right), \qquad \text{for a rectangular shape}$$

$$s_\gamma = 0.7, \qquad \text{for a square or circular shape}$$

$$s_c = \frac{s_q(N_q - 1)}{N_q - 1}, \qquad \text{for a rectangular, square or circular shape}$$

For inclination of the load caused by a horizontal load H (see Annex D):

$$i_c = i_q - \frac{(1 - i_q)}{\left[N_c \times \tan\left(\dfrac{\phi'}{\gamma_{\phi'}}\right)\right]}$$

$$i_q = \left[1 - \frac{H}{\left[V + A' \times c' \times \cot\left(\dfrac{\phi'}{\gamma_{\phi'}}\right)\right]}\right]^m$$

$$i_\gamma = \left[1 - \frac{H}{\left[V + A' \times c' \times \cot\left(\dfrac{\phi'}{\gamma_{\phi'}}\right)\right]}\right]^{(m+1)}$$

where $m = m_B = \dfrac{[2 + B'/L']}{[1 + B'/L']}$ when H acts in the direction of B'

$m = m_L = \dfrac{[2 + L'/B']}{[1 + L'/B']}$ when H acts in the direction of L

B' and L' are effective width and length of foundation base (see Figure D.1 of Annex D)

3.2.2   Spread Footing in Deep Strip Foundations

As described in Chapter 2, when the footing is founded to a considerable depth below the ground level (when the depth of foundation exceeds the width of footing), the weight of the overburden around the foundation changes the pattern of the zones of plastic shear failure. The effect of overburden pressure increases the bearing capacity factors and also the value of ultimate bearing capacity. The graphs in Figure 2.8 in Chapter 2, prepared by Meyerhop, shows the bearing capacity factors for net ultimate bearing capacity for a deep strip foundation.

Skempton, after a comprehensive study together with various experimental data and laboratory test results and full-scale observations, concluded that for cohesive soil the factor N_c increases with depth to a maximum of 7.5 for depths exceeding 2.5 times the width of footing. He prepared the graphs shown in Figure 2.9 in Chapter 2.

3.2.3   Spread Footing in Deep Square or Rectangular Foundations

When $\phi' = 0$; for footing at a depth exceeding 2.5 times the width, the value may be taken equal to $N_c = 9$ in Eq. (2.9) as stated in Chapter 2 (value of N_q and N_y from Figure 2.5). Therefore, ultimate bearing capacity in deep square foundation,

$$q_u = 1.3 \times 9 \times c + \gamma \times z \times N_q + 0.4 \times \gamma \times B \times N_y$$

and ultimate bearing capacity for deep rectangular foundation,

$$q_u = 1.3 \times 9 \times \left(0.84 + 0.16 \times \frac{B}{L} \right) \times c + \gamma \times z \times N_q + 0.4 \times \gamma \times B \times N_y$$

3.3 BENDING MOMENT AND SHEAR IN SQUARE AND RECTANGULAR FOOTINGS

3.3.1 For Square Footing

Contact pressure

Referring to Figure 3.3 (a), the contact pressures on four equal symmetrical trapezoidal areas, as defined by corner lines ('ap', 'bf', 'cm' and 'dn'), give the equal loads due to upward contact pressure, and thus generate equal bending moments and shears upon all four parts assuming that the parts act as cantilever about sides ('ab', 'bc', 'cd' and 'da') of column.

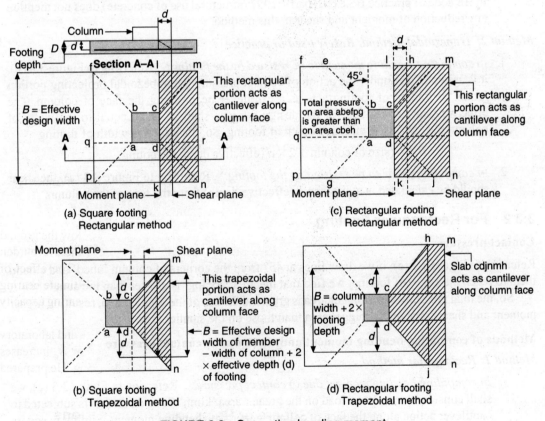

FIGURE 3.3 Computing bending moment.

Methods of computing bending moment and shear due to contact pressure as suggested by Dunham [3.2].

Method 1: Rectangular method

1. *In computing bending moment to be resisted by the footing:* It is assumed that the rectangular projecting portion 'klmn' or 'pqrn' as shown in Figure 3.3 (a) acts as a cantilever beam about line kl or qr subjected to upward contact pressure. As we find that the square 'kdrn' is taken twice in calculating the bending moments of rectangles at right angles to one another. So, 85% of computed moments may be considered in the design of footing.

2. *In computing shear to be resisted by the footing:* Under the action of contact pressure the rectangular projecting portion 'klmn' or 'pqrn' of footing is subjected to diagonal shear along a plane at a distance d (effective depth of footing), i.e. 45 degree from the face of column or pedestal. For the same reason as described before, the total shear should be multiplied by 0.85 to obtain the design shear. So, 85% of computed shear may be considered in the design of footing.

   In BS code of practice BS 8110 : part 1:1997 (structural use of concrete) does not mention any reduction of moment and shear in this method.

Method 2: Trapezoidal method. Rarely used in practice

1. *In computing, bending moment to be resisted by the footing:* Referring to Figure 3.3 (b), it is assumed that under the action of contact pressure the trapezoidal projecting portion 'cdmn' or 'adpn' of footing acts as a cantilever beam along the face of column. The effective width of footing for the design purpose shall be taken equal to the width of column plus twice the effective depth of footing. So, the effective width of footing

   $$B = b \text{ (size of column} + 2 \times d \text{ (effective depth of footing)}$$

2. *In computing shear to be resisted by the footing:* Referring to Figure 3.3 (a), the shear should be calculated at a distance d (effective depth) from the face of the column.

3.3.2   For Rectangular Footing

Contact pressure

Referring to Figure 3.3 (c), if we draw lines at 45° from the corners of column 'abcd' and extend them to reach the edges of footing, we find that the area 'abefpg' is greater than the area 'cbeh'.

So, the total pressure on the bigger area is greater than that of the smaller area, resulting higher moment and shear force on the bigger area than those on the smaller area.

Methods of computing bending moment and shear due to contact pressure

Method 1: Rectangular method

1. *In computing bending moment due to contact pressure:* Referring to Figure 3.3 (c), we shall consider that the total load on the greater area 'klmn' (long direction) is subjected to cantilever action along the face of column generating bending moment. Similar to square footing, 85% of total moment may be taken in the design of section.

2. *In computing shear due to contact pressure:* Referring to Figure 3.3 (c), shear should be calculated on the total load on the greater area 'klmn' at a distance d (effective depth) from the face of column, and 85% of total shear may be taken in the design. British codes of practice do not mention the reduction of design value.

Method 2: Trapezoidal method

Referring to Figure 3.3 (d), the slab 'cdjnmh' acts as cantilever along the column face. This method is not used much in practice.

3.4 REINFORCED CONCRETE DESIGN OF SPREAD FOOTING

The spread footing may be designed in plain concrete without any reinforcement. But for heavily loaded structures, the footing may have to be massive and it becomes uneconomical. So, it is a general practice and is economical to use reinforced concrete in the design of spread foundation. In the design, any standard code of practice may be followed in reinforced concrete design.

In reinforced concrete design we will follow British code of practice BS 8110 : part 1 : 1997; the structural use of concrete. Also we shall use Eurocode 7 (Geotechnical design) as a comparison. The following procedures should be followed as specified in the above codes.

3.4.1 Method of Design

The design of reinforced concrete spread footing shall be carried out by the ultimate limit state (ULS) method in structural strength calculations and serviceability limit state (SLS) method for calculating deflection and crack width and also the effect of temperature, creep and shrinkage of members.

3.4.2 Partial Safety Factors (γ_f)

In the ultimate limit state and servicibility limit state design, the characteristic values of loads are multiplied by the partial safety factors (γ_f) which varies according to types of loads and combinations of loads (say dead, imposed, wind, and earth and water pressure).

Using British code of practice (BS8110): part 1:1997 structural use of concrete [3.5]

The values of γ_f for various load combinations are specified (see Table 2.1).

Example 3.1:

γ_f for dead load (G_k) only = 1.4

γ_f for imposed load (Q_k) only = 1.6

γ_f for wind load (W_k) only = 1.4

γ_f for earth pressure (E_k) and water pressure (W_p) = 1.4

γ_f for (dead + imposed + earth + water) combinations = $1.4\,G_k + 1.6\,Q_k + 1.4\,E_k + 1.4\,W_p$

γ_f for (dead + imposed + earth + water + wind) combinations = $1.2\,(G_k + Q_k + E_k + W_p + W_k)$

Using Eurocode 2: Part 1: 2004 [3.6]

Referring to Table A 1.2 (B) of EC provides the partial factors γ for dead (permanent) and imposed (variable) loads in ultimate load combinations. Thus,

for dead loads, $\gamma G = 1.35$

for imposed loads (leading) $\gamma Q = 1.5$

for imposed loads (accompanying) $\gamma Q \times \psi_0 = 1.5 \times \psi_0$

where

ψ_0 = reduction factor for buildings

= 0.6 for wind

= 1.0 live loads on storage area

= 0.7 live loads on traffic, shopping, office areas

[ψ_0 values are given in Table A1.1 of EC Basis of structural design BS EN 1990:2002]

Design values of actions (STR/GEO) (Set B) of EN 1990:2002 (E) Eurocode—basis of structural design (partial factors on actions, γ). Moments and shear forces should be assessed by using structural combinations.

Unfavourable combinations

$$\gamma_{G,j} \times G_{k,j} + \gamma_{Q,1} \times Q_{k,i} + \gamma_{Q,1} \times Q_{k,1} \times \psi_{0,i} = 1.35\, G_{k,j} + 1.5\, Q_k$$

when wind force is not acting. For stability analysis: [Referring to Table A 1.2 (A)—Design values of actions (EQU) (Set A) of EN 1990-2002(E) Eurocode—basis of structural design].

Unfavourable combinations:

$$\gamma_{G,j} \times G_{k,j} + \gamma_{Q,i} \times Q_{k,i} + \gamma_{Q,1} \times Q_{k,i} \times \psi_{0,i} = 1.35\, G_{k,j} + 1.5\, Q_k \text{ with wind action} + 1.5 \times 0.6 \times Q_{k,j}$$

where

$\gamma_{G,j}$ = partial factor for permanent actions = 1.35

$\gamma_{Q,i}$ = partial factor for leading variable action i = 1.5

$\psi_{0,i}$ = partial factor for combination value of a variable action (wind = 0.6)

[recommended values for ψ_0 shall be obtained from Table A 1.1 of EN 1990–2002 (E)]

$\gamma_{G,j} \times G_{k,j}$ = design values for permanent action = ULT. D.L

$\gamma_{Q,i} \times Q_{k,i}$ = design value for leading variable action = ULT. L.L

$\gamma_{Q,1} \times Q_{k,i} \times \psi_{0,i}$ = design value for accompanying variable actions.

where

G_k = dead loads (D.L.)

Q_k = imposed loads (L.L, W.L, moving loads, etc. WL = Wind Loads)

3.4.3 Strength of Materials

In accordance with BS 8110:1997 [3.5]

For concrete: The strength of concrete for design purposes is based on tests made on cubes at an age of 28 days. These 28-day characteristic strengths determine the grade of concrete and it is important to select the correct grade appropriate for use. The concrete should have the quality of adequate durability and strength for the environmental conditions as well as loading requirements, respectively.

The grades of concrete is expressed in terms of strength in N/mm^2.

Example 3.2:   Grade C_{40} concrete indicates the concrete of 40 N/mm^2 design strength at 28-day cube strength.

The grades of concrete used in practice for structural members are C_{30}, C_{35}, C_{40}, C_{45} and C_{50}. The lowest recommended grade to be used in structures should be grade C_{30}.

For reinforcement: The characteristic strengths of reinforcement should comply with British codes of practices BS 4449, BS 4482, and BS 4483 and are shown in Table 3.1 (strength of reinforcement) in BS 8110: Part 1: 1997. In reinforced concrete design it is the normal practice to use high yield steel of characteristic strength f_y = 460 N/mm^2 as recommended by British code of practice BS 8110.

TABLE 3.1 Selected concrete properties (based on Eurocode 2, Part 1.1)

Symbol	Description	Properties								
f_{ck} (N/mm^2)	Characteristic cylinder strength	12	16	20	25	30	35	40	45	50
$f_{ck.cube}$ (N/mm^2)	Characteristic cube strength	15	20	25	30	37	45	50	55	60
F_{ct} (N/mm^2)	Mean tensile strength	1.6	1.9	2.2	2.6	2.9	3.2	3.5	3.8	4.1
E_{cm} (kN/mm^2)	Secant modulus of elasticity	27	29	30	31	33	34	35	36	37

Use of Eurocode 2 [3.6] In structural design, Eurocode 2 (design of concrete structures) shall be followed.

For concrete: The design of reinforced concrete is based on the characteristic cylinder strength of concrete rather than the cube strength (see Table 3.1).

Thus, if characteristic cylinder strength of concrete f_{ck} = 40 N/mm^2.

Then, characteristic cube strength of concrete $f_{ck.cube}$ = 50 N/mm^2.

So, the ratio of

$$\frac{f_{ck}}{f_{ck.cube}} = \frac{40}{50} = 0.8$$

For reinforcing steel: The characteristic yield strength of high tensile steel (f_{yk}) varies from 400 to 600 N/mm^2. The properties of steel reinforcement in the UK for use with Eurocode 2 are given in BS 4449 (2005): specification for carbon steel bars for the reinforcement of concrete are summarized in Table 3.2.

(*Note:* The required properties of reinforcement steel shall be verified in accordance with EN 10080)

TABLE 3.2 Characteristic tensile properties of reinforcement

Class (BS 4449) and designation (BS 8666)	A	B	C
Characteristic yield strength f_{yk} or $f_{0.2k}$ in N/mm^2	500	500	500
Minimum value of $k = (f_t/f_y)k$	≥ 1.05	≥ 1.08	≥ 1.15 < 1.35
Characteristic strain at maximum force (ε_{uk})	≥ 2.5	≥ 5.0	≥ 7.5

A characteristic yield strength of 500 N/mm^2 has been adopted by the UK reinforcement industry. There are three classes of reinforcement A, B, and C which provide increasing ductility. Class A is not suitable where redistribution of 20% or more has been assumed in the design. There is no provision for the use of plain or mild steel reinforcement.

3.5 EXAMPLE 1—DESIGN OF A SQUARE OR RECTANGULAR FOOTING

Design data

A column (size 500 × 500) of a storage bin for limestone and coke is subjected to the following loadings at ground level:

Characteristic dead load	$G_k = 1984$ kN
Characteristic live load	$Q_k =$ **negligible**
Characteristic wind load	$W_k = 141$ kN
Characteristic moment due to wind	$M_w = 116.6$ kNm
Characteristic shear due to wind at ground level	$H_w = 75.2/2 = 37.6$ kN

Characteristic moment developed due to shear at base level (2 m below GL)

$$37.6 \times 2 = 75.2 \text{ kN m}$$

Therefore, total characteristic moment developed at base level

$$M_w = 116.6 + 75.2 = 191.8 \text{ (say 192 kN m)}$$

Geotechnical data

Top 300 mm of soil is underlain by 1.5 m of sandy clay. Below sandy layer lies medium sand of adequate depth.

We are to design a square or rectangular footing foundation to sustain these loadings. The principles of design of square or rectangular footing are the same. In our case we adopt a square footing because the wind loads may act in either direction on the storage bin structure.

The following principal steps are taken in the design:

- To determine the bearing capacity of soil.
- To compute the size of footing.
- To calculate the actual pressure in soil due to vertical loads and moments.
- To calculate the net contact pressure under the footing due to vertical loads and moments.
- To design the reinforced concrete footing foundation.
- To calculate the ultimate moment.
- To calculate the reinforcement with an assumed thickness of footing.
- To check the shear stress in concrete. If the concrete shear stress exceeds the allowable shear stress in concrete, increase the thickness so as to lower down the shear stress in concrete to the allowable value of shear stress in concrete.
- To check the punching shear stress in concrete.

3.5.1   To Determine Bearing Capacity of Soil

To determine the allowable bearing capacity using of BS 8004:1986 (foundations)

Assume the foundation to be founded on soil of medium sand at a depth of 2 m from the ground level. From soil investigation report, the following geotechnical design data are obtained for medium sand:

Soil density,	$\gamma_b = 20$ kN/m^2
Angle of internal friction,	$\phi' = 30°$; $C_u = 0$ (assumed)
Number of blows in SPT tests,	$N = 25$

Ultimate bearing capacity for square footing may be calculated from the following semi-empirical equation:

$$q_u = 1.3 \times C_u \times N_c + \gamma_b \times z \times N_q + 0.4 \times \gamma_b \times B \times N_y$$

where

C_u = undrained shear strength of soil for cohesionless soil = 0

N_c = bearing capacity factor = 0

N_q = bearing capacity factor for ($\phi' = 30°$) = 22

N_y = bearing capacity factor for ($\phi' = 30°$) = 20

The bearing capacity factors are obtained from graph prepared by Terzaghi [3.1].

B = width of footing

z = depth of foundation below ground level = 2.0 m

Now, we have to find out the approximate value of B.

Refer to Table 2.3 in Chapter 2 (Geotechnics). In soil type medium sand at 2 m depth, allowable bearing capacity of soil

$$q = \frac{(220 + 330)}{2} = 275 \text{ kN/m}^2 \quad \text{(average between fine and course sand)}$$

In calculating the allowable bearing capacity of soil, the characteristic value of loads shall be considered. So,

the characteristic (dead + wind) loads = (1984 + 141) kN = 2125 kN

Area of footing required, $\qquad\qquad A = \dfrac{2125}{275} = 7.73 \text{ m}^2$

Therefore,

size of base required = 2.78 m × 2.78 m

Assume,

size of square footing = $B \times B$ = 2.8 m × 2.8 m

Now, referring to equation for ultimate bearing capacity of soil,

$$q_u = \gamma_b \times z \times N_q + 0.4 \times \gamma_b \times B \times N_y$$
$$= 20 \times 2 \times 22 + 0.4 \times 20 \times 2.8 \times 20 = 1328 \text{ kN/m}^2$$

and the net ultimate bearing capacity of soil is given by Eq. (2.6) by deducting the column of 2 m of soil.

Therefore,

$$q_u \text{ (net)} = \gamma_b \times z \times (N_q - 1) + 0.4 \times \gamma_b \times B \times N_y$$
$$= 20 \times 2 \times (22 - 1) + 0.4 \times 20 \times 2.8 \times 20 = 1288 \text{ kN/m}^2$$

Using a factor of safety of 3 taking into consideration the excessive differential settlement, net safe bearing capacity of soil

$$q \text{ (net)} = \frac{q_u}{3} = \frac{1288}{3} = 429 \text{ kN/m}^2$$

Adding the weight of 2 m column of soil, gross safe bearing capacity of soil

$$q \text{ (gross)} = 429 + 2 \times 20 = 429 + 40 = 469 \text{ kN/m}^2$$

So, adopt an allowable safe bearing capacity of soil, $q = 400 \text{ kN/m}^2$.

To determine allowable bearing capacity using of Eurocode 7: Part 1: 2004 (Geotechnical design)

To calculate the allowable bearing pressure of soil at 2 m depth of medium sand, assume

$$\phi' = 30° \text{ and } C_u = 0 \text{ and also } c' = 0$$

Following the expression, as given in Eurocode 7 (Annex D) for drained condition, the design allowable bearing pressure

$$q_d = \frac{R}{A'} = q' \times N_q \times b_q \times s_q \times i_q + 0.5 \times \gamma \times B' \times N_\gamma \times b_\gamma \times s_\gamma \times i_\gamma$$

(*Note:* the first term containing c' is neglected, since c' assumed = 0)
where

R = design bearing resistance
$A' = B' \times L'$ = design effective foundation base area
B' = the design effective foundation base width
L' = the design effective foundation base length.

with the design values of dimensionless factors for the bearing resistance factors.
Referring to Table A.2 in Annex A of EC 7: Partial factors for soil parameters:

1. Angle of shearing resistance, $\gamma_{\phi'} = 1.25$; this factor is applied to tan ϕ'
2. Undrained shear strength, $\gamma_{C_u} = 1.4$
3. Effective cohesion, $\gamma_{c'} = 1.25$

$$N_q = e^{\left(\pi \times \tan \frac{\phi'}{\gamma_{\phi'}}\right)} \times \tan^2 \left(45 + \frac{\phi'/2}{\gamma_{\phi'}}\right)$$

$$= e^{\left(\pi \times \tan \frac{30}{1.25}\right)} \times \tan^2 \left(45 + \frac{30/2}{1.25}\right) = 4.05 \times 2.37 = 9.60$$

$$N_\gamma = 2 \times (N_q - 1) \times \tan \left(\frac{\phi'/2}{1.25}\right) = 2 \times (9.6 - 1) \times \tan 12 = 3.66$$

The inclination factors of the foundation base:

$$b_q = b_y = \left[1 - \alpha \times \tan \left(\frac{\phi'/2}{1.25}\right)\right]$$

where

α = inclination of base with the horizontal = 0
Since

$$\alpha = 0$$

$$b_q = b_y = 1$$

The shape factors of foundation:

$$s_q = 1 + \sin\left(\frac{\phi'/2}{1.25}\right) = 1.2 \text{ for a square or circular shape}$$

$s_\gamma = 0.7$ for a square or circular shape.
The inclination of the load caused by a horizontal load H

$$i_q = \left[1 - \frac{H}{\left[V + A' \times c' \times \cot\left(\frac{\phi'}{\gamma_{\phi'}}\right)\right]}\right]^m$$

where

$$m = m_L = \frac{\left[2 + \dfrac{L'}{B'}\right]}{\left[1 + \dfrac{L'}{B'}\right]}$$

when H acts in the direction of L'.
Assumed, $B = 3.0$ m; $L = 3.0$ m, and H acts in the direction of L'

$$e_l = \text{eccentricity} = \frac{M}{P} = \frac{192}{(1984 + 141)} = \frac{192}{2125} = 0.09$$

$$L' = L - 2 \times e_l = 2.82 \text{ m}$$

$$B' = B = 3.0; \; A' = 2.82 \times 3 = 8.46 \text{ m}^2$$

Therefore,

$$m = \frac{2 + \dfrac{2.84}{3}}{1 + \dfrac{2.84}{3}} = 1.52$$

[Since $c' = 0$ (cohesion intercept in terms of effective stress)]

$$i_q = \left[1 - \frac{37.6}{2125}\right]^{1.52} = \left[1 - \frac{37.6}{2125}\right]^{1.52} = 0.97$$

$$i_\gamma = \left[1 - \frac{H}{V}\right]^{m+1} = 0.95$$

γ' = effective density of soil = 20 kN/m³
q' = effective overburden pressure at foundation base = $2 \times 20 = 40$ kN/m²

Hence,

q_d = design allowable bearing pressure

$$= 40 \times 9.6 \times 1 \times 1 \times 0.97 + 0.5 \times 20 \times 3 \times 3.66 \times 1 \times 0.7 \times 0.95 = 445 \text{ kN/m}^2$$

Adopt: q_d = allowable bearing capacity of soil = 400 kN/m².

3.5.2 Size of Footing

With the above value of allowable bearing capacity of soil, the area of base required is

$$\frac{2125}{400} = 5.3 \text{ m}^2$$

Required size of base = 2.3 m × 2.3 m

Till now, we have only considered the vertical loads. But the footing is also subjected to a moment is 192 kN m. So, the size of base should be increased to cater for this moment in order to keep the bearing pressure within the allowable value. Therefore, adopt the size of footing,

$$B \times B = 3.0 \text{ m} \times 3.0 \text{ m} \qquad \text{[see Figure 3.4(a)]}$$

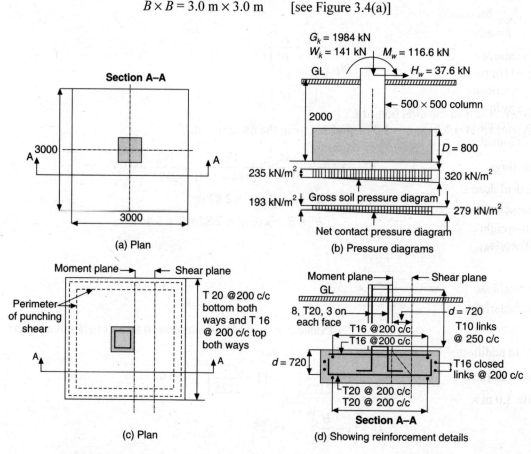

(a) Plan

(b) Pressure diagrams

(c) Plan

(d) Showing reinforcement details

Note:
1. All loads and moments are un-factored
2. Concrete strength f_{cu} = 40 N/mm^2
3. High strength reinforcement f_y = 460 N/mm^2

FIGURE 3.4 Size of footing.

3.5.3 To Calculate the Actual Gross and Net Pressures in Soil due to Vertical Loads and Moments

To assume the thickness of footing

It is desirable to design a footing thick enough so that no web reinforcement is required, in order to attain stiffness and simplicity of reinforcement.

The minimum design concrete shear stress at the edges of 45 degree slopes from the faces of column should not exceed $v_c = 0.34$ N/mm^2 for the thickness of 400 mm and more with minimum per cent of steel of $100 \times A_s/(b_v \times d) = 0.15$, where

  A_s = area of tension reinforcement

  b_v = breadth of section

  d = effective depth of section

(The above minimum design shear stress criterion is specified in British Standard Code of Practice BS 8110: part 1: 1997, Table 3.8 in ultimate limit state method).

Eurocode 2 states that it is not usual to provide shear reinforcement in a pad (spread) foundation. So, it is necessary to ensure that the allowable concrete shear stress without shear reinforcement is greater than the applied shear stress.

Considering this point, assume the total depth of footing, $D = 600$ mm

Loadings

Vertical dead load:

Characteristic dead load from column, G_k		= 1984 kN
Self-weight of footing	$= 3.0 \times 3.0 \times 0.6 \times 24 =$	130 kN
Soil overburden on footing	$= (3.0^2 - 0.5^2) \times 1.4 \times 20 =$	245 kN
	Total =	2359 kN

Vertical load due to wind:

Characteristic load W_k (already calculated)		= 141 kN
	Total vertical load, $W =$	2500 kN

In addition, the foundation is subjected to a moment due to wind, $M = 192$ kN m

Gross foundation pressures

With 3.0 m × 3.0 m footing, modulus of section

$$Z_x = 3 \times \frac{3^2}{6} = 4.5 \text{ m}^3$$

And area of footing base

$$A = 3^2 = 9 \text{ m}^2$$

Therefore, maximum gross pressure on soil

$$f_{max} = \frac{W}{A} + \frac{M}{Z} = \frac{2500}{9} + \frac{192}{4.5} = 320 \text{ kN/m}^2$$

and minimum pressure on soil

$$f_{min} = \frac{W}{A} - \frac{M}{Z} = \frac{2500}{9} - \frac{192}{4.5} = 235 \text{ kN/m}^2$$

So, maximum soil pressure is within the allowable bearing capacity of soil 400 kN/m².
Therefore, the size of footing 3.0 m square is adopted in the design is satisfactory [see Figure 3.4 (a)].

To calculate the net contact pressure at the underside of footing base

To calculate the net contact in the design of footing, the weight of overburden soil and the weight of concrete of footing shall be deducted. So

Total gross downward load   = 2359 kN
Deduct: self-weight of footing   = – 130 kN
            overburden soil weight   = –245 kN
Net vertical load, G_k = 1984 kN

Additional vertical load on column due to wind, W_k = 141 kN
Total net vertical load, = $G_k + W_k$ = (1984 + 141)   = 2125 kN
In addition, moment due to wind   =192 kN m
Therefore, maximum net upward contact pressure

$$p_{max} = \frac{W}{A} + \frac{M}{Z} = \frac{2125}{9} + \frac{192}{4.5} = 236 + 43 = 279 \text{ kN/m}^2$$

Minimum upward contact pressure

$$p_{min} = \frac{W}{A} - \frac{M}{Z} = 193 \text{ kN/m}^2 \qquad \text{[see Figure 3.4 (b)].}$$

3.5.4   Structural Design of Reinforced Concrete Footing

In the structural design of reinforced concrete spread footing, any standard codes of practice may be followed.

Structural design using BS 8110: part 1: 1997 (Structural use of concrete code of practice for design and construction)

Ultimate moment: The cantilever bending moment due to net upward soil pressure shall be calculated along the face of column [see Figure 3.4 (c) and (d)].
Upward pressure at the face of column

$$p = 193 + (279 - 193) \times \frac{1.75}{3} = 243 \text{ kN/m}^2$$

Considering whole 3.0 m width of slab cantilevered from the face of column, characteristic moment at the face of column

$$= \left[3.0 \times \frac{243 \times 1.25^2}{2} + 0.5 \times (279 - 243) \times \frac{1.25}{2} \times \frac{2}{3} \times 1.25 \right] = 3 \times 199.2 \text{ kN m} = 597.6 \text{ kN m}$$

Since (dead and wind) loads acting simultaneously, the partial safety factor (γ_f) for the ultimate moment calculation should be taken equal to 1.4. So, $\gamma_f = 1.4$

Therefore, ultimate moment

$$M_u = 1.4 \times 597.6 = 836.6 \text{ kN m}$$

Design of section: Assume: the depth of footing $D = 600$ mm, effective width of slab = 3000 mm. With cover = 50 mm, and assuming diameter of bar = 20 mm, effective depth of footing

$$d = 600 - 50 - 20 - \frac{20}{2} = 600 - 50 - 20 - \frac{20}{2} = 520 \text{ mm}$$

(*Note:*   As the reinforcement is provided in both directions, the centre line of upper layer of bar is considered in calculating the effective depth.)

Assumed:

the characteristic strength of reinforcement, $f_y = 460 \text{ N/mm}^2$

the characteristic cube strength of concrete, $f_{cu} = 40 \text{ N/mm}^2$

Then

$$K = \frac{M_u}{B \times d^2 \times f_{cu}} = \frac{836.6 \times 10^6}{3000 \times 520^2 \times 40} = 0.026$$

$$K' = 0.156$$

Since $K < K'$, compression reinforcement is not required.

$$z = d \left[0.5 + \left(\frac{0.25 - K}{0.9} \right)^{0.5} \right] = 520 \left[0.5 + \left(\frac{0.25 - 0.026}{0.9} \right)^{0.5} \right] = 519 \text{ mm}$$

But should not be greater than $0.95 \times 520 = 494$ mm

So, adopt

$$z = 494 \text{ mm}$$

Therefore, area of steel required

$$A_s = \frac{M_u}{0.95 \times f_y \times z} = \frac{836.6 \times 10^6}{0.95 \times 460 \times 487} = 3875 \text{ mm}^2$$

Therefore,

$$\frac{A_s}{m_{\text{width}}} = \frac{3875}{3} = 1292 \text{ mm}^2$$

Using 20 mm high strength bar at 200 mm c/c area provided = 1571 mm^2

Therefore, adopt T20 bar at 200 mm c/c bottom both ways [see Figure 3.4 (c) and (d)].

(*Note:*   T20 = High strength reinforcement bar of 20 mm diameter).

To check for shear: The shear to be checked at a distance d from the face of column and for the whole width of base. The concrete shear stress should not be greater than the allowable shear stress in concrete [Referring to Figure 3.4 (c) and (d)].

Shear at d (520 mm) from face of column

$$V = \text{Net upward soil pressure} \times \text{width of base } (B) = \frac{(258 + 279)}{2 \times 0.7 \times 3.0} = 588 \text{ kN}$$

(With a combined partial safety factor, $\gamma_f = 1.4$)

Ultimate shear at the face of column

$$V_u = \gamma_f \times V = 1.4 \times 588 = 823 \text{ kN}$$

(With depth of base, $D = 600$ mm; and $d = 520$ mm)

Therefore, concrete shear stress

$$v_u = \frac{V_u}{d \times B} = 823 \times \frac{10^3}{520 \times 3000} = 0.52 \text{ N/mm}^2$$

Percentage of steel provided

$$\frac{100 \times A_s}{1000 \times d} = 100 \times \frac{1571}{1000 \times 520} = 0.30$$

Referring to Table 3.8 of BS 8110 (values of v_c design concrete shear stress), and with effective depth of slab = 520 mm > 400, Allowable shear stress in concrete

$$v_c = 0.4 \text{ N/mm}^2 < v_u \; (0.52 \text{ N/mm}^2)$$

The values given in Table 3.8 of BS 8110 have been derived from the expression,

$$v_c = \frac{0.79}{\gamma_m} \left(\frac{100 \times A_s}{b \times d} \right)^{1/3} \times \left(\frac{400}{d} \right)^{1/4}$$

where $\gamma_m = 1.25$ and $400/d$ should not be greater than 1.

So, we need shear reinforcement, but it should be avoided for footing slab. In this case, it will be rather justified to increase the depth of base from 600 mm to 800 mm.

With increased value of $D = 800$ mm; $d = 800 - 50$ (cover) $- 30$ (1.5 × bar diameter) $= 720$ mm
Shear at a distance d (720 mm) from the face of column

$$V = \text{net upward soil pressure} \times \text{width of base}$$

$$(B = 3000 \text{ mm}) = (264 + 279) \times \frac{0.53}{2 \times 3.0} = 432 \text{ kN}$$

(With $\gamma_f = 1.4$)

Ultimate shear

$$V_u = 1.4 \times 432 = 604 \text{ kN}$$

(With increased depth $D = 800$ mm and $d = 720$ mm)

Concrete shear stress

$$v_u = \frac{V_u}{(B \times d)} = \frac{604 \times 10^3}{3000 \times 720} = 0.28 \text{ N/mm}^2$$

Percentage of steel provided

$$100 \times \frac{A_s}{1000 \times 720} = 100 \times \frac{1571}{1000 \times 720} = 0.22$$

Referring to Table 3.8 (BS 8110: part 1: 1997) with effective depth = 720 mm > 400 m, allowable shear stress in concrete

$$v_c = \frac{(0.34 + 0.40)}{2} = 0.37 \text{ N/mm}^2 \text{ (average)} > 0.22$$

Therefore, no shear reinforcement is required, and adopt 800 mm thick footing slab [see Figure 3.4 (d)].

To check for punching shear: Punching shear stress shall be calculated along the perimeter at a distance 1.5 × effective depth of base [see Figure 3.4 (c)].

The distance of perimeter line from the face of column

$$1.5 \times d = 1.5 \times 720 = 1080 \text{ mm}$$

Assume, average contact pressure

$$p(\text{ave}) = \frac{193 + 279}{2} = 236 \text{ kN/m}^2$$

Total punching shear

$$V_{\text{punch}} = p(\text{ave}) \times [B^2 - (1.5\ d \times 2 + c)^2] = 236 \times (3^2 - 2.66^2) = 454 \text{ kN}$$

Ultimate

$$V_{\text{punch}} = 1.4 \times 454 = 636 \text{ kN}$$

Punching shear stress

$$v_{\text{punch}} = \frac{V_{\text{punch}}}{\text{perimeter} \times \text{effective depth}} = \frac{636 \times 10^3}{4 \times 266 \times 720} = 0.08 \text{ N/mm}^2 < v_c\ 0.37 \text{ N/mm}^2$$

Therefore, the depth 800 mm provided is adequate in punching shear stress.

Structural design using Eurocode 2: 2004 (design of concrete structures)

Net upward pressure: From previous Section 3.5.3

Net characterisic upward pressure due to dead load

$$\frac{1984}{3^2} = 220 \text{ kN/m}^2$$

Characteristic maximum upward pressue due to wind load

$$= \frac{W_k}{A} + \frac{M_w}{Z}$$

$$\frac{141}{3^2} + \frac{192}{4.5} = 59 \text{ kN/m}^2$$

Characteristic minimum upward pressure due to wind load

$$\frac{W_k}{A} - \frac{M_w}{Z} = -27 \text{ kN/m}^2$$

At ultimate limit state, load combination = $1.35\,G_k + 1.5\,W_k$
Therefore, at ultimate load combination:

    Ultimate upward pressure due to dead load   = $1.35 \times W_k = 1.35 \times 220 = 297$ kN/m²
    Ultimate maximum pressure due to wind load = $1.5 \times 59 = 89$ kN/m²
    Ultimate minimum pressure due to wind load = $1.5 \times -27 = -41$ kN/m²
    So, total ultimate maximum upward pressure = $297 + 89 = 386$ kN/m²
    and total ultimate minimum upward pressure = $297 - 41 = 256$ kN/m²

Ultimate moment: Moment shall be calculated at the face of column with footing slab cantilevered from the face of column assuming whole width of slab of 3.0 m.
    Ultimate upward soil pressure at the face of column

$$256 + (386 - 256) \times \frac{1.75}{3} = 332 \text{ kN/m}^2$$

Therefore, ultimate moment at the face of column

$$M_u = 3\left(332 \times \frac{1.25^2}{2} + \frac{1}{2} \times 1.25 \times 54 \times \frac{2}{3} \times 1.25\right) = 863 \text{ kN m}$$

$$M_u/\text{m width} = \frac{863}{3} = 288 \text{ kN m}$$

Design of section: With characteristic cube strength of concrete (BS 8110) $= f_{ck.\text{cube}} = 40$ N/mm², characteristic cylinder strength of concrete (EC 2) $= f_{ck} = 30$ N/mm² (approx.) (see Table 3.1 of EC 2, part 1.1)
    Concrete class = C30/40

$f_{ck} = 30$ N/mm²; $f_{yk} = 500$ N/mm²
    Assumed depth, $D = 800$ mm (to ensure that actual shear stress in concrete does not exceed allowable shear stress).
    Effective depth $d = 800 - 40$ (cover) $- 10(1/2$ bar diameter$) = 750$ mm

$$K = \frac{M_u}{(b \times d^2 \times f_{ck})} = \frac{288 \times 10^6}{1000 \times 750^2 \times 30} = 750 \text{ mm}$$

$$K' = 0.60 \times \delta - 0.18 \times \delta^2 - 0.21 = 0.60 \times 1 - 0.18 \times 1 - 0.21 = 0.21$$
$$\text{(assuming } \delta = 1)$$

Since K is less than K', no compression reinforcement is required.

$$\text{Lever arm } z = \frac{d}{2[1 + (1 - 3.53K)^{0.5}]} = \frac{d}{2[1 + (1 - 3.53 \times 0.017)^{0.5}]} = 0.98d$$

but should be limited to $0.95d$.
Therefore, area of steel required

$$A_s = \frac{M_u}{(f_y \times d)} = \frac{288 \times 10^6}{(500 \times 750)} = 768 \text{ mm}^2$$

Adopt: T20 at 200 mm c/c bottom both ways (As provided = 1571 mm²)
Minimum % of tensile reinforcement,

$$0.0015 \times b \times d = 1000 \times 750 = 1125 \text{ mm}^2 < 1571 \text{ mm}^2 \quad \textbf{Satisfactory.}$$

Check for shear: Actual shear stress at a distance d from the face of column

$$v_{ed} = V_{ud/(b \times d)}$$

Upward pressure at a distance 750 mm from the face of column

$$256 + 130 \times \frac{2.5}{3} = 364 \text{ kN/m}^2$$

Total shear at 750 mm from the face of column

$$V_{ed} = \frac{1}{2} \times 0.5 \times (364 + 386) = 188 \text{ kN}$$

Applied shear stress in concrete

$$v_{ed} = \frac{V_{ed}}{b \times d} = \frac{188 \times 10^3}{1000 \times 750} = 0.25 \text{ N/mm}^2$$

Concrete shear stress capacity

$$v_{rdc} = 0.12 \times k \times (100 \times \rho_1 \times f_{ck})^{0.33}$$

where

$$\rho_1 = \frac{A_s}{b \times d} = \frac{1571}{1000 \times 750} = 0.0021$$

and

$$k = 1 + \left(\frac{200}{d}\right)^{0.5} = 1 + \left(\frac{200}{750}\right)^{0.5} = 1.52$$

Therefore,

$$v_{rdc} = 0.12 \times 1.52 \times (100 \times 0.0021 \times 30)^{0.33} = 0.33 \text{ N/mm}^2$$

and should be

$$\geq 0.035 \times k^{1.5} \times f_{ck}^{0.5} \geq 0.035 \times 1.52^{1.5} \times 30^{0.5} = 0.36 \text{ N/mm}^2$$

Therefore, concrete shear capacity stress

$$v_{rdc} = 0.36 \text{ N/mm}^2 > v_{ed} (0.25 \text{ N/mm}^2) \quad \textbf{So, OK}$$

To check for punching shear: The punching shear shall be calculated around a perimeter of d from the face of column. Assume, average upward soil pressure

$$q_d = \frac{1}{2}(256 + 386) = 321 \text{ kN/m}^2$$

Total shear in concrete around the perimeter of d from the face of column

$$V_{ed} = q_d [3 \times 3 - \pi \times (0.25 + 0.75)^2] = 321 \times (9 - \pi) = 1880 \text{ kN}$$

Applied punching shear stress

$$v_{ed} = \frac{V_{ed}}{2 \times \pi \times (0.25 + 0.75)} = \frac{1880 \times 10^3}{(2 \times \pi \times 1) 10^6} = 0.3 \text{ N/mm}^2$$

And concrete shear stress capacity

$$v_{rdc} = 0.36 \text{ N/mm}^2 > v_{ed} (0.3 \text{ N/mm}^2) \qquad \textbf{So, OK}$$

REFERENCES

[3.1] Terzaghi, K. and R.B. Peck, *Soil Mechanics in Engineering Practice*, Wiley, New York, 1962.

[3.2] Dunham, C.W., *Foundations of Structures*, McGraw-Hill, New York, 1950.

[3.3] BS 8004: 1986: British Standard Code of Practice for Foundations.

[3.4] Eurocode 7: 2004: Geotechnical Design, Part 1: General Rules.

[3.5] BS 8110: 1997: Structural Use of Concrete, Part 1: Code of Practice for Design and Construction.

[3.6] Eurocode 2: 2004: Design of Concrete Structures-Part-I: General Rules and Rules for Buildings.

[3.7] Skempton, A.W., The bearing capacity of clays, Building Research Congress, Division I, 1951, 180.

Chapter 4

Combined Spread Footing Foundations

4.0 DEFINITION AND DESCRIPTIONS

When the size of isolated footings for individual columns are large enough to nearly touch the footing of neighbouring column, it is advisable to use a large slab or combined footing under two or more columns instead of isolated spread footing under each one and connected together. This type of footing is defined as combined spread footing (Peck, Hansen and Thornburn [4.1]).

The following are some of the conditions under which the combined spread footings are adopted (Dunham [4.2]):

1. When a row of columns is so close to the neighbouring building line that the individual spread footing near the neighbouring building line will be loaded eccentrically, then the footing of the outer column is joined together to the footing of the interior column to form the combined footing [see Figure 4.1(a)].
2. When two nearby columns are so close that their individual spread footings nearly coincide, it is advisable to connect the individual footings to act as combined footing [see Figure 4.1 (b)].
3. When two columns in a row at the ground level are subjected to uplift, overturning moment and horizontal forces, the combined spread footing provides the most satisfactory solution in construction [see Figure 4.1 (c)]. Sometimes the columns are tied together by introducing a beam to create more structural rigidity and allowing the footing slab to act transversely, and also the beam to span between the columns.
4. When the individual footing of two or more columns is founded on soil of variable and low bearing value and subjected to differential settlements, a combined spread footing under the columns is recommended [see Figure 4.1 (d)].

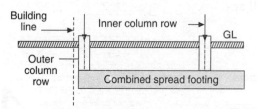

(a) Showing outer column row, so close to the building line that isolated footing will be eccentrically loaded. Combined footing recommended.

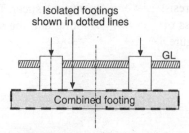

(b) Showing isolated footings (in dotted lines) of two nearby columns too close to nearly coincide. It is advisable to have combined footing.

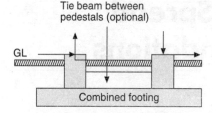

(c) Showing two pedestals of a trestle subjected to vertical loads, uplift and horizontal forces. A combined footing provides satisfactory solution. Sometimes, a beam is introduced to tie up the pedestals and also to bring rigidity to the foundation.

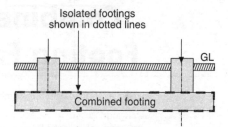

(d) Showing isolated footings (in dotted lines) subjected to differential settlements due to variable and low bearing value of soil and high differences in column loadings. In this condition, a combined footing is recommended.

FIGURE 4.1 Combined spread footings under various conditions.

5. The important point to be borne in mind in determining the dimensions of the combined footing that the dimensions of the footing should be so chosen that the resultant the column loads passes through the centroid of the base area to give a uniform bearing pressure so as to avoid differential settlements. A rectangular footing is always preferred.

4.1 BEHAVIOUR OF COMBINED FOOTING SUBJECTED TO UPWARD SOIL CONTACT PRESSURE

The combined spread footing under two or more vertically loaded columns will behave as a slab of simply supported or continuous member under the vertical point loads of columns and subjected to upward contact pressure. The contact pressure will tend to deflect the footing slab upwards in the regions between the spacing of columns, thus creating tensions at the top face of slab and also bottom face of slab under the column. The tension in the concrete is resisted by introducing reinforcement [see Figure 4.2 (a)].

When the upward contact pressure is very high and the spacing of columns is large, the beams are introduced between the columns to bring high stiffness to the footing and at the same time to resist greater moments and shear. The introduction of this inverted T-beam will reduce the thickness of slab of the footing and the slab will act transversely as cantilevers over the beam [see Figure 4.2 (b)].

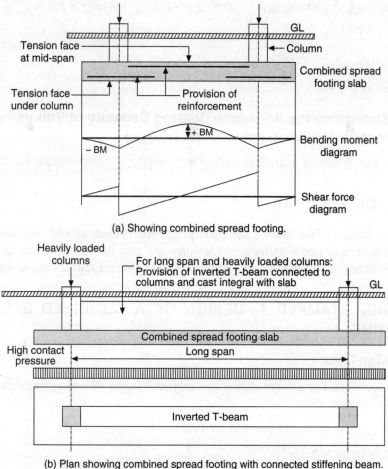

(a) Showing combined spread footing.

(b) Plan showing combined spread footing with connected stiffening beam.

FIGURE 4.2   Combined footing.

4.2   BEARING CAPACITY OF SOIL

4.2.1   To Determine the Allowable Bearing Capacity of Soil using BS 8004: 1986 (Foundations)

Before determining the size of footing, we should at first determine the bearing capacity of soil. Referring to Chapter 2 (Geotechnics):

Ultimate bearing capacity as formulated by Terzaghi [4.7] the semi-empirical equation for square footing given in Eq. (2.9) in Chapter 2,

$$q_u = 1.3 \times c \times N_c + \gamma \times z \times N_q + 0.4 \times \gamma \times B \times N_y$$

For rectangular footing, the above equation may be modified as skempton [4.8]

$$q_u = \left(0.84 \times 0.16 \times \frac{B}{L} \right) \times N_c + \gamma \times z \times N_q + 0.4 \times \gamma \times B \times N_y$$

where

B = width of footing

L = length of footing.

4.2.2 To Determine the Allowable Bearing Capacity of Soil using Eurocode 7: 2004 (Geotechnical Design)

Refer to Annex D: A sample analytical method for bearing resistance calculation.

4.3 SIZE OF FOOTING

In determining the size of the footing, the resultant of column loads should coincide with the CG of footing base area so that a uniform contact pressure may be obtained. The footing may be trapezoidal or of any shape, but rectangular base is preferable for reinforcement detailing.

4.4 DESIGN EXAMPLE 1—DESIGN OF A COMBINED SPREAD FOOTING

4.4.1 Design Data

Consider the foundation of a tower of two legs subjected to the following loadings:
The left leg loadings at base:

Vertical downward thrust (unfactored), $V_1 = -2000$ kN $\downarrow$

The right leg loadings at base:

Vertical downward thrust (unfactored), $V_2 = 2500$ kN $\downarrow$

The size of columns 600 mm × 600 mm; the foundation depth from ground level = 2.0 m; the spacing of column is 6.0 m
Geotechnical data of ground: The top 300 mm of soil is made up of ground underlain by sandy clay of considerable depth.

We are to design a combined spread footing.
The following procedures are carried out:

- To determine the bearing capacity of soil
- To obtain the sizing of the footing
- To calculate the net upward contact pressure of soil under the footing
- To design the reinforced concrete footing foundation.

4.4.2 The Bearing Capacity of Soil in Sandy Clay

To determine bearing capacity of soil using BS 8004: 1986 (Foundations) [4.3]

Referring to Table 2.4 (approximate allowable bearing capacity of soil) in Chapter 2, approximate bearing capacity of soil type clay and sand mixed at 2 m depth, $q = 275$ kN/m^2.

Total loads

$$V_1 + V_2 = (2000 + 2500) = 4500 \text{ kN}$$

Therefore, area of footing base required $= \dfrac{4500}{275} = 16.4 \text{ m}^2$

Assume the width of footing is 2.5 m.
So, the length of base required is

$$\frac{16.4}{2.5} = 6.5 \text{ m}$$

Assume a length,

$L = 6.0$ (spacing of columns) + 0.6 m (width of column) + 1.4 (overhang) = 8.0 m

Therefore, assume approximate size of footing base is 2.5 m × 8.0 m.
Now, referring to Eq. (2.9) for ultimate bearing capacity of soil

$$q_u = \gamma_b \times z \times N_q + 0.4 \times \gamma_b \times B \times N_y, \quad \text{assuming } c = 0 \text{ and } N_c = 0$$

Assuming

$\gamma_b = 20$ kN/m^3
$B = 2.5$ m (width of footing)
$z = 2.0$ m (depth of foundation below ground)
$\phi' = 30°$

and referring to Terzaghi's graph (Figure 2.5, Chapter 2) of bearing capacity factors

$$N_q = 22 \text{ and } N_y = 20$$

Therefore,

$$q_u = 20 \times 2 \times 22 + 0.4 \times 20 \times 2.5 \times 20 = 1280 \text{ kN/m}^2$$

Deduct the weight of overburden 2 m of soil at foundation depths

$$20 \times 2 = 40 \text{ kN/m}^2$$

Hence, net ultimate bearing capacity of soil,

$$q_{u(net)} = 1280 - 40 = 1240 \text{ kN/m}^2$$

using a factor of safety = 3.0 (as the footing is subjected to heavy unequal loadings).
Hence, net safe bearing capacity of soil,

$$q_n = \frac{1240}{3} = 413 \text{ kN/m}^2$$

again adding 2 m column of soil excavated.
Thus, gross safe bearing capacity of soil,

$$q_{gross} = 413 + 40 = 453 \text{ kN/m}^2$$

So, adopt a safe bearing capacity of soil,
$$q = 450 \text{ kN/m}^2.$$

To determine bearing capacity of soil using Eurocode 7: 2004 (Geotechnical design) [4.4]

Referring to Annex D of Eurocode 7, allowable bearing pressure in clayey sand at 2 m depth (assuming $c' = 0$)

$$q_d = \frac{R}{A'} = q' \times N_q \times b_q \times s_q \times i_q + 0.5 \times \gamma' \times B' \times N_\gamma \times b_\gamma \times s_\gamma \times i_\gamma$$

(For drained condition)

where

R = design bearing resistance

$A' = B' \times L'$ (where B' and L' are effective foundation width and length, respectively)

$B' = B = 2.5$ m; $L' = L = 8.6$ m

q' = design effective overburden pressure at 2 m depth = 2×20 kN/m^3 = 40 kN/m^2

$b_q = b_\gamma$ = inclination factor of foundation = $[1 - \alpha \times \tan (\phi'/\gamma_m)]$

where

ϕ' = effective angle of shearing resistance of soil = 30°

γ_m = partial factor for angle of shearing resistance = 1.25

(see Table A.2 of Eurocode 7)

$$\frac{\phi'}{1.25} = \frac{30}{1.25} = 24°$$

α = inclination of foundation base = 0°

$$b_q = b_\gamma = 1.0$$

s_q = for rectangular shape factor of foundation

$$1 + \left(\frac{B'}{L'}\right) \times \sin\left(\frac{\phi'}{\gamma_m}\right) = 1 + \left(\frac{2.5}{8.6}\right) \times \sin 24 = 1.19$$

s_γ = for rectangular shape factor of foundation

$$1 - 0.3 \times \left(\frac{B'}{L'}\right) = 1 - 0.3 \times \left(\frac{2.5}{8.6}\right) = 0.91$$

i_q = inclination factor of the load, caused by a horizontal load H

$$= \left[1 - \frac{H}{\left[V + A' \times c' \times \cot\left(\frac{\phi'}{\gamma_{\phi'}}\right)\right]}\right]^{(m)} \quad \text{(since } H = 0 \text{ and } c' = \text{cohesion} = 0\text{)}$$

$$i_\gamma = \left[1 - \frac{H}{\left[V + A' \times c' \times \cot\left(\frac{\phi'}{\gamma_{\phi'}}\right)\right]}\right]^{(m+1)} \quad \text{(since } H = 0 \text{ and } c' = 0\text{)}$$

where

$$m = m_B = \frac{[2+(B'/L')]}{[1+(B'/L')]}$$

when H acts in the direction of B'

$$m = m_L = \frac{[2+(L'/B')]}{[1+(L'/B')]}$$

when H acts in the direction of L'

B' and L' are effective width and length of foundation base.

γ' = design effective weight of soil = 20 kN/m³

$$N_q = e^{\left[\pi \times \tan\left(\frac{\phi'}{\gamma_m}\right)\right]} \times \tan^2\left[\frac{45+\left(\frac{\phi'}{\gamma_m}\right)}{2}\right]$$

$$= e^{[\pi \times \tan 24°]} \times \tan^2[45+12] = 9.6$$

$$N_\gamma = 2 \times (N_q - 1) \times \tan\left(\frac{\phi'}{\gamma_m}\right) = 2 \times 8.6 \times \tan 24 = 7.66$$

Therefore,

q_d = Allowable design bearing capacity of soil

$= q' \times N_q \times b_q \times s_q \times i_q + 0.5 \times \gamma' \times B' \times N_\gamma \times b_\gamma \times s_\gamma \times i_\gamma$

$= 40 \times 9.6 \times 1 \times 1 \times 1 + 0.5 \times 20 \times 2.5 \times 7.66 \times 1 \times 0.91 \times 1$

$= 558$ kN/m²

Adopt allowable design bearing capacity of soil

$$q_d = 450 \text{ kN/m}^2$$

4.4.3   To Calculate the Size of Footing

With the above safe bearing capacity of soil of 450 kN/m².
Area of combined footing required is

$$\frac{4500}{450} = 10 \text{ m}^2$$

Till now we have considered only the vertical loads without considering the eccentricity developed due to unequal loadings.

Moment developed due to unequal loadings,

$$M_e = (V_2 - V_1) \times 3 = (2500 - 2000) = 500 \times 3 = 1500 \text{ kN m.}$$

So, the size of the footing should be increased to keep the actual contact pressure within allowable value. In order to attain equal uniform contact pressure (that is ideal), the CG of load system should coincide with the CG of base. To find the CG of load system, take moments about left hand load line. Therefore,

$$(V_1 + V_2) \times x = V_2 \times 6; \quad 4500 \times x = 250 \times 6; \quad x = 2500 \times \frac{6}{4500} = 3.33 \text{ m}$$

The CG of load system acts at a distance 3.33 m from left load.

So, to bring the contact pressure uniform for the whole length of footing, the footing to be extended is 1.6 m from the centre of right-hand column.

Therefore, adopt the size of footing,

$$B \times L = 2.5 \text{ m} \times 8.6 \text{ m} \quad \text{[see Figure 4.3 (a)]}$$

4.4.4 To Calculate the Actual Gross Contact Pressure due to Vertical Loads and Moments Developed

As it is difficult to install shear reinforcement in slab, the thickness is to be so designed that the actual shear stress in concrete shall be within the allowable value.

The minimum design concrete shear stress (v_c) should not exceed 0.34 N/mm² for concrete thickness of 400 mm or more with minimum % of steel (0.15).

Considering the above point, assume a minimum thickness of footing slab, $D = 800$ mm.

Vertical loads

Characteristic dead load from column, G_k		= 984 kN
Unfactored vertical loads from columns	= (2000 + 2500) kN	= 4500 kN
Self-weight of footing	= 2.5 × 8.6 × 0.8 × 24 =	413 kN
Soil overburden over footing = (2.5 × 8.6 – 2 × 0.6 × 0.6) × 1.2 × 20 =		499 kN
Total		= 5412kN

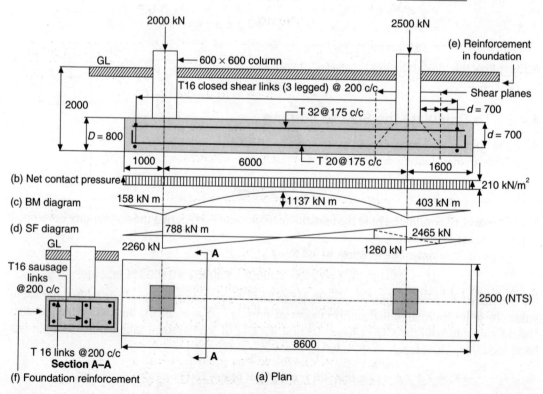

FIGURE 4.3 Combined spread footing.

Therefore, gross uniform contact pressure

$$p_{(gross)} = \frac{5412}{(2.5 \times 8.6)} = 252 \text{ kN/m}^2 < \text{allowable } 450 \text{ kN/m}^2$$

4.4.5 To Calculate Net Contact Pressure

Net uniform contact pressure

$$p_{(net)} = \frac{252 - (413 + 499)}{(2.5 \times 8.6)} = 210 \text{ kN/m}^2 \qquad \text{[see Figure 4.3 (b)]}$$

4.4.6 To Design Reinforced Concrete Footing Slab

The reinforced concrete design of footing foundation using The British Standard Code BS 8110: part 1: 1997 [4.5]

In the design, the following procedures are carried out:

To calculate bending moment and shear forces: Assuming a partial safety factor $\gamma_f = 1.5$ (average) [since the individual value of dead and live loads are unknown, the average value of partial safety factors $(1.4 + 1.6)/2 = 1.5$ in load combination of dead and live loads are taken].

Net ultimate uniform upward contact pressure

$$p_{u\,(net)} = 1.5 \times 210 = 315 \text{ kN/m}^2$$

To calculate the moments and shear, consider the whole width of slab.

1. *To calculate moments at various sections:* ultimate cantilever −ve moment at right-hand support

$$= -315 \times \frac{1.6^2}{2} \times 2.5 = -403 \times 2.5 = 1008 \text{ kN m}$$

and ultimate cantilever −ve moment at left-hand support

$$315 \times \frac{1}{2} \times 2.5 = -158 \times 2.5 = 395 \text{ kN m}$$

and net +ve moment at mid-span

$$315 \times \frac{6^2}{8} - \left(\frac{(403 + 158)}{2}\right) \times 2.5 = 2843 \text{ kN m} \qquad \text{[see Figure 4.3 (c)]}$$

2. *To calculate shears at various sections* [see Figure 4.3 (d)]: To find reaction at left hand support, take moments about right hand support. So,

$$R_1 \times 6 = \left(315 \times 7 \times \frac{7}{2} - 315 \times 1.6 \times \frac{1.6}{2}\right) \times 2.5$$

$$R_1 = 1219 \times 2.5 = 3048 \text{ kN}$$

$$R_r = 315 \times 8.6 \times 2.5 - 3048 = 3725 \text{ kN}$$

Hence,

V_1 = shear at a distance

$d = 700$ from face of right support (600 mm) $1 = 315 \times 2.5 \times 0.6 = 473$ kN

V_2 = shear at right of right-hand support = $315 \times 2.5 \times 1.6 = 1260$ kN

V_3 = shear at left of right-hand support = $R_r - V_2 = 3725 - 1260 = 2465$ kN

V_4 = shear at d from left face of right support = $2465 - 315 \times 1 \times 2.5 = 1678$ kN

V_5 = shear at left of left support = $315 \times 2.5 \times 1 = 788$ kN

V_6 = shear at right of left support = $R_1 - V_5 = 3048 - 788 = 2260$ kN

V_7 = shear at d from face of left support = $V_6 - 315 \times 2.5 \times 1 = 1473$ kN.

To calculate the reinforcement and depth of footing slab at mid span: Consider section at mid span, $M_u = 2843$ kN m (calculated above). Assume, the depth of footing, $D = 800$ mm.

The effective depth,

$$d = 800 - 75 \text{ (cover)} - 12 \text{ (link)} - \frac{25}{2} \text{ (main bar)} = 700 \text{ mm}$$

(with $f_{cu} = 40$ N/mm^2; $f_y = 460$ N/mm^2)

$$K = \frac{M_u}{B \times d^2 \times f_{cu}} = 2843 \times \frac{10^6}{2500 \times 700^2 \times 40} = 0.058$$

$K' = 0.156$ (where redistribution does not exceed 10% and assumed NA depth = 0.5) Since K is less than K', no compression reinforcement is required.

z = lever arm

$$= d \left[0.5 - \left(0.5 - \frac{K}{0.9} \right)^{0.5} \right] = d \left[0.5 + \left(0.025 - \frac{0.058}{0.9} \right)^{0.5} \right] = 0.93d$$

which is within $0.95d$.

Hence,

$$A_s = \text{area of steel} = \frac{M_u}{0.95 f_{yz}} = 2843 \times \frac{10^6}{0.95 \times 460 \times 0.93 \times 700} = 9993 \text{ mm}^2$$

Area required per m width of footing $= \dfrac{9993}{2.5} = 3997$ mm^2

Adopt: T32 @ 175 mm c/c top and T20 @ 175 mm c/c bottom [see Figure 4.3 (e)]. Area of reinforcement provided = 4596 mm^2, and 800 mm depth of footing slab.

To check the shear stress: Maximum shear at d from left face of right support, $V_4 = 1674$ kN Shear stress

$$v = \frac{V_4}{(B \times d)} = \frac{1674 \times 10^3}{2500 \times 700} = 0.96 \text{ N/mm}^2$$

less than

$$0.8 \sqrt{f_{cu}} = 0.8 \times \sqrt{40} = 5 \text{ N/mm}^2$$

Now, to check if shear reinforcement is required % of reinforcement

$$100 \times \frac{A_s}{(b \times d)} = 100 \times \frac{4596}{(1000 \times 700)} = 0.66$$

Therefore,

$$v_c = 0.79 \left(100 \times \frac{A_s}{b_d} \right)^{0.5} \times \frac{\left(\frac{400}{700} \right)^{0.25}}{1.25} = 0.45 \text{ N/mm}^2$$

As v is greater than $(v_c + 0.4)$, i.e. $(0.45 + 0.5) = 0.95$, the area of shear reinforcements as links to be provided

$$A_{sv} = b_v \times s_v \frac{(v - v_c)}{0.95 f_y}$$

where

b_v = breadth of section = 2500 mm

s_v = spacing of links = 200 mm

f_y = shear strength of links = 460 N/mm²

Hence,

$$A_{sv} = 2500 \frac{200 (0.96 - 0.45)}{(0.95 \times 460)} = 583 \text{ mm}^2$$

Adopt: 3, T16 close links @ 200 c/c for the whole length of slab (area provided = 603 mm²) [see Figure 4.3 (f)].

To design the reinforced concrete footing foundation using Eurocode 2: 2004 [4.6]

Net upward soil pressure p_{net}: Assuming a thickness of slab of 800 mm to avoid the application of shear reinforcement,

Net upward soil pressure p_{net} = 210 kN/m² (as calculated in previous section)

Ultimate moment: As the vertical column loads are combined dead and live loads, we may assume an average partial safety factor

$$\gamma_f = \frac{1.35 + 1.5}{2} = 1.43$$

Therefore, net ultimate uniform upward contact pressure = $1.43 \times 210 = 300$ kN/m².

Now to calculate moments and shear at various sections for whole width of slab:

(a) ultimate cantilever −ve moment at right support $= 300 \times \frac{1.6^2}{2} \times 2.5 = 960$ kN m

(b) ultimate cantilever −ve moment at left support $= 300 \times \frac{1}{2} \times 2.5 = 375$ kN m

(c) ultimate +ve moment at mid span of slab $= 300 \times \dfrac{6^2}{8} \times 2.5 - \dfrac{(960 + 375)}{2} = 2708$ kN m

Design of section: Consider the section at mid span:

Ultimate design moment = 2708 kN m

Assume depth $D = 800$ mm;

$$d = 800 - 40 \ (\text{cover}) - 16 \ (1/2 \ \text{bar diameter}) - 12 \ (\text{link}) = 732 \ \text{mm}$$

$$K = \frac{M_u}{(bd^2 f_{ck})} = 2708 \times \frac{10^6}{(2500 \times 732^2 \times 30)} = 0.067$$

and

$$K' = 0.6 - 0.18 - 0.21 = 0.21$$

Since $K < K'$, no compression reinforcement is required.

$$z = \frac{d}{2[1 + (1 - 3.53 \times 0.067)^{0.5}]} = \frac{d}{2 \times 1.87} = 0.93d$$

$$A_s = \frac{M_u}{(f_y \times z)} = \frac{2708 \times 10^6}{(500 \times 0.93 \times 732)} = 7956 \ \text{mm}^2$$

A_s required per m width

$$\frac{7956}{2.5} = 3182 \ \text{mm}^2$$

Adopt: T32 at 175 mm c/c top and T20 at 175 mm c/c bottom
(Area of reinforcement provided = 4596 mm^2).

Check for shear: Consider shear at a distance d from left face of right column:
Shear at a distance d (0.732 m) from left face of right support

$$2500 - 210 \times 2.63 \times 2.5 = 1180 \ \text{kN}$$

With a partial safety factor $\gamma_f = 1.43$ (average)
Ultimate shear

$$V_{ed} = 1.43 \times 1180 \ \text{kN} = 1687 \ \text{kN}$$

Ultimate applied shear stress

$$v_{ed} = \frac{V_{ed}}{(b \times d)} = \frac{1687 \times 10^3}{(2500 \times 732)} = 0.92 \ \text{N/mm}^2$$

$$\rho_1 = \frac{A_s}{b \times d} = \frac{4596}{1000 \times 732} = 0.0063$$

$$k = 1 + \left(\frac{200}{d}\right)^{0.5} = 1 + \left(\frac{200}{732}\right)^{0.5} = 1.52 \leq 2.0$$

v_{rdc} = allowable design shear stress

$$= 0.12 \times k \times (100 \times \rho_1 \times f_{ck})^{1/3}$$

$$= 0.12 \times 1.52 \times (100 \times 0.0063 \times 30)^{1/3} = 0.48 \text{ N/mm}^2 < 0.92 \text{ N/mm}^2.$$

As allowable design shear stress is less than the applied shear stress, the slab shall be designed as beam with shear reinforcement in form of links. In Eurocode, the capacity of assumed concrete strut in beam shall be considered.

Maximum strut capacity in terms of stress

$$v_{rd} \times \max \cot \theta = 0.48 \times 2.5 = 1.2 \text{ N/mm}^2$$

Ultimate applied shear stress at d from left face of right support

$$v_{ed} = \frac{V_{ed}}{(b_w \times z)} = \frac{1687 \times 10^3}{2500 \times 0.9 \times 732} = 1.02 \text{ N/mm}^2$$

Since $v_{ed} < v_{rd} \times \cot \theta$, calculate area of shear reinforcement by the following expression:

$$\frac{A_{sw}}{s} = \frac{v_{ed} \times b_w}{0.9 \times f_{ywd} \times \cot \theta} = \frac{1.02 \times 2500}{0.9 \times 500 \times 2.5} = 2.27$$

where

s = spacing of stirrups = 200 mm (assumed)

b_w = width of beam = 2500 mm

$\cot \theta = 2.5$

f_{ywd} = strength of shear reinforcement links = 500 N/mm^2

A_{sw} = area of shear links in mm^2

Therefore,

$$A_{sw} = 200 \times 2.27 = 453 \text{ mm}^2 \text{ for 2500 mm wide slab}$$

Using T16 (area = 201 mm^2) links, number of legs required = 453/201 = 2.25

Use, T16 links at 200c/c, with 4 legs in 2500 mm width of slab

(Area of shear steel provided = $4 \times 201 = 804$ mm^2).

4.5 DESIGN EXAMPLE 2

The foundation of a dead-end tower at a substation is subjected to the following loadings:

At base of left leg of tower: uplift = 150 kN ↑; horizontal force = 40 kN →

At base of right leg of tower: downward vertical = 200 kN ↓; horizontal force = 40 kN →

The foundation is placed at a depth 3.0 m from the ground level.

Geotechnical data of ground: Top two metre of made-up ground is underlain by alluvium of 5 m depth under which lies 2 m of gravel river terrace deposits.

γ_b = weight of soil = 20 kN/m^3

C_u = undisturbed undrained shear strength of soil = 20 kN/m²

ϕ' = effective angle of shearing resistance of soil in degrees = 25

To design a combined footing.

4.5.1 To Determine the Bearing Capacity of Soil at 3 m Depth

To calculate the bearing capacity using BS 8004: 1986 (Foundations)

Referring to Eq. (2.9) in Chapter 2, ultimate bearing capacity of soil for square bases:

$$q_u = 1.3 \times c \times N_c + \gamma_1 \times z \times N_q + 0.4 \times \gamma_b \times B \times N_\gamma$$

where

$C_u = 20$ kN/m²

$N_c = 25$ (from Figure 2.5);

$\gamma_{\text{submersed}} = (20 - 10) = 10$ kN/m³

$z = 3.0$ m from GL

$N_q = 12$ (from Figure 2.5)

As the water table is nearly at ground level, weight of water to be deducted

$B = 2.5$ m (assumed) and $N_y = 10$ (from Figure 2.5)

As the base is rectangular, the value of N_c is modified as

$$\left(0.84 + 0.16 \times \frac{B}{L}\right) \times N_c = \left(0.84 + 0.16 \times \frac{2.5}{9}\right) N_c = \left(0.84 + 0.16 \times \frac{2.5}{9}\right) 25 = 22$$

Hence,

$$q_u = 1.3 \times 20 \times 22 + 10 \times 3 \times 12 + 0.4 \times 10 \times 2.5 \times 10 = 1032 \text{ kN/m}^2$$

Deduct 3 m of soil overburden

Therefore, net ultimate bearing capacity of soil

$$q_{u \text{ (net)}} = 1032 - 60 = 972 \text{ kN/m}^2$$

Assuming a factor of safety = 4 (subjected to high overturning moment), net safe bearing capacity of soil

$$q = \frac{972}{4} = 243 \text{ kN/m}^2$$

Again adding 3 m of overburden soil excavated, gross safe bearing capacity of soil

$$q_{\text{gross}} = 243 + 60 = 303 \text{ (say 300 kN/m}^2)$$

To calculate the bearing capacity of soil using Eurocode 7: 2004 (Referring to Annex D)

With undrained conditions

$$C_u = 20 \text{ kN/m}^2$$

Design bearing capacity

$$q_d = (\pi + 2) \times \frac{C_u}{1.4 \times b_c \times s_c \times i_c} + q$$

where

b_c = factor for the inclination of foundation base $= 1 - 2 \times \dfrac{\alpha}{(\pi + 2)}$

$\quad = 1.0 \quad$ (since α = inclination of base = 0)

s_c = shape factor for the foundation base $= 1 + 0.2 \times \left(\dfrac{B'}{L'}\right)$ for rectangular base

$$= 1 + 0.2 \times \frac{2.5}{9} = 1.06$$

(where B' and L' = effective width and length = 2.5 m and 9 m)

i_c = factor due to horizontal force

$$H = \frac{1}{2\left[1 + \left(1 - \dfrac{H}{A' \times C_u}\right)\right]} = \frac{1}{2\left[1 + \left(1 - \dfrac{80}{2.5 \times 9 \times 20}\right)\right]} = 0.91$$

Therefore, design bearing capacity of soil

$$q_d = (\pi + 2) \times \frac{20}{1.4 \times 1 \times 1.06 \times 0.91 + (20 - 10)3} = 100 \text{ kN/m}^2$$

4.5.2 To Calculate the Size of Footing

Assume,

The size of footing = 2.5 m wide × 9 m long × 0.5 m thick

The size of pedestal = 500 mm^2

Connecting beam   = 0.4 m wide × 2.2 m depth

Weight of foundation:

Base	= 2.5 × 9 × 0.5 × 24	= 270 kN
Pedestal	= 0.5 × 0.5 × 2.7 × 24	= 16 kN
Beam	= 5.5 × 2.2 × 0.4 × 24	= 116 kN
Total		= 402 kN

Soil overburden $= (9 \times 2.5^2 - 2 \times 0.5^2 \times 2.7 - 5.5 \times 2.2 \times 0.4) \times 10 =$ 509 kN

(submerged weight of soil considered) total   = 911 kN

Net vertical column loads   = (200 – 150) =   50 kN

Total vertical downward load, W   = 961 kN

In addition, moments due to unbalanced loads and horizontal forces:
Take moments about the right-hand edge of base slab,

$$M = 150 \times 7.5 - 200 \times 1.5 + 40 \times 2 \times 3.2 = 1081 \text{ kN m}$$

Z_y (section modulus),

$$\frac{2.5 \times 9^2}{6} = 33.75 \text{ m}^3$$

Therefore, maximum soil pressure

$$f_{\text{max}} = \frac{W}{A} + \frac{M}{Z_y} = \frac{961}{9 \times 2.5} + \frac{1081}{33.75} = 75 \text{ kN/m}^2 < 100 \text{ kN/m}^2$$

Minimum soil pressure,

$$f_{\text{min}} = 43 - 32 = 11 \text{ kN/m}^2$$

So, the assumed size of base (2.5 m × 9 m) is satisfactory. Hence, adopt size of footing base.

2.5 m wide × 9 m long × 0.5 m thick   [see Figure 4.4(a)].

4.5.3   To Design the Reinforced Concrete Foundation

To design the reinforced concrete foundation using BS 8110: Part 1: 1997

The design of bottom slab:

1. *To calculate the net upward contact pressure:*   Maximum net upward contact pressure

$$p_{\text{max}} = \frac{W}{A} + \frac{M}{Z_y}$$

$$= \frac{200 - 150}{2.5 \times 9} + \frac{1081}{33.8} = 2.2 + 32 = 34.2 \qquad \text{(say 34 kN/m}^2\text{)}$$

Minimum net upward contact pressure

$$p_{\text{min}} = \frac{W}{A} - \frac{M}{Z_y} = -29.8 \qquad \text{(say } -30 \text{ kN/m}^2\text{)} \qquad \text{[see Figure 4.4 (b)]}$$

To calculate the distance where the pressure is zero, let x be the distance from maximum contact pressure to zero pressure.
Then

$$\frac{x}{(9-x)} = \frac{34}{30}$$

Therefore, $x = 4.8$ m.
To calculate the net contact pressure at centre of right-hand pedestal

$$p \text{ at } 3.3 = 34 \times \frac{3.3}{4.8} = 23 \text{ kN/m}^2$$

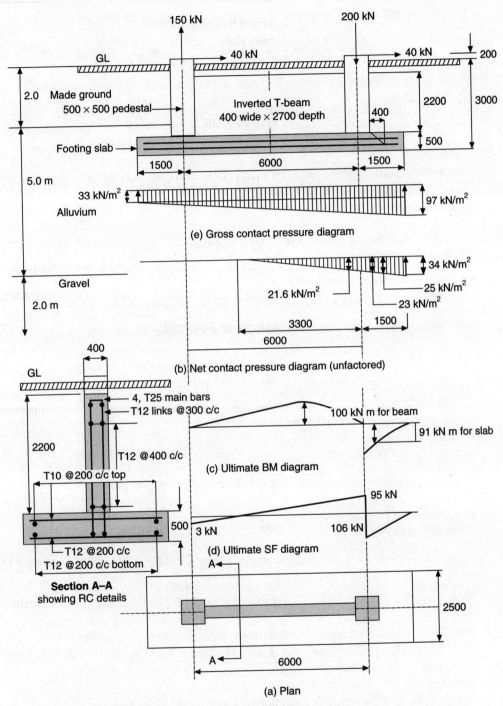

FIGURE 4.4 Combined spread footing subjected to uplift and horizontal shear.

To calculate the net contact pressure at right face of right-hand pedestal

$$p \text{ at } 3.55 = 34 \times \frac{3.55}{4.8} = 25 \text{ kN/m}^2 \quad \text{[see Figure 4.4 (b)]}$$

2. *To calculate the cantilever moment at the face of pedestal:*   Consider the whole width of slab = 2.5 m

$$M = 2.5 \left(25 \times \frac{1.25^2}{2} + \frac{1}{2} \times 1.25 \times 9 \times \frac{2}{3} \times 1.25 \right) = 60.5 \text{ kN m}$$

Assuming a partial safety factor γ_f =1.5 (as the foundation is subjected to abnormal loadings of cable tensions and wind)
Ultimate moment

$$M_u = 1.5 \times 60.5 = 91 \text{ kN m} \quad \text{[see Figure 4.4 (c)]}$$

3. *To determine the reinforcement:*   Assume the slab thickness

$$D = 500 \text{ mm};$$

$$d = 500 - 75 \text{ (cover)} - 1.5 \times 16 \text{ (bar diameter)} = 400 \text{ mm}.$$

Also assume the whole width of slab of 2500 mm resisting the moment

$$K = \frac{M_u}{(Bd^2 f_{cu})} = \frac{91 \times 10^6}{2500 \times 400^2 \times 40} = 0.00057$$

$K' = 0.156 > K$
So, no compression reinforcement is required.
z = lever arm factor

$$d \left[\left(0.5 + 0.25 - \frac{K}{0.9} \right)^{0.5} \right] = d \left[0.5 + \left(0.25 - \frac{0.00057}{0.9} \right)^{0.5} \right] = 0.99d$$

But should not be more than 0.95d.
Therefore, area of steel per m

$$A_s = \frac{M_u}{0.95 \times f_y \times z} = \frac{\left[\frac{91 \times 10^6}{(0.95 \times 460 \times 0.95 \times 400)} \right]}{2.5} = 219 \text{ mm}^2.$$

Therefore, adopt T12 @ 200 c/c bottom both ways (area provided = 565 mm^2 [see Figure 4.4(e)]. Minimum area of steel required = 0.013 × 1000 × 400 = 520 mm^2 < 565 mm^2. It is satisfactory.
Also, provide T10 @ 200 c/c top bothways.

4. *To check for shear stress:*   Contact pressure at d from face of pedestal

$$p \text{ } (3.95) = 34 \times \frac{3.95}{4.8} \approx 28 \text{ kN/m}^2$$

Consider the whole width of slab of 2500 mm.
Ultimate shear at a distance 400 mm from the face of pedestal,

$$V_u = 1.5 \times 2.5 \times \frac{28 + 34}{2 \times 0.85} = 99 \text{ kN}$$

Shear stress,

$$v_u = \frac{V_u}{B \times d} = \frac{99 \times 10^3}{2500 \times 400} = 0.1 \text{ N/mm}^2$$

% of steel,

$$100 \times \frac{A_s}{b \times d} = 100 \times \frac{565}{1000 \times 400} = 0.14$$

Allowable shear stress,

$$v_c = 0.79 \left(100 \times \frac{A_s}{(b \times d)}\right)^{0.5} \times \left(\frac{400}{d}\right)^{0.25} \gamma_m$$

$$= 0.79 \times 0.14^{0.5} \times \frac{1}{1.25} = 0.24 > v_u$$

Therefore, no shear reinforcement is required.

Design of inverted T-beam connecting the pedestal

1. *Net contact pressure:*

Net contact pressure at 1.5 m from right support = 34 kN/m² (calculated before)
Net contact pressure at centre of right support = 23 kN/m² (calculated before)

Net contact pressure at left face of right support = $34 \times \dfrac{3.05}{4.8} = 21.6$ kN/m²

Net contact pressure at d (2500 mm) from left of right support = $34 \times \dfrac{0.55}{4.8} = 4$ kN/m²
At 3.3 m left of right support = 0

Total net upward contact pressure on the beam $= \dfrac{1}{2} \times 3.3 \times 23 \times 2.5 = 95$ kN/m²

To find reactions at supports, take moments about right support

$$R_1 \times 6 = 2.5 \left(\frac{1}{2} \times 3.3 \times 23 \times \frac{3.3}{3} - 23 \times \frac{1.5^2}{2} - \frac{1}{2} \times 1.5^2 \times 11 \times \frac{2}{3}\right) = 3 \text{ kN m}$$

$$R_r = \frac{1}{2} \times 4.8 \times 34 \times 2.5 - R_1 = 201 \text{ kN} \qquad \text{[see Figure 4.4(b)]}$$

2. *To calculate moments:* Moment at the inner face of pedestal

$$M = -R_1 \times 5.75 + \frac{1}{2} \times 3.05 \times 21.6 \times \frac{3.05}{3} \times 2.5 = 66.5 \text{ kN m}$$

With a partial safety factor $\gamma_f = 1.5$

$$M_u = 1.5 \times 66.5 = 100 \text{ kN m} \qquad \text{[see Figure 4.4 (c)]}$$

3. *To calculate the reinforcement:* The beam will be designed as inverted T-beam with the bottom slab acting as compression member.

Beam width, $b = 2500$ mm

Rib width, $b_w = 400$ mm

Depth, $\quad D = 2600$ mm

$\qquad\quad d = 2500$ mm

$\qquad\quad Z = 0.95 \, d$

x = neutral axis depth = $(d - z)/0.45 = 278$ mm is within the slab. So, to be treated as beam.

$$A_s = \frac{M_u}{0.95 \times f_y \times z} = \frac{100 \times 10^6}{0.95 \times 460 \times 0.95 \times 2500} = 28 \text{ mm}^2$$

With

$$\frac{b_w}{b} = \frac{400}{2500} = 0.16 < 0.4$$

Minimum area of steel required

$$A_s = 0.0018 \times b_w \times D = 0.0018 \times 400 \times 2600 = 1872 \text{ mm}^2$$

Adopt: 4,T25 bar at bottom and 2,T20 bar at top
Area of tension steel provided = 1963 m [see Figure 4.4(e)]

4. *To check shear stress:* Shear at a distance d (2500 mm) from left face of right-hand column

$$V = \left[R_1 - \frac{1}{2} \times (3.3 - 2.75) \times 2.1 \times 2.5 \right] = 1.55 \text{ kN};$$

$$V_u = 1.5 \times V = 2.3 \text{ kN} \qquad \text{[see Figure 4.4 (d)]}$$

$$v_u = \frac{V_u}{b_w \times d} = 2.3 \times \frac{10^3}{400 \times 2500} = 0.002 \text{ N/mm}^2 \qquad \textbf{(Negligible)}$$

Percentage of steel

$$p = 100 \times \frac{A_s}{(b_w \times d)} = 100 \times \frac{1963}{400 \times 2500} = 0.2$$

Allowable shear stress

$$v_c = \frac{0.79}{1.25} \times p^{0.33} = \frac{0.79}{1.25} \times 0.2^{0.33} = 0.37 \text{ N/mm}^2 \gg v_u$$

Theoretically, no shear reinforcement required.
Provide nominal T12 shear links @300 c/c for the whole length of beam [see Figure 4.4 (e)].

To design the reinforced concrete foundation using Eurocode 2: 2004: Refer to Figure 4.5.

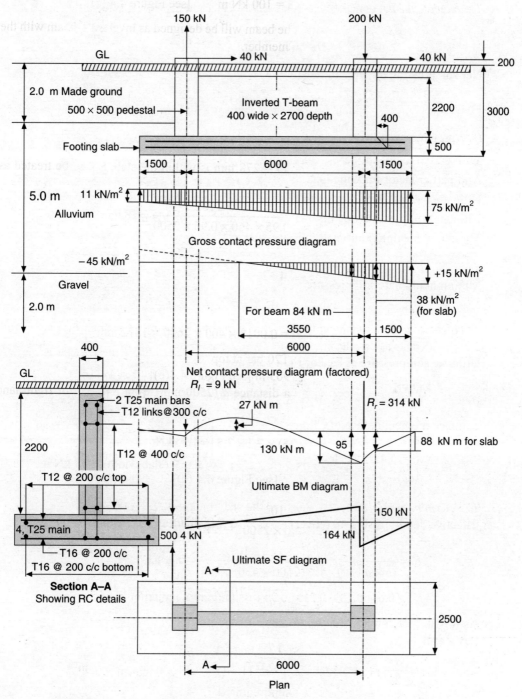

FIGURE 4.5 Combined spread footing subjected to uplift and horizontal thrust.

Design of bottom slab

1. *To calculate the net upward contact pressure:* Net soil pressure due to vertical dead load,

$$G_k = \frac{50}{(9 \times 2.5)} = 2.2 \text{ kN/m}^2$$

Net soil pressure due to wind load

$$W_k = \pm \frac{M}{Z} = \pm \frac{1081}{33.2} = \pm 32 \text{ kN/m}^2$$

(see previous section)

With partial factor for dead load, $G_k = \gamma_f = 1.35$
And partial factor for wind load, $W_k = \gamma_f = 1.5$
Ultimate net soil pressure due to $G_k = 1.35 \times 2.2 = 3 \text{ kN/m}^2$
Ultimate soil pressure due to $W_k = \pm 1.5 \times 32 = \pm 48 \text{ kN/m}^2$
Therefore, maximum ultimate soil pressure

$$p_{\text{ul.max}} = 3 + 48 = 51 \text{ kN/m}^2$$

Minimum ultimate soil pressure

$$p_{\text{ul.max}} = -45 \text{ kN/m}^2$$

2. *To calculate ultimate moment in slab at face of right column:* Consider the slab of full
2.5 m wide acts as cantilever.
Ultimate soil pressure at face of right column

$$51 \times \frac{3.55}{4.8} = 38 \text{ kN/m}^2$$

Ultimate moment at face of column

$$M_u = \left(38 \times \frac{1.25^2}{2} + \frac{1}{2} \times 1.25 \times 13 \times \frac{2}{3} \times 1.25 \right) \times 2.5 \ \text{(slab width)} = 88 \text{ kN m}$$

3. *To determine reinforcement:* Assume the slab thickness, $D = 500$ m
Effective depth = $500 - 40$ (cover) $- 1.5 \times 16$ (bar diameter) = 436 mm

$$K = \frac{M_u}{(b \times d^2 \times f_{ck})} = \frac{88 \times 10^6}{(2500 \times 436^2 \times 30)} = 0.0062$$

$K' = 0.6 - 0.18 - 0.21 = 0.21$ (assuming 0% redistribution)

As $K < K'$, no compression reinforcement is required.
Lever arm

$$z = \frac{d}{2} [1 + (1 - 3.53 \times K)] = \frac{d}{2} [1 + (1 - 3.53 \times 0.0062)] = 0.99 \, d$$

But z should not be more than $0.95 \, d$. So, adopt $z = 0.95 \, d$

Therefore, area of tension steel required

$$A_s = \frac{M_u}{(f_y \times z)} = 88 \times \frac{10^6}{(500 \times 0.95 \times 436)} = 425 \text{ mm}^2$$

$$A_s \text{ per m width} = \frac{425}{2.5} = 170 \text{ mm}^2$$

Minimum % requirment of tension steel = 0.15

$$= 0.0015 \times 1000 \times 436 = 654 \text{ mm}^2 > A_s \text{ required}$$

Therefore, adopt: T16 @ 200 c/c bottom both ways (area provided = 1005 mm²)
And T12 @ 200 c/c top both ways (see Figure 4.5).

4. *To check for shear stress in slab:* The shear stress to be calculated at a distance d from the face of column:

Ultimate soil pressure at a distance 436 mm from the face of column

$$51 \times \frac{3.986}{4.8} = 42 \text{ kN/m}^2$$

Ultimate shear at a distance 436 mm from the face of column

$$V_{ed} = \frac{1}{2} \times 0.814 \times (42 + 51) \times 2.5 = 95 \text{ kN}$$

Ultimate applied shear stress

$$v_{cd} = \frac{V_{ed}}{(b \times d)} = \frac{95 \times 10^3}{(2500 \times 436)} = 0.09 \text{ N/mm}^2$$

Concrete shear stress capacity without shear reinforcement

$$v_{rd} = 0.12 \times k \times (100 \times \rho_1 \times f_{ck})^{1/3}$$

where

$$k = 1 + \left(\frac{200}{d}\right) = 1 + \left(\frac{200}{436}\right) = 1.45 < 2 \qquad \textbf{(OK)}$$

$$\rho_1 = \frac{A_s}{(b \times d)} = \frac{1005}{(1000 \times 436)} = 0.0023$$

Therefore,

$$v_{rd} = 0.12 \times 1.45 \times (100 \times 0.0023 \times 30)^{1/3} = 0.33 \text{ N/mm}^2 >> v_{ed} (0.09 \text{ N/mm}^2)$$

So, no shear reinforcement is required in slab.

Design of inverted T-beam connecting the pedestal

1. *Net ultimate contact pressure:* From net ultimate pressure diagram as stated previously and assuming whole width of slab of 2.5 m:

Maximum net ultimate upward soil pressure/m at 1.5 m from the right support

$$51 \times 2.5 = 128 \text{ kN/m}$$

Net ultimate soil pressure at the centre of right-hand pedestal

$$128 \times \frac{3.55}{5.05} = 90 \text{ kN/m}$$

Net ultimate soil pressure at the inner face of right support

$$128 \times \frac{3.3}{5.05} = 84 \text{ kN/m}$$

Net ultimate soil pressure at a distance d from inner face of right column

$$90 \times \frac{0.7}{3.55} = 18 \text{ kN/m} \quad \text{(see Figure 4.5)}$$

Right reaction

$$R_r = \frac{1}{2} \times 5.05 \times 128 \times \frac{5.82}{6} = 314 \text{ kN}$$

Left reaction

$$R_l = \frac{1}{2} \times 5.05 \times 128 - 314 = 9 \text{ kN}$$

2. *Ultimate moment and shear:*
   Ultimate moment at the centre of right support,

$$-90 \times \frac{1.5^2}{2} - \frac{1}{2} \times 38 \times 1.5 \times \frac{2}{3} \times 1.5 = -130 \text{ kN m}$$

Ultimate moment at inner face of right support,

$$-84 \times \frac{1.75^2}{2} + \frac{1}{2} \times 44 \times 1.75 \times \frac{2}{3} \times 1.75 = -95 \text{ kN m}$$

Ultimate moment at 3.55 m from right support,

$$-\frac{1}{2} \times 5.05 \times 128 \times \frac{2}{3} \times 5.05 + 314 \times 3.55 = +27 \text{ kN m}$$

With the above values, draw BM diagram (see Figure 4.5).
Ultimate shear at centre of right support

$$\frac{1}{2} \times 1.5 (90 + 128) = 164 \text{ kN}$$

Ultimate shear at $d = 2.6$ m from inner face of right support,

$$\frac{1}{2} \times 4.35 (18 + 128) - 314 = 4 \text{ kN}$$

With the above values, draw SF diagram (see Figure 4.5).

3. *Design of section:* The beam will be designed as inverted T-beam with bottom slab acting as compression member.

Width of beam, $b = 2500$ mm
Width of rib, $b_w = 400$ mm

Depth of beam   = 2700 m

Effective depth, d = 2600 mm.

Ultimate moment at left face of right support,

$$M_u = 95 \text{ kN m}$$

$$K = \frac{M_u}{b_w \times d^2 \times f_{ck}} = \frac{95 \times 10^6}{400 \times 2600^2 \times 30} = 0.0012$$

$$K' = 0.6 - 0.18 - 0.21 = 0.21$$

Since $K < K'$, no compression reinforcement required.

$$Z = \frac{d}{2}[1 + (1 - 3.53\,K)^{0.5}] = \frac{d}{2} \times 1.99 = 0.99\,d \quad \text{(but should not be less than } 0.95\,d)$$

Therefore,

$$A_s = \frac{M_u}{f_y \times 0.95\,d} = \frac{95 \times 10^6}{500 \times 0.95 \times 2600} = 80 \text{ mm}^2$$

Minimum % of steel required = $0.0015 \times 400 \times 2600 = 1560$ mm^2

Adopt: 4,T25 at bottom (A_s provided = 1963 mm^2); 2,T25 top (see Figure 4.5).

   4. *To check for shear:*

Ultimate shear at 2.6 m from inner face of right column,

$$V_{ed} = 4 \text{ kN}$$

Applied shear stress,

$$\frac{V_{ed}}{(b \times 0.95 \times d)} = \frac{4 \times 10^3}{(400 \times 0.95 \times 2600)} = 0.004 \text{ N/mm}^2 \quad \textbf{(Negligible)}$$

Provide : Nominal shear reinforcement T12 stirrups @ 300 c/c.

REFERENCES

[4.1] Peck, R.B., W.E. Hanson and T.H. Thornburn, *Foundation Engineering,* Asia Publishing House, New Delhi, 1962.

[4.2] Dunham, C.W., *Foundation of Structures*, McGraw-Hill, New York, 1950.

[4.3] BS 8004:1986. British Standard Code of Practice for Foundations.

[4.4] Eurocode 7: 2004. Geotechnical design.

[4.5] BS 8110: 1997: part 1. Structural use of concrete. Codes of practice for design and construction.

[4.6] Eurocode 2: 2004: Design of concrete structures.

[4.7] Terzaghi, K. and R.B. Peck, *Soil Mechanics in Engineering Practice*, John Wiley and Sons, Inc., New York, 1962.

[4.8] Skempton, A.W., The Bearing Capacity of Clays, Building Research Congress, Division I, 180, 1951.

Chapter 5

Strip Footing Foundations

5.0 DEFINITION AND DESCRIPTIONS

When a series of columns in a row, not far apart, is subjected to loadings, the foundations of individual columns are connected together to form strip footing foundation. The spacing of columns and the loading of individual columns may be equal, and the distribution of ground pressure is uniform. When the column loadings are not equal and the spacing of columns are not the same, the distribution of ground pressure is not uniform [Figures 5.1 (a) and (b)].

5.1 BEHAVIOUR OF FOUNDATION UNDER THE ACTION OF COLUMN LOADS

In case of equal column spacing and if the footing is subjected to uniform contact pressure, it is treated as a continuous slab under the columns and the bending moments and shear forces can be calculated from standard moment and shear factors found in design handbook.

When the spacing of columns are unequal and subjected to unequal pressure distribution, the moments and shear forces may be analyzed by any suitable theory of moment distribution by Hardy Cross or any other method, Dunham [5.1] [Figures 5.1 (c) and (d)].

5.2 ALLOWABLE BEARING PRESSURE

Before analyzing the strip footing foundation, we should determine the allowable bearing pressure of soil under the footing. Terzaghi derived the following expression for the ultimate bearing capacity of soil under a shallow strip footing which will cause general shear failure:

$$Q_u = c \times N_c + \gamma \times z \times N_q + 0.5 \times \gamma \times B \times N_y \quad \text{[see Eq.(2.4), refer to Chapter 2]}$$

where

c = cohesion (undisturbed undrained shear strength of soil in kN/m^2)

γ = density of soil in kN/m^3

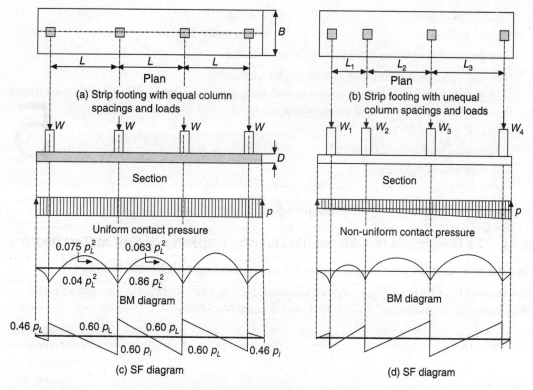

FIGURE 5.1 Strip footing foundations.

B = width of strip in metre

N_c, N_q, N_y = bearing capacity factors

[These factors can be obtained from Figure 2.5 (Terzaghi's bearing capacity factors).]

5.3 TO DETERMINE THE SIZE OF FOOTING

In determining the size:

    (i) Add up all vertical column loads and calculate the CG of resultant load system.

    (ii) Add up total column spaces.

    (iii) Ensure that the CG of resultant load system should coincide the CG of foundation, so that a uniform soil pressure will occur.

If the item (iii) is difficult to achieve, a non-uniform soil pressure will have to assume in the analysis of footing.

5.4 DESIGN EXAMPLE 1—DESIGN OF A CONTINUOUS STRIP FOOTING

5.4.1 Design Data

A series of internal columns in a row of an industrial building is subjected to the following loadings:

Dead load   = 650 kN

Imposed load   = 370 kN

Spacing of columns   = 4.5 m

Size of column   = 400 mm × 400 mm

The depth of foundation from ground level = 2.0 m

The geotechnical condition of ground is given below:

The ground consists of 1 m of top soil underlain by alluvium. Water table = 1 m below ground. So, the foundation will be placed on alluvium soil.

The geotechnical properties of alluvium:

γ_b = density of soil = 20 kN/m³

C_u = cohesion = 20 kN/m²

ϕ' = effective angle of shearing resistance = 25°

We are to design a strip footing foundation under the columns.

5.4.2 To Determine the Allowable Bearing Capacity of Soil at 2 m Depth

To calculate the allowable bearing capacity in accordance with BS 8004: 1986

Referring to Eq. (2.9) and Figure 2.5 (in Chapter 2) of net ultimate bearing capacity of soil: With undrained condition, C_u = 20 kN/m² and drained condition,

$$C' = w$$
$$\phi' = 25°$$
$$\gamma = 18 \text{ kN/m}^3$$

Assume partial factors for soil parameter angle of shearing resistance, $\gamma_{\phi'}$ = 1.25

Therefore, design angle of shearing resistance

$$\phi'_d = \frac{25}{1.25} = 20$$

Water table = 2.5 m below ground level

$$q_u = \gamma \times z \times (N_q - 1) + 0.5 \times \gamma \times B \times N_y$$

(where z = depth below ground; B = 2 m width)

$$= 18 \times 2 \times (12.5 - 1) + 0.5 \times 18 \times 2 \times 10 = 594 \text{ kN/m}^2$$

With a factor of safety = 3

$$q_n = \text{Net safe bearing capacity of soil} = \frac{594}{3} = 198 \text{ kN/m}^2$$

Adding 2 m of overburden soil, gross safe bearing capacity of soil

$$198 + 18 = 216 \text{ kN/m}^2$$

Adopt: safe bearing capacity of soil

$$q_{\text{gross}} = 200 \text{ kN/m}^2$$

To calculate the allowable bearing capacity in accordance with Eurocode 7: 2004

Applying the analytical method in Annex D, the design bearing capacity may be calculated from Eq. (D.2).

$$q = C' \times N_c \times b_c \times s_c \times i_c + q' \times N_q \times b_q \times s_q \times i_q + 0.5 \times \gamma \times B' \times N_\gamma \times b_\gamma \times s_\gamma \times i_\gamma$$

[(D.2) see Annex D of Eurocode 7]

Since

$C' = 0$, the first part = 0

$q' =$ overburden pressure $= 2 \times 18 = 36$ kN/m^2

Assume partial factor for soil parameter of angle of shearing resisrance, $\gamma_{\phi'} = 1.25$
(See Table A.2 of Eurocode 7)

Therefore, design angle of shearing resistance,

$$\phi'_d = \frac{25}{1.25} = 20°$$

$$N_q = e^{\pi} \times \tan \phi' \times \tan^2 \left(45 + \frac{\phi'}{2} \right) = e^{\pi} \times \tan 20 \times \tan^2 \left(45 + \frac{22}{2} \right) = 8.422 \times 2.039 = 17.17$$

$N_\gamma = 2 \times (N_q - 1) \times \tan \phi'_d = 2 \times 6.17 \times \tan 20 = 11.77$

$b_q =$ inclination factor $= 1$

$b_\gamma = 1$

$s_q =$ shape factor for foundation $= 1 + \left(\dfrac{B'}{L'} \right) \times \sin \phi'_d$ for rectangular shape

where B' and L' are the effective dimensions of foundation slab.

Since, the ground upwardward contact pressure is uniform, the effective dimensions are the same as assumed dimensions
Therefore,

$$s_q = 1 + \left[\frac{2}{13.5} \text{ (three spans)} \right] \times \sin 20 = 1 + 0.05 = 1.05$$

$$s_i = 1 - 0.3 \times \left(\frac{B'}{L'} \right) = 1 - 0.3 \times \frac{2}{13.5} = 0.95$$

Therefore,

$$q = 36 \times 17.17 \times 1 \times 1.05 \times 0.95 + 0.5 \times 18 \times 2 \times 11.77 \times 1 \times 1.05 \times 0.95$$

$$= 616.6 + 211.33 = 827 \text{ kN/m}^2$$

Using soil as undrained condition

$$Q = (\pi + 2) \times C_u \times b_c \times s_c \times i_c + q, \qquad \text{where } C_u = 20 \text{ kN/m}^2$$

Assuming, partial factor for undrained soil parameter, $\gamma_{C_u} = 1.4$

$\quad C_{ud}$ = design undrained shear strength of soil = $\dfrac{20}{1.4}$ = 14.3 kN/m²

$\quad b_c$ = inclination factor = 1

$\quad s_c$ = shape factor for rectangular foundation = $1 + 0.2 \times \left(\dfrac{B'}{L'}\right) = 1 + 0.2 \times \dfrac{2}{13.5} = 1.03$

$\quad i_c$ = inclination of load caused by a horizontal thrust

$$H = \frac{1}{2}\left[1 + \left(\frac{1-H}{\dfrac{A'}{C_u}}\right)\right]^{0.5}$$

where
$\quad H$ = horizontal thrust = 0
$\quad A'$ = effective foundation area.

Since no horizontal thrust is acting, no eccentricity is developed and the effective area is the same as original foundation area.

$$2 \times 13.5 = 27$$

$$i_c = \frac{1}{2}[1-0]^{0.5} = 0.5$$

Therefore,

$$q = (\pi + 2) \times 14.3 \times 1 \times 1.03 \times 0.5 + 36 = 75.05 + 36 = 111 \text{ kN/m}^2$$

Hence, adopt, design bearing pressure of soil, q = 100 kN/m².

5.4.3   To Calculate the Size of Footing

Total (dead + imposed) loads	= (650 + 370) = 1020 kN
With spacing of column	= 4.5 m

Assume,

Width of footing	= 2 m
Thickness	= 0.8 m
Weight of foundation:	$2 \times 4.5 \times 0.8 \times 24$ = 173 kN
Weight of overburden soil = $(4.5 \times 2 - 0.4 \times 0.4) \times 1 \times 10$ =	88 kN
Total	= 261 kN
Total vertical load	= 1020 + 261 = 1281 kN
Actual bearing pressure	$= \dfrac{1281}{4.5 \times 2}$ = 142 kN/m² > q = 100 kN/m²

Increase the width of foundation to 4 m.

So, revised weight of foundation, considering one span,

Weight of base	$= 4 \times 4.5 \times 0.8 \times 24 =$	346 kN
Weight of overburden	$= (4 \times 4.5 - 0.4 \times 0.4) \times 1 \times 18 =$	321 kN
Total		$=$ 667 kN
Plus vertical column load		$=$ 1020 kN
Total Dead Load + Live Load		$=$ 1687 kN

Therefore, actual bearing pressure

$$p = \frac{1687}{4 \times 4.5} = 94 \text{ kN/m}^2 < 100 \text{ kN/m}^2$$

Hence, adopt: 4.0 m wide and 800 mm thick strip footing continuous under columns [see Figure 5.2 (a)].

5.4.4 To Design the Reinforced Concrete Strip Footing

To design in accordance with BS 8110: 1997

Ultimate net contact pressure: With Load combinations for ultimate loads: 1.4 × characteristic dead load + 1.6 × characteristic live load. So, total ultimate column loads

$$1.4 \times \text{dead} + 1.6 \times \text{ imposed load} = 1.4 \times 630 + 1.6 \times 370 = 1474 \text{ kN}$$

Therefore, ultimate upward contact pressure

$$\frac{1474}{4 \times 4.5} = 82 \text{ kN/m}^2$$

and upward contact pressure per m run of slab

$$82 \times 4 = 328 \text{ kN/m}$$

Downward loads:

Self-weight of foundation per m	$= 0.8 \times 4 \times 24 = 76.8$ kN/m
Weight of soil overburden	$= 1.2 \times 4 \times 18 = 86.4$ kN/m
Total ultimate downward load	$= 1.4 \times (76.8 + 86.4) = 228$ kN/m

Net upward pressure under the foundation

$$p_u = 328 - 228 = 100 \text{ kN/m}$$

Ultimate bending moments and shear forces: Considering continuous slab of equal spans and referring to Table 3.12 of (BS 8110: part 1: 1997),
Assume that the slab simply supported at end support.

- *Bending moments* [Figure 5.2 (b)]

  – ve moment at first interior support,

$$-0.086 \times p_u \times l^2 = -0.086 \times 100 \times 4.5^2 = 174 \text{ kN m}$$

+ ve moment near middle of end span

$$0.075 \times p_u \times l^2 = -0.086 \times 100 \times 4.5^2 = 152 \text{ kN m}$$

+ ve moment at middle of interior span

$$0.063 \times p_u \times l^2 = 0.063 \times 100 \times 4.5^2 = +128 \text{ kN m}$$

– ve moment at interior support

$$-0.063 \times p_u \times l^2 = 0.063 \times 100 \times 4.5^2 = -128 \text{ kN m}$$

- *Shear*
  Shear at end support $= 0.4 \times p_u \times l = 0.4 \times 100 \times 4.5 = 180 \text{ kN}$
  Shear at first interior support $= 0.6 \times p_u \times l = 0.6 \times 100 \times 4.5 = 270 \text{ kN}$
  Shear at interior supports $= 0.5 \times p_u \times l = 0.5 \times 100 \times 4.5 = 225 \text{ kN}$ [Figure 5.2 (c)]

To calculate the thickness and the longitudinal and transverse reinforcement:

1. *Longitudinal reinforcement:*   Consider moment near the middle of end span

$$M_u = 152 \text{ kN m}$$

Assume

$$f_{cu} = 40 \text{ N/mm}^2;$$
$$f_y = 460 \text{ N/mm}^2$$

Width of slab, $B = 4000 \text{ mm}$
Thickness of slab, $D = 800 \text{ mm};$
Effective thickness,

$$d = 800 - 40 \text{ (cover)} - 16 \text{ (transverse bars)} - 10 \text{ (half main bar diameter)}$$

$$= 734 \text{ mm (assuming 150 mm lean concrete under main slab)}$$

$$K = \frac{M_u}{Bd^2 f_{cu}} = \frac{152 \times 10^6}{(4000 \times 734^2 \times 40)} = 0.00176; \; K' = 0.156$$

Since $K < K'$, compression reinforcement is not required.
Lever arm,

$$z = d \left[0.5 + \left(0.25 - \frac{K}{0.9} \right) \right]^{0.5} = d \times 0.98$$

But should not be greater than $0.95d$. So,

$$z = 0.95 \times 734 = 697 \text{ mm}$$

Area of steel required

$$A_s = \frac{M_u}{(0.95 \times f_y \times z)} = \frac{152 \times 10^6}{(0.95 \times 460 \times 0.95 \times 734)} = 499 \text{ mm}^2$$

Minimum % of reinforcement required

$$0.0013 \times 4000 \times 800 = 4160 \text{ mm}^2 > A_s \quad \textbf{(Satisfactory)}$$

A_s required per m $\qquad = \dfrac{4160}{4} = 1040 \text{ mm}^2$

Adopt: T20 @ 250 mm c/c top and bottom (area = 1257 mm²)

2. *To calculate transverse reinforcement:* Cantilever transverse moment per m at face of column

$$p_u \times \frac{1.8^2}{2} = 100 \times \frac{1.8^2}{2} = 162 \text{ kN m/m}$$

$$d = 800 - 40 - 8 \left(\frac{1}{2} \text{ bar diameter} \right) = 752 \text{ mm}$$

$$A_s \text{ required} = \frac{162 \times 10^6}{(0.95^2 \times 460 \times 752)} = 519 \text{ mm}^2$$

Minimum % of steel required = 0.0013 × 1000 × 800 = 1040 mm²
Adopt: T16 @ 150 mm c/c bottom and bottom (area provided = 1149 mm²) [Figure 5.2 (d)]

To check shear stress: Shear at distance d from the face of first interior column

$$V_u = 0.6 \times p_u \times l - p_u \times (d + 0.2)$$
$$= 0.6 \times 100 \times 4.5 - 100 \times 0.9 = 180 \text{ kN}$$

Shear stress

$$v_u = \frac{180 \times 10^3}{4000 \times 734} = 0.06 \text{ N/mm}^2$$

Referring to Table 3.8 of BS 8110: part 1: 1997:
With % of steel less than 0.13 and d greater than 400,

$$v_c = 0.34 \text{ N/mm}^2 < v_u$$

Thus, no shear steel is required.

To design the RC foundation in accordance with Eurocode 2: 2004 [5.5]

Ultimate contact pressure: For moment and shear calculations, the combination to be used is

$$1.35 \times G_k + 1.5 \, Q_k$$

Therefore, total ultimate dead and live load from columns

$$1.35 \times 650 + 1.5 \times 370 = 1433 \text{ kN}$$

Upward ultimate contact pressure

$$\frac{1433}{(4 \times 4.5)} = 80 \text{ kN/m}^2$$

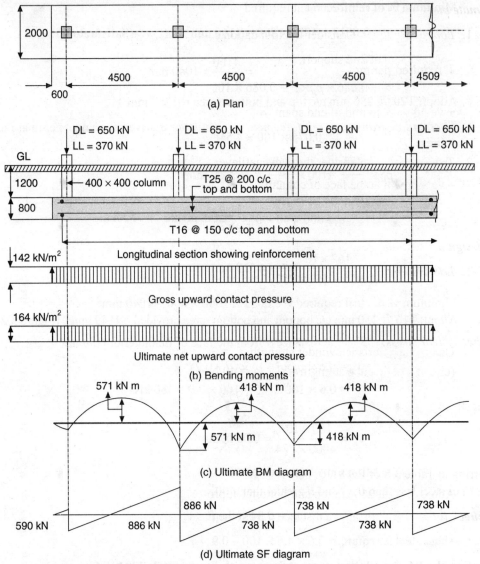

FIGURE 5.2 Continuous strip footing foundation.

Downward ultimate pressure due to self-weight of (concrete + overburden),

$$1.35 \times (0.8 \times 24 + 1.2 \times 18) = 55 \text{ kN/m}^2$$

Therefore, net ultimate upward contact pressure

$$80 - 55 = 25 \text{ kN/m}^2$$

Assuming, 4 m wide foundation slab, net upward load per m of slab,

$$25 \times 4 = 100 \text{ kN/m}$$

Ultimate moment

1. *Longitudinally:* Consider the foundation slab is continuous over columns.

   – ve moment at 2nd support,

   $$0.086 \times p_u \times l^2 = 0.086 \times 100 \times 4.5^2 = 174 \text{ kN m}$$

   + ve moment at mid of end span

   $$0.075 \times 100 \times 4.5^2 = 152 \text{ kN m}$$

2. *Transversely:* Consider the slab cantilever from the face of column

   – ve moment at the face of column,

   $$p_u \times \frac{l^2}{2} = 100 \times \frac{1.8^2}{2} = 162 \text{ kN m}$$

To design the section

1. *Longitudinally:*

   $b = 4000$ mm

   $d = 734$ mm

   $f_y = 500$ N/mm^2.

   Using characteristic cylinder strength, $f_{ck} = 30$ N/mm^2

   (characteristic cube strength $= f_{ck \text{ .cube}} = 40$ N/mm^2)

   $$z = 0.95 \times d$$

   $$A_s = \frac{M_u}{(f_y \times z)} = \frac{174 \times 10^6}{(500 \times 0.95 \times 734)} = 500 \text{ mm}^2$$

   Minimum % of steel $= 0.0015 \times 1000 \times 734 = 1101$ mm^2

   Adopt: T20 at 250 c/c top and bottom (A_s provided $= 1257$ mm^2)

To check for shear: Shear at a distance d from the face of column

$$V_u = 0.6 \times 4.5 \times 100 - 0.9 \times 100 = 180 \text{ kN}$$

$$v_u = \frac{V_u}{b \times d} = \frac{180 \times 10^3}{4000 \times 734} = 0.06 \text{ N/mm}^2$$

$$v_c = 0.12 \times k \times (100 \times \rho \times f_{ck})^{1/3}$$

where

$$k = 1 + \left(\frac{200}{d}\right)^{0.5} = 1 + \left(\frac{200}{734}\right)^{1/3} = 1.65 < 2$$

$$\rho = \frac{A_s}{(b \times d)} = \frac{1257}{(1000 \times 734)} = 0.0017$$

$$v_c = 0.12 \times 1.65 \times (100 \times 0.0017 \times 30)^{0.33} = 0.34 \text{ N/mm}^2 \gg 0.06 \text{ N/mm}^2$$

So, no shear reinforcement is required.

To check for punching shear: Punching shear along the perimeter at a distance d from the face of column

$$V_{ed} = [B \times L - (2 \times d + w)^2] \times p_u = [4 \times 4.5 - (2 \times 0.734 + 0.4] \times 100 = 1451 \text{ kN}$$

where

B = width of slab = 4.0 m

L = span = 4.5 m

d = effective slab depth

w = column side.

Ultimate punching shear stress

$$v_{ed} = \frac{V_{ed}}{\left[(2 \times d + w) \times 4 \times d\right]} = \frac{1451 \times 10^3}{\left[(2 \times 734 + 400) \times 4 \times 734\right]} = 0.26 \text{ N/mm}^2$$

Allowable punching shear stress v_{rd} for f_{ck} = 30 N/mm^2

$$v_{rd} = 0.34 \text{ N/mm}^2 \gg v_{ed}$$

(calculated in previous subsection, **Satisfactory**)

Refer to BS 8004: 1986 [5.2], Eurocode 7: 2004 [5.3], and BS 8110: 1997 [5.4].

REFERENCES

[5.1] Dunham, C.W., Foundations of structures, McGraw-Hill, New York, 1950.

[5.2] BS 8004: 1986: British Standard Code of Practice for Foundations.

[5.3] Eurocode 7: 2004: Geotechnical design. Part 1: General rules.

[5.4] BS 8110: part 1: 1997 Structural use of concrete. Code of practice for design and practice.

[5.5] Eurocode 2: 2004: Design of concrete structures.

Chapter 6

Mat or Raft Foundation

6.0 DEFINITION AND DESCRIPTIONS

Mat foundation is defined as the substructure that distributes the loads of several columns of a superstructure over the whole area of foundation by means of continuous slab. The mat foundation may also be described as raft or float foundation as it acts as raft to spread the concentrated unequal column loads evenly over the large area of the foundation soil which supports the loads (Terzaghi and Peck [6.1]).

This type of foundation is particularly applicable where the bearing capacity of soil is poor and also the geotechnical properties of soil is variable even within short distance. Also, sometimes the individual spread footing for each column load becomes so large that it almost nearly coincides with the adjoining footings. And sometimes due to unequal column loadings in the structure and variation of bearing pressure within the substructure, the individual spread footing size varies to a large extent. To overcome all these problems, it is advisable to adopt mat foundation.

6.1 STRUCTURAL BEHAVIOUR OF MAT FOUNDATION

The elastic deformation of continuous reinforced concrete slab in both directions and the nature of the stiffness of slab makes it possible to transmit the concentrated point loads of columns and distribute evenly over the large area of foundation. This behaviour provides the bridging action over the local weak spot in the supporting soil and results a reasonable contact pressure within the allowable bearing capacity of soil.

If we consider that the stiffness of slab is quite high and the mat is subjected to several heavy column loads of nearly equal value, then the plastic clayey soil under the mat will yield at the load points and the soil will be compressed and will adjust itself so that each column load will spread almost uniformly under the raft.

The mat foundation is generally applied in the construction of basement substructure of office buildings and powerhouse substructure (Dunham [6.2]).

6.2 ALLOWABLE BEARING CAPACITY OF SOIL

Before we analyze the raft foundation, we should determine the bearing capacity of soil under the foundation. In soil mechanics, it is not anywhere mentioned about the behaviour of soil under the raft foundation extended over a large area. In these circumstances, Terzaghi's basic equation for strip footing may be applicable to determine the ultimate bearing capacity of soil under the raft foundation.

The Terzaghi's equation for ultimate capacity is given by

$$Q_u = c \times N_c + \gamma \times z \times N_q + 0.5 \times \gamma \times B \times N_y, \qquad \text{(see Eq. 2.4)}$$

For square footing, Terzaghi suggests the following equation:

$$Q_u = 1.3 \times c \times N_c + \gamma \times z \times N_q + 0.4 \times B \times N_y, \qquad \text{(see Eq. 2.9)}$$

(Refer to Chapter 2—Geotechnics)

Skempton suggests that the value of N_c for a rectangular footing of length L and breadth B may

be given by the expression N_c for rectangle $= \left(0.84 + 0.16 \times \dfrac{B}{L} \right) N_c$ for square. In our case, we

may assume the dimensions L and B as the length and breadth of the whole foundation raft. The values of bearing capacity factors N_c, N_q and N_y for deep foundation may be obtained from the graphs as shown in Figure 2.5 in Chapter 2 described previously.

6.3 METHOD OF ANALYSIS OF MAT FOUNDATION

The mat foundation slab is generally analyzed in the following methods:

The grid beam method

This method is suggested by Dunham [6.2]. In this method, the column strips along the column lines act as stiff grid beams along the column lines in either direction carrying the upward contact pressure of soil.

The effective width of grid beam, B = Width of column (or width of pedestal) + $3 \times d$ or $4 \times d$ when the contact pressure is considered high, where d = effective depth of slab.

The effective depth is assumed as equal to approximately 100 mm per 1200 mm of clear span between columns.

Referring to Figure 6.1 (a), for the base slab of a basement to act as a mat, consider the diagonal lines drawn between the columns. Then the contact pressure under the area 'abcd' will be resisted by the portion of mat between 'a' and 'b' forming the grid beam. Similarly, the pressure under the area 'bcfe' will be resisted by the portion of the mat between 'e' and 'f' as another grid beam right angles to the previous one. The loadings on these column strips (as grid beams) are in triangular shape as shown in Figure 6.1 (c).

With these triangular loadings, the grid beams are analyzed as continuous beams subjected to triangular loadings. With these loadings the bending moment diagrams are shown in Figure 6.1 (d).

The reinforcement calculated for the above bending moments are spread within these column strips. The remaining area of slab between the column strips is analyzed as a slab fixed at edges with the column strips.

Flat slab method

In this method the base slab is divided into panels of width equal to the spacing of columns in either direction and run along the centre lines of columns at right angles to each other. These panels, subjected to upward contact pressure, are analyzed as continuous members under the columns. The moments and shears in the panels are then apportioned between column strips and middle strips as stipulated in codes of practice, (BS 8110 :1997 [6.3] [see Figure 6.1 (b)]).

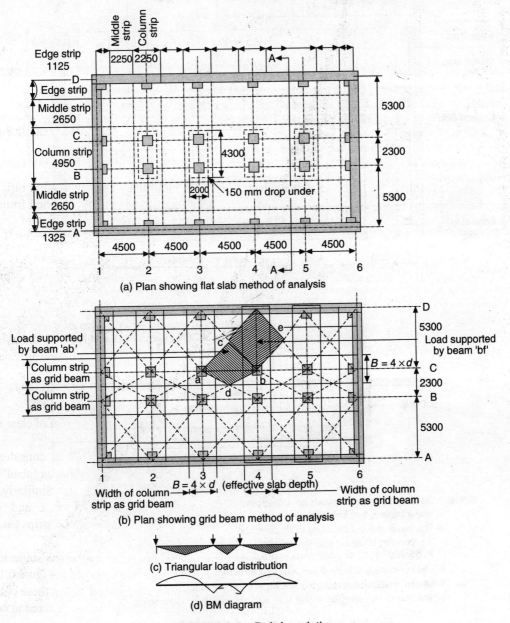

(a) Plan showing flat slab method of analysis

(b) Plan showing grid beam method of analysis

(c) Triangular load distribution

(d) BM diagram

FIGURE 6.1 Raft foundation.

6.4 DESIGN EXAMPLE 1

We are to design a mat (raft) foundation of a basement substructure with the dimensions as given in Figure 6.2 and subjected to the following loadings:

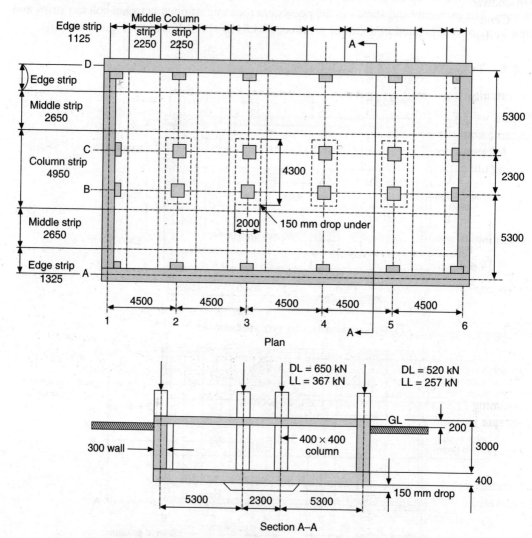

Plan

Section A–A

Notes: 1. Dead and live loads shown are unfactored.
2. Water table is 1 m below ground level.
3. The basement substructure to be designed for retaining aqueous liquids according to BS 8007:1987 or latest code of practice.
4. The concrete grade shall be C40 ($f_{cu} = 40$ N/mm^2).
5. Maximum allowable design crack width to be 0.2 mm.
6. The mat to be designed as flat slab with column and middle strips.

FIGURE 6.2 Mat (raft) foundation of a basement.

At basement level: loads on interior columns, DL = 650 kN; LL = 367 kN

Loads on exterior columns: DL = 520 kN; LL = 257 kN

300 mm basement wall and 400 basement slab

Groundwater table = 1 m below ground level.

Geotechnical ground conditions: Top 4 m of ground is made up soil underlain by alluvium of 3 m depth under which lies gravel river terrace deposits.

6.4.1 To Determine the Bearing Capacity of Soil at 3 m Depth

To calculate the bearing capacity in accordance with BS 8004: 1986

Before we analyze the raft foundation, we should determine the safe bearing capacity of soil underneath the foundation. The raft is placed on made-up soil at a depth 3.4 m from GL.

Adopting the equation suggested by Terzaghi and modified by Skempton for rectangular footing ultimate bearing capacity of soil

$$q_u = 1.3 \times c \times \left(0.84 + 0.16 \times \frac{B}{L} \right) \times N_c + \gamma \times z \times N_q + 0.4 \times \gamma \times B \times N_y$$

Assuming the geotechnical design data as shown in Table 2.1 in Chapter 2:

γ_b = 18 kN/m³; C_u = 20 kN/m²; ϕ' = 25°; B = 13.3 m; L = 22.9 m; γ_{net} = 18 − 10 = 8 kN/m³

From graphs in Figure 2.5

N_c = 25; N_q = 12.5; and N_y = 10

Therefore, net ultimate bearing capacity

$$q_u = 1.3 \times 20 \times \left(0.84 + 0.16 \times \frac{13.3}{22.9} \right) \times 25 + 8 \times 3 \times (12.5 - 1) + 0.4 \times 8 \times 13.3 \times 10 = 1308 \text{ kN/m}^2$$

Assuming a factor of safety = 3 to take into account of weak soil of made-up ground
Net safe bearing capacity of soil

$$q = \frac{1308}{3} = 436 \text{ kN/m}^2$$

A further overburden pressure may then be added, equal to the weight of the column of soil excavated. Thus, gross safe bearing capacity of soil

$$q = 436 + 3.4 \times 8 = 463 \text{ kN/m}^2$$

Adopt: a safe bearing capacity of soil

$$q = 300 \text{ kN/m}^2$$

to allow any differential settlement.

To calculate the allowable bearing capacity in accordance with Eurocode 7:

Assume:

$$\gamma_b = 18 \text{ kN/m}^3$$

Water table below ground level = 1.0 m

So, the soil is submersed. Therefore, weight of submersed soil

$$\gamma = 18 - 10 = 8 \text{ kN/m}^3$$

with the given soil parameter of $C_u = 20$ kN/m^2 and neglecting ϕ'.

Referring to Annex D.3 undrained soil conditions, the design bearing pressure may be calculated from

$$q = (\pi + 2) \times \frac{C_u}{\gamma_{C_u} \times b_c \times s_c \times i_c} + q$$

where

γ_{C_u} = partial safety factor for undrained shear strength of soil = 1.4

q = overburden surcharge 8×3.2 kN/m^2 = 25.6 kN/m^2

b_c = inclination of foundation base = 1

s_c = shape factor of foundation = $1 + 0.2 \times \left(\dfrac{B'}{L'}\right) = 1 + 0.2 \times \left(\dfrac{13.2}{22.8}\right) = 1.12$

where

B' = effective width of foundation base = B = 13.2 m

L' = effective length of foundation base = L = 22.8 m

Since no eccentricity developed on the foundation base.

i_c = the inclination of load caused by horizontal load H acting on the foundation

$$= \frac{1}{2}\left[1 + \left(1 - \frac{H}{A'} \times C_u\right)^{0.5}\right], \qquad \text{(since } H = 0\text{)}$$

$$= \frac{1}{2}(1 + 1) = 1$$

Hence,

q = Allowable bearing capacity of soil

$$= \left[(\pi + 2) \times \frac{20}{1.4} \times 1 \times 1.12 \times 1 + 25.6\right] \text{kN/m}^2 = 107.9 \text{ kN/m}^2$$

Adopt: Allowable bearing capacity of soil 100 kN/m^2.

6.4.2 To Calculate the Contact Pressure under the Foundation Raft

Consider the whole area of foundation slab = $22.8 \times 13.2 = 301$ m^2

Total DL at base level

From interior columns:	8 nos. × 650 kN = 5200 kN
From exterior columns (long walls):	8 nos. × 520 kN = 4160 kN
From exterior columns (short walls):	4 nos. × 650/2 kN = 1300 kN
From exterior columns (corner long walls):	4 × 520/2 kN = 1040 kN

Peripheral wall (assumed 300 mm thick): $2 \times (22.5 + 12.9) \times 2.85 \times 0.3 \times 24 =$ 1453 kN

Total   = 13153 kN

Foundation slab (assumed 400 mm thick): $22.8 \times 13.2 \times 0.4 \times 24 =$ 2889 kN

All total DL   = 16042 kN

Total LL at base level

From interior columns: 8 nos. $\times$ 367 kN = 2936 kN

From exterior columns (long walls):   8 nos. $\times$ 257 kN = 2056 kN

From exterior columns (short walls):   4 nos. $\times$ 367/2 kN =   734 kN

From exterior columns (corner long walls):4 nos. $\times$ 257/2 kN =   514 kN

All total LL   = 6240 kN

Total (DL + LL) = (16042 + 6240) kN = 22282 kN

Therefore, gross contact soil pressure

$$\frac{22282}{301} = 74 \text{ kN/m}^2 < \text{allowable } 100 \text{ kN/m}^2 \quad \textbf{(Satisfactory)}.$$

And net contact soil pressure = $(74 - 0.4 \times 24) = 64.4 \text{ kN/m}^2$

To calculate net ultimate contact pressure

Using BS 8004: 1986—Foundations: Assuming, partial safety factors γ_f for DL and LL are 1.4 and 1.6, respectively,

Total ultimate DL and LL = $1.4 \times 13153 + 1.6 \times 6240 = 28398$ kN

Therefore, net ultimate upward contact pressure,

$$p_u = \frac{28398}{301} = 94.3 \text{ kN/m}^2$$

Using Eurocode 7: 2004:   Referring Table A3: partial safety factors (γ_f) on actions:

For DL (permanent) $\gamma_f = 1.35$;

For live load (variable) $\gamma_f = 1.5$

Total net ultimate DL and LL = $1.35 \times 13153 + 1.6 \times 6240 = 27741$ kN

Therefore, net ultimate upward contact pressure

$$p_u = \frac{27741}{301} = 92 \text{ kN/m}^2$$

6.4.3   To Design the Reinforced Concrete Foundation Mat (Raft)

To design the foundation raft using BS 8110: 1997

Loading: Net ultimate upward contact soil pressure under the raft slab = 94.3 kN/m^2

(calculated before)

Analysis of raft slab

Methods of analysis: The slab may be analyzed as an inverted flat slab by empirical method subjected to upward contact soil pressure when the spacing of columns in either direction are approximately equal. In our case, the spacing of columns are not equal. So, the empirical method cannot be applied. Therefore, the frame analysis method, as mentioned in British Standard BS 8110, should be applied. The following design considerations are made in the analyais of raft slab by frame method:

- The slab shall be designed as inverted flat slab subjected to net upward ultimate contact soil pressure (p_u = 94.3 kN/m^2)
- The flat slab panels shall be divided into a series of longitudinal and transverse frames along column lines each way, consisting of columns and strips of slab. The width of strip is equal to the spacing of columns.
- The effective width of column strips may be taken equal to width of column w_p (or pedestal) + 3 to 4 times the effective depth of raft. So,

$$w_s = w_p + 4 \times \text{effective depth} = 0.4 \text{ (column width)} + 4 \times 0.3 = 1.6 \text{ m.}$$

The loadings on the column strip may be taken equal to triangular distribution by the diagonal lines drawn between the columns.

British Standard codes of practice BS 8110 stipulates the following:

- The width of the panel is to be divided into column strip and middle strip.
- The width of the column strip and middle strip shall be equal to half the panel width.
- The loading on the strip shall be taken as the full width of panel.

Each frame shall be analyzed in its entirety by the Hardy Cross method or any other suitable elastic methods.

The value of output results shall be distributed in column and middle strip as percentages of total negative and positive moments in accordance with Table 3.18 of BS 8110 as shown here (see Table 6.1).

TABLE 6.1   Table 3.18 (BS 8110: Part 1: 1997)

Design moment	Apportionment between column and middle strip as % of total negative or positive design moment		
Negative	Column strip 75%	!	Middle strip 25%
Positive	Column strip 55%	!	Middle strip 45%

We shall follow the frame analysis method as stipulated in BS 8110. Firstly, consider a transverse panel width = 4.5 m (see Figure 6.2 plan). Referring to Frame analysis method (BS 8110), assume, the slab is continuous under columns and the ends are hinged with the vertical basement walls. The connection between column end with slab is assumed hinged so that no column stiffness shall be taken into account in the analysis. Analyze the slab by Hardy Cross moment distribution method subjected to upward contact pressure due to soil reaction.

Net upward ultimate contact soil pressure per m = 94.3 × 4.5 = 424.4   (say 425 kN/m)

Consider the column supports at points A, B, C, and D, respectively, from left support A.

Spans AB and CD = 5.3 m; Span BC = 2.3 m

Fixed end moments:

$$M_{fab} = 0 \text{ (assumed simply supported at A)}$$

$$M_{fba} = 425 \times \frac{5.3^2}{2} = 1492 \text{ kN m} = M_{fcd}$$

$$M_{fbc} = 425 \times \frac{2.3^2}{12} = 187 \text{ kN m}$$

Stiffness: Assume the slab has constant moment of inertia due to constant width and thickness.

$$K_{ba} = \frac{3}{4} \times \frac{I_{ba}}{L_{ba}} = \frac{3}{4} \times \frac{I_{ba}}{5.3} = 0.14$$

$$K_{bc} = \frac{I_{bc}}{L_{bc}} = \frac{I_{bc}}{2.3} = 0.43$$

(Since I is constant, we can omit in the above expression).

Distribution factors:

$$D_{ba} = \frac{K_{ba}}{(K_{ba} + K_{bc})} = \frac{0.14}{(0.14 + 0.43)} = 0.25 = D_{cd}$$

$$D_{bc} = \frac{K_{bc}}{(K_{ba} + K_{bc})} = \frac{0.43}{(0.14 + 0.43)} = 0.75 = D_{cb}$$

With the above values, the moment distribution was carried out as shown in Table 6.2.

TABLE 6.2 Moment distribution

Supports

A		B	C		D
Distribution factors	0.25	0.75	0.75	0.25	
Fixed end moments	+1492	−187	+187	−1492	
Distribution	−326	−979	+979	+326	
Carried over		+489	−489		
Distribution	−122	−367	+367	+122	
Carried over		+184	−184		
Distribution	−46	−138	+138	+46	
Final moments	+998	−998	+998	−998	0.0

Span moment for

$$AB = w \times \frac{L_{ab}^2}{8} - \frac{998}{2} = 425 \times \frac{5.3^2}{8} - \frac{998}{2} = 993 \text{ kN m}$$

The moments calculated above shall be distributed in column and middle strip.

Referring to Table 3.18 (BS 8110), we have the following distribution of moments:

For column strip:

−ve moment at support = 75% of 998 kN m = 749 kN m

+ ve moment at mid span = 55% of 993 kN m = 546 kN m

For middle strip:

−ve moment at support = 25% of 998 kN m = 249 kN m

+ ve moment at mid span = 45% of 993 kN m = 447 kN m

Now,

$$\text{the width of column strip} = \frac{4.5}{2} = 2.25 \text{ m}$$

and

$$\text{the width of middle strip} = \frac{4.5}{2} = 2.25 \text{ m}$$

Next, consider the longitudinal panel along the interior along column row B

$$\text{Width of panel} = \left(\frac{5.3 + 2.3}{2}\right) = 3.8 \text{ m}$$

Span = 4.5 m continuous under columns and ends are considered hinged.

Net upward contact pressure/m = 94.3 × 3.8 = 358.4 (say 359 kN/m).

As the spans are equal, the moments and shears shall be calculated based on Table 3.12 of BS 8110 (Ultimate bending moment and shear forces in one-way spanning slab). Hence,

−ve BM at first of interior support = − 0.086 × 359 × 4.5² = 625 kN m

+ve BM near middle of end span = + 0.086 × 359 × 4.5² = 625 kN m

For column strip:

−ve BM at support = 75% of 625 kN m = 469 kN m

+ve BM at mid span = 55% of 625 kN m = 344 kN m

For middle strip:

−ve BM at support = 25% of 625 kN m = 156 kN m

+ve BM at mid span = 45% of 625 kN m = 281 kN m

Now,

$$\text{the width of column strip} = \frac{5.3}{4} + \frac{2.3}{2} = 2.475 \text{ m}$$

and

$$\text{width of middle strip} = \frac{5.3}{2} = 2.65 \text{ m}$$

Design of section: Refer to Figure 6.3 for RC details of mat (raft) foundation of a basement. Firstly, consider the transverse panel of width 4.5 m.

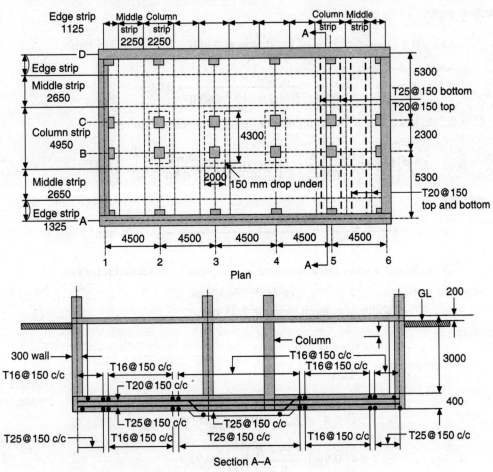

FIGURE 6.3 RC details of mat (raft) foundation of a basement.

Notes: 1. The basement substructure should be designed for retaining aqueous liquids according to BS 8007:1987 or latest code of practice.
2. The concrete grade shall be C 40 (f_{cu} = 40 N/mm²).
3. Maximum allowable design crack width to be 0.2 mm.
4. The mat should be designed as flat slab with column and middle strips.

Column strip:

At support: $-$ve $M_u = -749$ kN m

Width of column strip = 2.25 m

Hence,

BM/m width $= \dfrac{749}{2.25} = 333$ kN m

Assume, depth of slab D = 400 mm

Effective depth

$$d = D - \text{cover} - \frac{1}{2} \text{ of bar diameter} = 400 - 75 - 10 = 315 \text{ mm}$$

$$K = \frac{M_u}{(b \times d^2 \times f_{cu})} = \frac{333 \times 10^6}{(1000 \times 315^2 \times 400)} = 0.083$$

$K' = 0.156$, since $K < K'$ no compression reinforcement is required.

$$z = d\left[0.5 + \left(\frac{0.25 - K}{0.9}\right)^{0.5}\right] = d\left[0.5 + \left(\frac{0.25 - 0.083}{0.90}\right)^{0.5}\right] = 0.897d$$

A_s required

$$\frac{M_u}{(0.95 \times f_y \times z)} = \frac{333 \times 10^6}{(0.95 \times 460 \times 0.897 \times 315)} = 2696 \text{ mm}^2$$

Adopt: T25 @150 c/c bottom (area provided = 3272 mm²)   **(Satisfactory)**

Near mid span: + ve M_u = 546 kN m

Width of column strip   = 2.25 m

Therefore,

$$M_u \text{ per m width } = \frac{546}{2.25} = 243 \text{ kN m}$$

$$K = \frac{M_u}{(b \times d^2 \times f_{cu})} = \frac{243 \times 10^6}{(1000 \times 315^2 \times 40)} = 0.061$$

$$z = d\left[0.5 + \left(\frac{0.25 - K}{0.9}\right)^{0.5}\right] = 0.92\,d$$

$D = 400$ mm; $d = 315$ mm;
A_s required

$$\frac{M_u}{(0.95 \times f_y \times z)} = \frac{243 \times 10^6}{(0.95 \times 460 \times 0.92 \times 315)} = 1919 \text{ mm}^2$$

Adopt: T20 @ 150 c/c top (area provided = 2094 mm²)   **(Satisfactory)**

Middle strip:

At support: $M_u/\text{m} = \dfrac{249}{2.25} = 111 \text{ kN m}$

At mid span: $M_u/\text{m} = \dfrac{447}{2.25} = 199 \text{ kN m}$

Consider, at mid span:

$$\frac{M_u}{(d \times d^2)} = \frac{199 \times 10^6}{(1000 \times 315^2)} = 2.0$$

Instead of calculating the finding lever arm factor, it is easy to follow the chart given in part 3 of BS 8110:1985.

So, referring to Chart 2,

$$100 \times \frac{A_s}{(b \times d)} = 0.55$$

Hence,

$$A_s = 0.55 \times 1000 \times \frac{315}{100} = 1733 \text{ mm}^2$$

Provide: T20 @ 150 c/c top (area provided = 2094 mm²)   **(Satisfactory)**

To consider at support, adopt the same as at mid span: T20 @ 150 c/c bottom

Next, the consider the longitudinal panel

Column strip:

At support: $M_u/m = \dfrac{469}{2.475} = 190 \text{ kN m}$

At mid span: $M_u/m = \dfrac{344}{2.475} = 139 \text{ kN m}$

At support: Assumed

$$D = 400 \text{ mm}; \ d = 400 - 75 \text{ (cover)} - 25 - \frac{20}{2} = 290 \text{ mm}$$

$$\frac{M_u}{(b \times d^2)} = \frac{190 \times 10^6}{(1000 \times 290^2)} = 2.26$$

Referring to Chart 2 of BS 8110:

$$A_s = 1000 \times 290 \times \frac{0.6}{100} = 1740 \text{ mm}^2$$

Adopt: T25 @ 150 c/c bottom (A_s provided = 3272 mm² to reduce the shear stress)

At mid span:

$$\frac{M_u}{(b \times d^2)} = \frac{139 \times 10^6}{(1000 \times 290^2)} = 1.65$$

Referring to Chart 2 of BS 8110:

$$A_s = 0.43 \times 1000 \times \frac{290}{100} = 1247 \text{ mm}^2$$

Adopt: T16 @ 150 c/c top A_s provided = 1340 mm²

Middle strip:

At support: $M_u/m = \dfrac{156}{2.65} = 59 \text{ kN m}$

At mid span: $M_u/m = \dfrac{281}{2.65} = 106 \text{ kN m}$

Adopt: T16 @ 150 c/c top and bottom at support and at mid span (A_s provided = 1340 mm²)

Check for shear: Shear should be checked along the perimeter at a distance $1.5 \times d$ from the face of support. So, ultimate shear

V_u = Net upward ultimate soil contact pressure × (Area of slab supported by column − Area at $1.5 \times d$ from column face) = $p_u [A - (1.5 \times 0.315 \times 2 + 0.4)^2]$

$$= 94.3 [3.8 \times 4.5 - 1.35^2] = 1440 \text{ kN}$$

Perimeter of slab at $1.5 \times d$ from the face of column

$$u = 4 \times [1.5 \times 0.315 \times 2 + 0.4] = 5.38 \text{ m} = 5380 \text{ mm}$$

Therefore, shear stress,

$$v_u = \frac{V_u}{(u \times d)} = \frac{1440 \times 10^3}{(5380 \times 315)} = 0.85 \text{ N/mm}^2$$

% of steel,

$$\rho = 100 \times \frac{A_s}{(b \times d)} = \frac{100 \times 3272}{(1000 \times 315)} = 1.04$$

Allowable shear stress,

$$v_c = \frac{0.79}{1.25 \times p^{0.33} \times \left(\frac{400}{d}\right)^{0.25} \times \left(\frac{f_{cu}}{25}\right)^{0.33}}$$

$$= \frac{0.79}{1.25 \times 1.04^{0.33} \times \left(\frac{400}{315}\right)^{0.25} \times \left(\frac{40}{25}\right)^{0.33}} = 0.79 \text{ N/mm}^2 < v_u$$

As the actual shear stress exceeds the permissible value, shear reinforcement is necessary. But, it is difficult to apply the shear reinforcement in slab and also time consuming. It will be advisable to increase the slab thickness locally under the columns. Therefore, increase the thickness of slab to 550 mm locally under the column below foundation level. The dimensions of increased thickness = 2000 mm × 4300 mm × 550 mm.

With increased thickness:

$$D = 550 \text{ mm}; d = 550 - 75 \text{ (cover)} - 1.5 \times 25 \text{ (bar diameter)} = 438 \text{ mm}$$

Ultimate shear,

$$V_u = 94.3 \times [3.8 \times 4.5 - (1.5 \times 0.43882 + 0.4)^2] = 1138 \text{ kN}$$

Perimeter of slab at $1.5 \times d$ from the face of column,

$$u = 4 \times (1.5 \times 0.438 \times 2 + 0.4) = 6.856 \text{ m} = 6856 \text{ mm}$$

Therefore, shear stress,

$$v_u \frac{V_u}{(\text{perimeter} \times d)} = \frac{1138 \times 10^3}{(6856 \times 438)} = 0.38 \text{ N/mm}^2$$

% of steel,

$$\rho = \frac{100 \times A_s}{(b \times d)} = \frac{100 \times 3272}{(1000 \times 438)} = 0.75$$

Allowable shear stress,

$$v_c = \frac{0.79}{1.25 \times 0.75^{0.33} \times \left(\dfrac{40}{25}\right)^{0.33}} = 0.67 \text{ N/mm}^2 > v_u$$

So, no shear reinforcement is required.

To design the RC foundation raft in accordance with Eurocode 2: 2004

Loading: As previously calculated, net upward ultimate contact soil pressure, $p_u = 92$ kN/m².

Analysis of raft slab: For a flat slab, assume a series of longitudinal and transverse frames consisting of column strips of width equal to the spacing of columns. Consider the transverse frames of 2 end spans AB and CD = 5.3 m and a central span BC = 2.3 m (see Figure 6.3).

Assume that the end supports are simply supported and the frame is continuous over interior supports.

Width of frame = 4.5 m = c/c of longitudinal spacing of columns.

Therefore, net upward ultimate soil pressure per m = 92 × 4.5 = 414 kN/m run.

Following the Hardy Cross moment distribution method:
Fixed end moment,

$$M_f\text{BA} = M_f\text{CD} = w \times \frac{L^2}{8} = 414 \times \frac{5.3^2}{8} = 1454 \text{ kN m}$$

Fixed end moment,

$$M_f\text{BC} = M_f\text{CB} = 414 \times \frac{2.3^2}{12} = 183 \text{ kN m}$$

Distribution factor for BA = 0.25
Distribution factor for BC = 0.75

Following the moment distribution (done before):
Final moments:

$$M_{ba} = 998 \times \frac{414}{425} = 972 \text{ kN m} = M_{bc}$$

Distribution of moments:
In column strip:

$$\frac{1}{2} \text{ of longitudinal column spacing} = \frac{4.5}{2} = 2.25 \text{ m}$$

– ve moment at support = 75% of 972 = 729 kN m

+ ve moment at span = 55% of 972 = 535 kN m

In middle strip: 2.25 m wide

– ve moment at support = 25% of 972 = 243 kN m

+ ve moment at span = 45% of 972 = 437 kN m

Design of sections: Consider the column strip.

Moment at support per m width = $\dfrac{729}{2.25}$ = 324 kN m

Assumed depth of slab at support, D = 550 mm;
Effective depth

$$d = 550 - 40 \text{ (cover)} - (25 - 13) \text{ bar diameter} = 472 \text{ mm}$$

(Assumed 75 mm lean concrete under RC slab)

$$K = \frac{M_u}{(bd^2 f_{ck})} = \frac{324 \times 10^6}{(1000 \times 472^2 \times 30)} = 0.048$$

$K' = 0.205 > K$; so no compression reinforcement is required.
$z = 0.95d$

$$A_s = \frac{M_u}{(f_y d \times z)} = \frac{324 \times 10^6}{(500 \times 0.95 \times 472)} = 1445 \text{ mm}^2$$

Adopt: T25 at 150 c/c bottom (A_s provided = 3272 mm^2)
(*Note:* The higher area of steel is provided to reduce the shear stress in concrete)

Moment at mid span per m width $= \dfrac{535}{2.5} = 214$ kN m

$$A_s = \frac{214 \times 10^6}{500 \times 0.95 \times 472} = 955 \text{ m}^2$$

Adopt: T20 at 150 mm c/c top (A_s provided = 2094 mm^2) (see Figure 6.3).

To check for punching shear: Assume that the punching shear occurs along the perimeter at distance d from the face of column. The effective depth of slab around the central columns = 474 (calculated before).

The punching shear length = 2.3 (spacing of column) + 2 × 0.672 (distance from c/c line of column to a distance d) = 3.644 m

The punching shear width = 0.4 + 2 × 0.472 = 1.344 m

Length of perimeter = 2 (3.644 + 1.344) = 9.976 m

Punching shear,

$V_{ed} = p_u \times$ Area covered by spacing of longitudinal and transverse columns – area covered by punching perimeter

$$= 92 \times (6.8 \times 4.5 - 3.644 \times 1.344) = 2365 \text{ kN}$$

Punching shear stress,

$$v_{ed} = \frac{2365 \times 10^3}{(9.976 \times 1000 \times 472)} = 0.5 \text{ N/mm}^2$$

% of steel,

$$\rho = \frac{A_s}{(b \times d)} = \frac{3272}{(1000 \times 372)\,100} = 0.88$$

Allowable shear stress,

$$v_{rd} = 0.12 \times k \times (\rho \times f_{ck})^{0.33}$$

where

$$k = 1 + \left(\frac{200}{d}\right)^{0.5} = 1 + \left(\frac{200}{472}\right)^{0.5} = 1.65 < 2$$

Therefore,

$$v_{rd} = 0.12 \times 1.65 \times (0.88 \times 30)^{0.33} = 0.58 \text{ N/mm}^2 > v_{ed}\ (0.5 \text{ N/mm}^2) \qquad \textbf{(Satisfactory)}$$

Therefore, no shear reinforcement is required. Refer BS 8004: 1986 [6.4] and Eurocode 7: 2004[6.5].

REFERENCES

[6.1] Terzaghi, K. and R.B. Peck, Soil Mechanics in Engineering Practice.

[6.2] Dunham, C.W., Foundations of Structures, McGraw Hill, New York, 1950.

[6.3] BS 8110: part 1: 1997: Structural Use of Concrete; Code of Practice for Design and Construction.

[6.4] BS 8004:1986: British Standard Code of Practice for Foundations.

[6.5] Eurocode 7:2004 Geotechnical design. Part 1: General rules.

Chapter7

Piled Foundation

7.0 GENERAL PRINCIPLES

When we find that the soil for a considerable depth (5–10 m) depth below ground level is composed of soft silty clay with fine sand of very low shearing strength and bearing capacity, it is not practical and economical to use conventional isolated or strip footing carrying heavy and variable column loads in building the foundation extending to such a depth of soil adequate shearing strength.

In this situation, we transfer the heavy column loads deep down into such a depth of soil of high shearing strength to support the loads by means of pile foundations. The piled foundation may be defined as a single or a group of structural vertical long strut (sometimes acting as tension member) members, driven or bored (in case of cast-*in situ*) to a depth to attain sufficient capacity to support the external column loads from the superstructure. The pile cap tying up the pile group is built near ground level to support the column.

The supporting capacity of piles is gained by the shear frictional resistance developed between the surface of strut member and the adjoining soil and also the bearing strength of soil at the base area of piles.

7.1 CHOICE OF ALTERNATIVE TYPES OF FOUNDATIONS

Before we start the structural layout to meet the requirements of machines and equipment, it is the fundamental principle to know the soil conditions in the project area.

So, first of all, the geotechnical soil investigation at site are carried out, and from the laboratory tests the geotechnical data are established. The geotechnical soil data will determine the type of foundations for different structures and machines and equipment. For soil of very low shearing strength for appreciable depth below ground level, the piled foundation is the most appropriate.

7.2 FUNCTIONS OF PILES

The functions of piles is to transmit load to the soil of high shearing strength at sufficient depth and act as compression or tension members when the structure is subjected to wind and wave forces in addition to vertical direct thrust.

7.3 SELECTION OF CONSTRUCTION MATERIAL

Timber piles

From the early age of human civilization the timber piles have been used in civil engineering construction. Recently, they have been replaced by concrete and steel piles. Even nowadays, in underdeveloped countries and developing countries, timber piles are in use in light civil engineering works. The advantages of timber piles are that these are light, easily manoeuvrable, and easily available in medium length. They have high stiffness ratio in relation to the weight and long life when immersed in water without any atmospheric contact.

Concrete piles

Heavy civil engineering works in modern industrial age demand high strength material in compression, tension and bending to resist very heavy loads from superstructure and adverse climatic conditions. To meet all the above requirements, reinforced concrete piles are best suited. They can be cast to any shape and size to suit the required design load and location.

1. *In situ pile foundation:*   The concrete piles may be of *in situ* construction where holes are drilled to the required depth and concrete is poured in the hole after the insertion of reinforcement cage. The *in situ* construction avoids noise, vibration and ground heave.
2. *Pre-cast concrete pile foundation:*   The reinforced precast and prestressed concrete piles are manufactured in shop to design requirements and are transported to the site. They are driven in the ground to the depth to attain the required design capacity.
3. *Steel pile foundation:*   Due to easy fabrication and handling facility and to withstand high driving stress, steel piles are more used in recent times particularly in off-shore structures. They are resistant to marine conditions by the application of special durable coatings and cathodic protection.

7.4 TYPES OF PILE

The British Standard Code of Practice for Foundations (BS 8004) classifies the following three types of piles:

1. *Large displacement piles:*   Large displacement piles are mainly the piles that displace the soil entirely when driven into the ground. The are usually of solid or hollow section with driven end closed. Some large displacement piles are: Timber, precast concrete (solid and hollow section), precast prestressed concrete (solid and hollow section with driven end closed), and large hollow steel tube and box section.
2. *Small displacement piles:*   These types of piles are also solid but displace small amount of soil due to their small sectional area. They include steel I and H section, and also

hollow section with driven end open. Some small displacement piles are: precast concrete and precast prestressed hollow section with open driven end, steel I and H section, steel tube and box section with open driven end (quantity of soil inside shell removed as required). Sheet piles may also be called small displacement piles.

3. *Replacement piles:* The replacement piles are the cast-*in situ* piles where holes are bored in the ground and the soil is removed during boring machine operation. The bored hole is filled with concrete after placing reinforcement cage. Sometimes, steel casing is inserted in the bored hole before concrete is poured and the casing may be withdrawn after the concrete pouring operation is complete. In places, the steel sections are inserted in the bored hole and filled up with concrete. The diaphragm wall and contiguous pile construction may be classified as replacement piles. This type of wall construction has been used extensively in several underground rail and road cut and cover tunnel, metro station and basement civil engineering works.

7.5 BEHAVIOUR OF PILES SUBJECTED TO COMPRESSIVE AND LATERAL LOADS

The behaviour of soil in contact with pile surface, i.e. the soil–pile interaction phenomenon is highly complex. The vertical and lateral loads on pile are supported mainly by the skin friction and shear resistance of soil in contact with pile surface area. During the installation of a pile by any method (by driving, drilling, vibration, etc.), the soil in contact with pile face is entirely disturbed. The soil–pile interaction changes over a long period of time that may significantly affect the skin frictional resistance of pile.

Also, the soil beneath the toe of the piles becomes compressed to a large degree. As a result the end–bearing resistance of pile is significantly changed. These changes might have caused due to the dissipation of excess pore pressure by the installation of piles, and relative soil–pile or pile–soil movement. In the installation of individual piles for pile-group foundation in close spacing, the piles already installed undergo changes in load carrying capacity and load settlement characteristics.

Considering the above points on the complex behavioural characteristics, it is a difficult task to determine the exact load bearing capacity of soil by adopting a highly theoretical approach.

We shall, therefore, consider a more simplified method in calculating the capacity of piles by taking into account the factors on the method of installation, experience and field loading tests.

7.6 PRINCIPLES IN THE ANALYSIS OF THE LOAD BEARING CAPACITY OF PILES

The principles in the analysis capacity of piles may be explained in the following way based on the theory of soil mechanics:

Shear frictional or skin frictional resistance of piles

When a pile is subjected to a compressive load from the superstructure, the load is transferred deep into the ground through the shear frictional resistance generated by the soil around the perimeter of skin of the pile. This resistance may be termed as skin frictional resistance of pile. The mechanism of generation (development) of frictional resistance occurs only when a slight movement (displacement) pile occurs (see Figure 7.1).

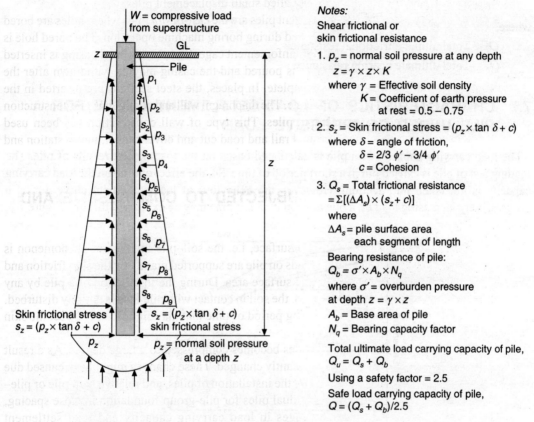

Notes:
Shear frictional or skin frictional resistance

1. p_z = normal soil pressure at any depth
   $z = \gamma \times z \times K$
   where γ = Effective soil density
   K = Coefficient of earth pressure
   at rest = $0.5 - 0.75$

2. s_z = Skin frictional stress = $(p_z \times \tan \delta + c)$
   where δ = angle of friction,
   $\delta = 2/3\ \phi' - 3/4\ \phi'$
   c = Cohesion

3. Q_s = Total frictional resistance
   $= \Sigma[(\Delta A_s) \times (s_z + c)]$
   where
   ΔA_s = pile surface area
   each segment of length
   Bearing resistance of pile:
   $Q_b = \sigma' \times A_b \times N_q$
   where σ' = overburden pressure
   at depth $z = \gamma \times z$
   A_b = Base area of pile
   N_q = Bearing capacity factor

Total ultimate load carrying capacity of pile,
$Q_u = Q_s + Q_b$
Using a safety factor = 2.5
Safe load carrying capacity of pile,
$Q = (Q_s + Q_b)/2.5$

Labels in figure:
W = compressive load from superstructure
GL
Pile
Skin frictional stress $s_z = (p_z \times \tan \delta + c)$
$s_z = (p_z \times \tan \delta + c)$ skin frictional stress
p_z = normal soil pressure at a depth z

FIGURE 7.1 Principles in the analysis of load carrying capacity of piles.

The frictional resistance is dependant on the angle of shearing resistance of cohesionless sandy soil or the undisturbed undrained cohesion of cohesive clay soil and the surface area of pile in contact with soil.

As the pile goes down through soil strata of different geotechnical characters (i.e. varying angle of shearing resistance and cohesion), the frictional resistance increases with depth and, at the same time, the carrying capacity of pile increases. The total frictional resistance of pile shall be the summation of individual resistance values of each stratum.

End bearing resistance

In addition to frictional resistance, the pile receives the bearing resistance when its end bears on a very hard incompressible stratum. The end bearing resistance is dependant on the effective overburden pressure at the base level of pile and the base area of pile.

Total resistance of piles

Hence, the total ultimate pile resistance

$$Q_u = \text{total frictional resistance} + \text{end bearing resistance}$$

Or, the ultimate load carrying capacity of pile,

$$Q_u = Q_s + Q_b$$

where,

Q_s = Total ultimate frictional resistance

Q_b = Total ultimate bearing resistance

7.7 CHARACTERISTICS OF LOAD-SETTLEMENT CURVE FOR A PILE UNDER COMPRESSIVE LOAD

The load carrying capacity of a pile is calculated based on the loading test results of pile. The loading test of pile is carried out in a short period of time. So, the effect of time on the load carrying capacity is not taken into account. However, the behaviour of load-settlement curve during a progressively increasing load on a pile at a rapid rate of time may be explained through Figure 7.2.

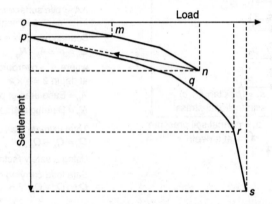

Notes: Loading sequence
1. During initial loading the load-settlement curve is almost a straight line as shown by *om*.
2. As the load increases progressively, the spoil–pile interface yields and slippage occurs when the curve reaches the point *n*. At this point, maximum skin friction on the pile has been mobilized.
3. Now, release the load from the pile gradually. The curve bounces back to the point *p*. Then, *op* is the permanent settlement due to the mobilization of full skin friction which is only 1% (maximum) of pile diameter.
4. Again, reload the pile gradually when the base resistance starts to act. For full mobilization of base resistance, higher downward movement of pile has taken place and the curve reaches the point *r*. The settlement accounts to 10-20% of pile diameter.
5. After the full mobilization of base resistance takes place, even a slight increase in loading a large settlement will take place, and the curve will slide downwards sharply.
6. So, the point on the curve r indicates the ultimate load resistance of pile.

FIGURE 7.2 Characteristics of load-settlement curve under compressive load.

- Initially, the load-settlement relationship is almost a straight line up to point *m*.
- Beyond point *m*, as the load is increased progressively, the soil–pile interface yields and slippage occurs when we reach the point *n* on the curve. At this point, maximum skin friction on the pile shaft has been mobilized.

- Now, we release the load gradually from the pile head. A settlement of amount op is measured. This amount is the 'permanent set'. This amount of displacement, required to mobilize the total skin friction, is only 0.3 to 1% of the diameter of pile.
- Again, we reload the pile gradually when the base resistance started to act. For the full mobilization of base resistance, higher downward movement takes place when the curve reaches the point r. The settlement accounts to 10 to 20% of the pile diameter.
- After the full mobilization of base resistance, a slight increase of load will tend to slide the curve downwards indicating large increase of settlement to point s, as shown in Figure 7.2.
- Based on the load-settlement curve indicating the failure of pile after reaching the maximum skin friction and base resistance, we determine the total ultimate load carrying capacity of pile. So, the point r on the curve indicates the ultimate resistance of pile.

Therefore, ultimate load carrying capacity of pile,

$$Q_u = Q_s + Q_b$$

7.8 ALLOWABLE LOAD CARRYING CAPACITY OF PILES

It is not safe to design the load carrying capacity of pile to support the load from the superstructure by adopting the ultimate load carrying capacity of pile. There may be significant variations in the properties of soil in soil data through which the pile penetrates. There may also be variations in soil character within few distance apart. So, a safety factor should be assumed by which the ultimate capacity is to be divided to arrive at the design safe capacity of pile.

The best way to assume a factor of safety will be to carry out a number of loading tests at different locations of the site and also geotechnical soil investigation of ground at the site, and to arrive at a reasonable factor of safety.

In general, a value of factor of safety is taken equal to 2.5 under normal condition.

Thus, safe load carrying capacity of pile,

$$Q = \frac{(Q_s + Q_b)}{2.5}$$

7.9 PILES IN COHESIONLESS SOIL

7.9.1 Based on British Standard Codes of Practice for Foundations BS 8004: 1986

To calculate the bearing resistance of pile

Referring to the following general expression of Terzaghi's ultimate bearing capacity of soil [see Eq. (2.4)]:

$$q_u = C_u \times N_c + \gamma \times z \times N_q + 0.5 \times g \times B \times N_y$$

Since the soil is cohesionless, the first term is zero and can be neglected in the expression where

$$\gamma = (\gamma_b - \gamma_w) = \text{effective density of soil}$$

γ_b = bulk density of soil

γ_w = density of water

and

$\gamma \times z$ = effective overburden pressure = σ'

B = width of base = diameter of pile

N_q and N_y are the bearing capacity factors.

Let

Q_b = end bearing resistance = $q_u \times A_b$ (where A_b = base area of pile)

Multiply the expression (2.4) by A_b. So, the above expression becomes

$$q_u \times A_b = \sigma' \times N_q \times A_b + 0.5 \times \gamma \times B \times A_b \times N_y$$

Since B is small compared to the length of pile, the last term may be neglected. Therefore, ultimate end bearing resistance of pile

$$Q_b = q_u \times A_b = \sigma' \times A_b \times N_q \tag{7.1}$$

To calculate the shear frictional resistance of pile

Let

σ' = effective overburden pressure at a depth z below ground level = $(\gamma_b - \gamma_w) \times z$

Let

p = normal soil pressure on the side of pile at any depth z.

Then,

$$p = \sigma' \times K_{ps}$$

where

$K_s = K_0$ = coefficient of horizontal soil stress at rest.

The value of K_s varies between 0.5 and 1.0 (see Tables 7.1 and 7.2).

Let

s = shear frictional (skin) stress = $p \times \tan \delta$

where

δ = angle of friction between pile surface and the surrounding soil mass.

The value of δ may be taken as $2/3 \phi$ to $3/4 \phi$, where ϕ is the angle of shearing resistance.

The value of shear frictional stress is maximum at bottom and zero at top, where $z = 0$

Therefore, average shear frictional stress,

$$s = \frac{p}{2} \times \tan \delta$$

Multiply the expression $s = p/2 \times \tan \delta$ by A_s, where A_s = surface area of pile in contact with soil.

Then, the above expression becomes

$$s \times A_s = \frac{p}{2} \times \tan \delta \times A_s$$

where

$\sigma \times A_s = Q_s$ = average frictional resistance of pile.

Therefore, average frictional resistance of pile,

$$Q_s = \frac{1}{2} \times p \times \tan \delta \times A_s = \frac{1}{2} \times \sigma' \times K_s \times \tan \delta \times A_s \qquad (7.2)$$

Therefore, total ultimate load carrying capacity of pile in cohesionless soil,

$$Q_u = Q_b + Q_s = \sigma' \times A_b \times N_q + \frac{1}{2} \times \sigma' \times K_s \times \tan \delta \times A_s \qquad (7.3)$$

using a safety factor (2.5).

Therefore, safe load carrying of pile in cohesionless soil,

$$Q = \frac{(Q_b + Q_s)}{2.5} \qquad (7.4)$$

7.9.2 Based on Eurocode 7: 2004 (Geotechnical Design)

To calculate the bearing resistance of piles

Referring to the general expression of Terzaghi's ultimate bearing capacity of soil [see Eq. (2.4)]

$$q_u = C_u \times N_c + \gamma \times z \times N_q + 0.5 \times \gamma \times B \times N_y$$

Referring to Annex D.4 [Eq. (D.2)] of Eurocode 7: 2004 (drained condition), the design bearing resistance of pile may be expressed in the following form

$$Q_{bd} = (C' \times N_c \times b_c \times s_c \times i_c + q' \times N_q \times b_q \times s_q \times i_q + 0.5 \times \gamma' \times B' \times N_\gamma \times b_\gamma \times s_\gamma \times i_\gamma) \times A_b$$

where

C' = Cohesion intercept in terms of effective stress

N_c, N_q and N_γ = Bearing capacity factors

$$N_q = e^{(\pi \times \tan \phi'/\gamma_{\phi'})} \times \tan^2 \left(45° + \frac{\phi'}{\gamma_{\phi'}} \right)$$

where

ϕ' = Effective angle of shearing resistance of soil.

$\gamma_{\phi'}$ = Partial factor for angle of shearing resistance.

b_c, b_q, b_γ = Inclination factor for the pile base

s_c, s_q, s_γ = Shape factor for pile base

i_c, i_q, i_γ = Shape factor (rectangular or circular)

B' = Effective width or diameter of pile.

A_b = Base area of pile

q' = Design effective overburden pressure at foundation level

γ' = Design effective density of soil

Since $C' = 0$ for cohesionless soil, the first term in the above expression is zero. Again, since B' is insignificant compared to the pile length, the last term is zero. Therefore,

$$Q_{bd} = [q' \times N_q \times b_q \times s_q \times i_q] \times A_b$$

Therefore, design end bearing resistance of pile,

$$Q_{bd} = \left[q' \times e^{\pi \times \tan\left(\frac{\phi'}{\gamma_{\phi'}}\right)} \times \tan^2\left(\frac{45 + \dfrac{\phi'}{\gamma_{\phi'}}}{2}\right) \times b_q \times s_q \times i_q \right] \times A_b \qquad (7.1a)$$

To calculate the design shear frictional resistance of pile

Let, q' = The effective overburden pressure at a depth z below ground level = $(\gamma_b - \gamma_w) \times z$
And let p = Normal soil pressure on the side of pile at any depth z
Then,

$$p = q' \times K_s$$

(where $K_s = K_o$ = Coefficient of horizontal soil stress at rest)

The value of K_s varies between 0.5 and 1.0 (see Tables 7.1 and 7.2)
Let
$\quad s$ = Shear frictional (skin) stress = $p \times \tan \delta = q' \times K_s \times \tan \delta$
where
$\quad \delta$ = Angle of friction between pile surface and the surrounding soil mass.

The value of δ varies between $\dfrac{2}{3}$ and $\dfrac{3}{4}$ of $(\phi'/\gamma_{\phi'})$
where

$\quad \phi'$ = effective angle of shearing resistance of soil
$\quad \gamma_{\phi'}$ = partial factor for soil parameter.

The value of soil frictional stress is maximum at bottom and zero at top, where $z = 0$
Therefore, average shear frictional stress,

$$s = \frac{p}{2} \times \tan \delta = q' \times \frac{K_s}{2} \times \tan \delta$$

Multiply the above axpression by A_s, where A_s = Surface area of pile in contact with soil.
Then, the above expression becomes

$$s \times A_s = \frac{p}{2} \times \tan \delta \times A_s = q' \frac{K_s}{2} \times \tan \delta \times A_s$$

where
$\quad s \times A_s = Q_{sd}$ = average design frictional resistance of pile.
Therefore, average design frictional resistance of pile,

$$Q_{sd} = \frac{1}{2} \times q' \times K_s \times \tan \delta \times A_s \qquad (7.2a)$$

Therefore, total design load carrying capacity of pile in cohesionless soil,

$$Q_d = Q_{bd} + Q_{sd} = q' \times A_b \times N_q \times b_q \times s_q \times i_q + \frac{1}{2} \times q' \times K_s \times \tan \delta \times A_s \qquad (7.3a)$$

The value of bearing capacity factor N_q is dependent on the ratio of penetration depth to the diameter of pile and on the angle of shearing resistance ϕ' of soil. The value of ϕ' is normally obtained from field standard penetration tests. The relationship between standard penetration resistance N and ϕ has been established by Peck, Hansen and Thornburn as shown by the curve in Figure 2.2a (Chapter 2).

The base resistance increases with depth but the rate of increase is not constant and also vary considerably in loose and very dense sand, as shown in Figure 7.3 by Kulhawy [7.1].

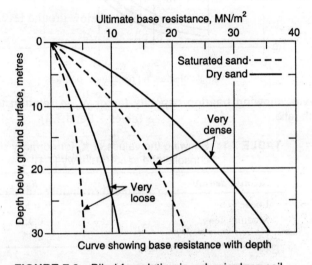

FIGURE 7.3   Piled foundation in cohesionless soil.

The value of N_q decreases as the depth of penetration of pile increases as shown by Berezantsev et al. [7.2]. The value of N_q, in relationship to the angle of shearing resistance and depth to width (diameter) ratio, is shown in Figure 7.4 by Berezantsev et al. [7.2].

The value of K_s is dependant on the relative density and state of consolidation of soil, the volume of displacement of the pile, the material of the pile and its shape. The evaluation of the value of K_s in calculating the skin friction is difficult, and is very complex phenomenon as it depends on the stress history of the soil which changes during the installation of the pile.

For driven piles, the displacement of soil increases the horizontal soil stress from the original K_o value.

For bored piles, drilling operation during the pile installation causes the loosening of dense sand, thereby resulting the decrease of horizontal soil stress. For the normally consolidated sand, the value of K_o at site is constant with depth and the value of K_s is modified by the installation method, as shown in Tables 7.1 and 7.2.

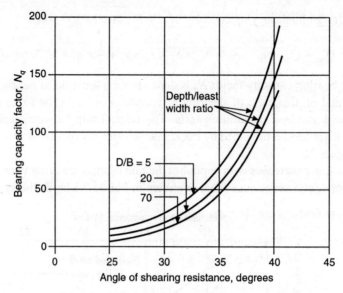

FIGURE 7.4 Curves showing bearing capacity factor N_q in relation to ϕ and depth/least width ratio.

TABLE 7.1 Showing the values of K_o for normally consolidated sand (Kulhawy [7.1])

Relative density	K_o
Loose	0.5
Medium dense	0.45
Dense	0.35

TABLE 7.2 Showing the values of coefficient of horizontal stress K_s (Kulhawy [7.1])

Installation method	K_s/K_o
Driven piles, large displacement	1 to 2
Driven piles, small displacement	0.75 to 1.25
Bored and cast-*in situ* piles	0.70 to 1
Jetted piles	0.5 to 0.7

For overconsolidated sand deposit that had been subjected to overburden pressure during the prehistoric period and where the pressure is released due to removal of overburden in recent times, the value of K_o is higher than those stated in Table 7.1 and reaches to 1 or even higher.

In normally-consolidated sand, the rate of penetration is slow at shallow depth and increasing linearly as the depth increases.

Kulhawy has also established the relationship between the angle of friction δ (between soil and type of pile surface) and effective angle of shearing resistance of soil ϕ' as shown in Table 7.3.

TABLE 7.3   Showing the values of δ/ϕ' for various types of material of pile

Pile/soil interface condition	δ/ϕ'
Smooth (coated) steel/sand	0.5–0.7
Rough (corrugated) steel/sand	0.7– 0.9
Precast concrete/sand	0.8–1.0
Cast-in-place concrete/sand	1.0
Timber/sand	0.8–0.9

Note: Tapered piles offer higher skin friction due to tapering shape.

7.10   CHARACTERISTICS OF PILES IN COHESIONLESS SOIL

7.10.1   Characteristics of Driven Piles in Cohesionless Soil

During driving, the sand in contact with pile particular the loose sand becomes more compact and solidified. So, the skin friction increases, and a higher value of K_s may be assumed relating to K_o, as shown in Tables 7.1 and 7.2.

Higher value of ϕ' should not be relied upon based of higher compaction of soil at the toe of pile. So, the increase in the value of N_q should not be taken into account for the estimation of the end bearing resistance of pile as the impact of hammer blows may transform the sandy soils containing weak deposits to the silt sized particle reducing the angle of shearing resistance. Referring to Figure 7.3, it shows that rate of increase of end bearing resistance decreases as the depth of penetration increases.

7.10.2   Characteristics of Driven and Cast-in-place Piles in Cohesionless Soil

In the operation of cast-in-place piles in cohesionless soil, an open tube is driven to the required design depth to avoid any possibility of collapse of sandy soil from the surface of hole and the removal of soil within the hole during driving. The reinforcement case is lowered in the hole. The concrete is poured in the hole and vibrated and, at the same time, the tube is gradually withdrawn. The sequence of casting the pile and withdrawal of tube continues until the full length of the pile is cast.

In this process the concrete fills the gap between tube casing and soil. So, there is no possibility of loosening of soil around pile shaft and the base. Therefore, no reduction of the value of N_q and ϕ' need to be considered.

Thus, the full value of calculated design skin frictional and end bearing resistance is maintained.

7.10.3   Characteristics of Bored and Cast-in-place Piles in Cohesionless Soil

In the installation of bored and cast-in-place piles in cohesionless soil, normally the hole is bored by means of boring machines and is filled with bentonite slurry during boring operation. The reinforcement casing is inserted in the hole. Concrete is then poured in with the gradual replacement of betonite slurry.

In this process of installation, there will be no reduction of angle of shearing resistance of soil and the value of N_q to be considered, except in the case, the slurry by any chance, is entrapped at the base of pile when the end bearing resistance should be reduced.

Referring to Fleming and Sliwinski [7.3], a reduction in the value of ϕ' by 10–30% should be considered when bentonite slurry is used in the installation of bored and cast-in-place piles, and so, a reduction of value of skin frictional and end bearing resistance is suggested in computing the total load carrying capacity of the pile.

The most reliable information regarding the load carrying capacity of pile should be obtained by means of load tests.

7.10.4 The Influence of Time Period on the Load Carrying Capacity of Piles in Cohesionless Soil

Referring to Peck, Hanson and Thornburn [7.4], most of the settlement generally takes place within 24 hours of driving piles in field load tests, and any reduction of pile capacity in coarse-grained sandy soil is insignificant on the time period after loading from the superstructure.

In the case of fine sand and silty soil, there may be some possibility of reduction of pile capacity during time period due to degradation of soil at the base area of pile. But it is difficult to quantify the percentage of reduction in the pile capacity. It is left to the judgement of engineers to decide the reduction factor to be considered in calculating the design capacity of pile.

7.11 PILES IN COHESIVE SOIL

7.11.1 Load Carrying Capacity of Driven Displacement Piles

When a pile is driven into cohesive soil (clay), the soil is displaced sideways and upwards and the quantity of soil displacement equals the volume of pile driven, and the structure of the clay is disturbed. The soil close to the pile surface is highly remoulded with the generation of high pore water pressure. So, the load carrying capacity of pile is minimum after pile driving. Due to thixotropic processes the shear strength of soil increases with time. Under high pressure develops in the clay by the insertion of pile, the clay immediately surrounding the pile consolidates, and regains the shear strength with time, thus increasing ultimate frictional resistance of pile.

The research project carried out by M.J. Tomlinson [7.5] for Construction Industry Research and Information Association (CIRIA) established the behaviour of piles driven into clay as follows:

For soft clay, the dissipation of pore water pressure takes long time. So, the skin frictional and end bearing resistance develop gradually with the displaced soil coming back to the original position, thus regaining the full contact to the pile surface and disappearance of heave at surface.

For stiff clay, the soil is displaced sideways and upwards. The soil in contact with the pile surface becomes highly fractured in radial direction around the pile and, for the top part, the soil completely looses contact with pile surface and never regains with time. The pore water pressure occupying the cracks around the soil contact surfaces dissipates quickly, and the major portion of load from the pile is transmitted to the lower portion of soil in contact with pile by means of adhesion (skin friction). No significant load transfer takes place from pile to the upper part of soil (see Figure 7.5).

Based on BS 8004: 1986 [7.17]

In cohesive soil the load carrying capacity of driven displacement pile is given by the following equations

To calculate the end bearing carrying capacity of piles: Ultimate end bearing stress of soil

$$q_b = N_c \times C_u = 9 \times C_u$$

where

N_c = bearing capacity factor, the value may be taken equal to 9

C_u = undisturbed, undrained cohesive strength of clay.

If A_b is the base area of pile at toe, then, end bearing resistance of pile,

$$Q_b = q_b \times A_b = 9 \times C_u \times A_b \tag{7.5}$$

Shaft skin-frictional resistance on pile shaft: The ultimate skin friction is dependent on horizontal effective stress acting on the pile shaft and the effective remoulded angle of friction between pile shaft and cohesive soil, i.e.

$$q_s = \sigma'h \times \tan \delta$$

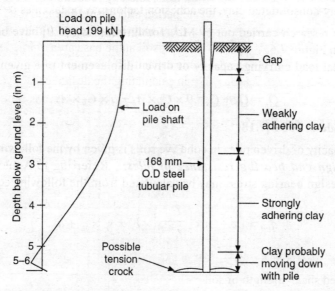

FIGURE 7.5   Characteristics of load transfer of pile in stiff clay. (*Source:* M.J. Tomlinson, CIRIA report **26**, 1970)

The horizontal effective stress (σ'_h) is related to vertical effective overburden pressure σ'_v. The value of effective overburden pressure changes and so does the horizontal effective stress during the installation and loading of pile due to the complex behaviour of soil mass surrounding the pile shaft. Therefore, it is difficult to quantify the effective frictional stress theoretically.

Burland [7.6] and Meyerhop [7.7] suggested the following equation based on semi-empirical method for the shaft skin frictional resistance:

$$Q_s = \alpha \times C_u \times A_s \tag{7.6}$$

where

A_s = pile surface area;

α = adhesion factor;

$\alpha \times C_u$ = effective frictional stress.

The value of adhesion factor (α) depends on the undisturbed shear strength of soil and the type of clay soil penetrated by the pile.

CIRIA research established the following facts:

- In stiff clay, the formation of cavity and fractured soil around the pile and non-contact surface of clay at the top portion of pile reduces the adhesion factor. So, a low adhesion factor should be considered for short penetration of piles into clay. For higher penetration piles higher adhesion factor may be considered.
- In soft clay, the fractured soil around pile regains its original contact surface quickly. So, a higher adhesion factor may be recommended.
- In sensitive clays, the remoulding of the soil around pile contact surface during pile driving decreases the adhesion. Though considerable recovery of strength of cohesive strength of soil takes place as time passes after the driving, the adhesion factor should be lowered in the carrying capacity calculation of pile.
- For normally-consolidated clay, the adhesion factor may be taken as $\alpha = 0.5$.

The results of research carried out by M.J. Tomlinson [7.8], [7.9] have been shown by the curves as shown in Figure 7.6.

Therefore, total load carrying capacity of driven displacement pile given by the following equation:

$$Q_u = Q_b + Q_s = 9 \times C_u \times A_b + a \times C_u \times A_s \tag{7.7}$$

Based on Eurocode 7: 2004 [7.18]

Load carrying capacity of driven piles in cohesive soils is given by the following equations:

To calculate design end bearing resistance of piles: Referring to Annex D.3 (undrained conditions), the design bearing stress may be calculated from the following equations:

$$q_{bd} = (\pi + 2) \times \left(\frac{C_u}{\gamma_{C_u}}\right) \times b_c \times s_c \times i_c + q$$

where

C_u = undrained shear strength of soil

γ_{C_u} = partial factor for soil parameter of undrained shear strength of soil

b_c = inclination factor of the pile base = $1 - \left[\dfrac{2\alpha}{(\pi + 2)}\right]$ (see Annex D)

where

α = inclination. The inclination of base is considered horizontal. So, $b_c = 1$

s_c = the shape factor of pile for square or circular shape = 1.2

i_c = inclination factor of the load caused by the horizontal thrust

$$H = \frac{1}{2}\left[1 + \left(\frac{1 - H}{(A \times C_u)}\right)^{0.5}\right]$$

(Since the effect of H is insignificant considering the length of pile, $i_c = 1$)

q = overburden pressure

Therefore,

$$q_{bd} = (\pi + 2) \times \left(\frac{C_u}{\gamma_{C_u}}\right) \times 1.2 + q$$

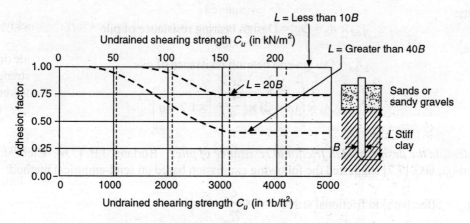

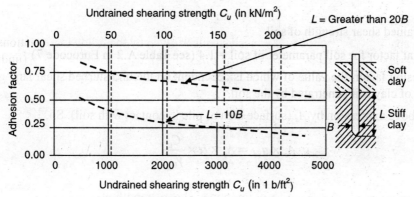

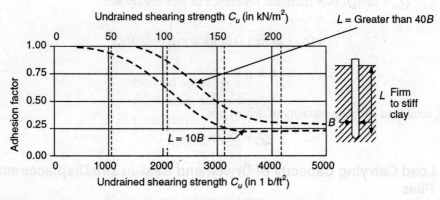

FIGURE 7.6 Curves showing values of adhesion factors relating to shear strength of stiff clay (by M.J. Tomlinson).

Multiply both sides by A_b (area of base of pile). So,

$$q_{bd} \times A_b = A_b \times \left[(\pi + 2) \times \left(\frac{C_u}{\gamma_{C_u}} \right) \times 1.2 + q \right]$$

Assume

$$q_{bd} \times A_b = Q_{bd} = \text{Design bearing resistance of pile}$$

Hence,

$$Q_{bd} = \text{Design end bearing resistance of pile}$$

$$= A_b \times \left[(\pi + 2) \times \left(\frac{C_u}{\gamma_{C_u}} \right) \times 1.2 + q \right] \qquad (7.5a)$$

To calculate the design of skin frictional resistance of pile: Burland, J.B. [7.6], Clerk, J.I. and Meyerhop, G.G. [7.7] suggested the following expression based on semi-empirical method:

$$q_{sd} = \text{effective skin frictional stress} = \alpha \times \frac{C_u}{\gamma_{C_u}}$$

where

C_u = undrained shear strength of soil

γ_{C_u} = partial factor for soil parameter of soil = 1.4 (see Table A.2 in Eurocode 7)

α = adhesion factor, the value of which is dependent on the undisturbed shear strength and type of clay soil penetrated by the soil.

Multiply the above expression by A_s (surface area of pile in contact with soil). So,

$$A_s \times q_{sd} = A_s \times \alpha \times \frac{C_u}{\gamma_{C_u}}$$

Now,

$A_s \times q_{sd} = Q_{sd}$ = design skin frictional resistance of pile in clay soil.

Therefore,

$$Q_{sd} = \text{design skin frictional resistance}$$

$$= A_s \times \alpha \times \frac{C_u}{\gamma_{C_u}} \qquad (7.6a)$$

Therefore, total load carrying capacity of driven pile

$$Q_d = Q_{bd} + Q_{sd} \qquad (7.7a)$$

7.11.2   Load Carrying Capacity of Driven and Cast-*in situ* Displacement Piles

End bearing resistance

The soil at the toe area of pile after the withdrawal of closed end tube behaves in the same way as driven pile. So, value of the end bearing resistance may be taken the same as driven displacement pile.

Therefore, ultimate end bearing resistance

$$Q_b = N_c \times C_u \times A_b = 9 \times C_u \times A_b \qquad \text{[see Eq. (7.5)]}$$

Skin frictional resistance

As the tube with the closed end is driven in the clay soil, the soil surrounding the pile shaft becomes remoulded, fractured and attains the same condition at the soil–pile interface as the driven pre-formed displacement pile. After the pile is driven, the hole is immediately filled up with concrete with the withdrawal of tube. So, the space between the tube and soil surface is closed. The soil surrounding the pile does not get time to swell. Only the soil surrounding the green concrete absorbs some water from the concrete that softens the soil, and may reduce slightly the adhesion factor for stiff clay. But for practical design purposes the adhesion factor for the driven cast-in-situ displacement piles shall be taken same as driven displacement piles.

Therefore, ultimate skin frictional resistance

$$Q_s = \alpha \times C_u \times A_s \qquad \text{[see Eq. (7.6)]}$$

and ultimate total load carrying capacity

$$Q_u = Q_b + Q_s = 9 \times C_u \times A_b + \alpha \times C_u \times A_s \qquad \text{[see Eq. (7.7)]}$$

7.11.3   Load Carrying Capacity of Bored and Cast-*in situ* Non-displacement Piles

Based on BS 8004: 1986

Skin frictional resistance: In the installation of this type of piles, borehole operation is carried out by borehole machines with the removal of soil within the hole. Due to the effect of this operation, the soil along the surface of hole becomes relieved of lateral stress and the soil swells with the pore water reaching to the exposed surface of hole. This condition weakens the clay, and thus affects the skin friction of the pile shaft and reduces the adhesion factor. The reduction of value of adhesion factor is not significant compared to the value in driven and cast-*in situ* displacement piles, as shown by the graphs in Figure 7.7 (prepared by Weltman and Healy [7.10]) from the results of a number of loading tests carried out in glacial till.

Skempton [7.11] studied the behaviour of skin friction on bored pile in London clay on a number of loading test results of bored piles and found that the adhesion factor varies between 0.3 and 0.6. He suggests that for practical purposes the value of adhesion factor $\alpha = 0.45$ for London clay, where drilling and pouring of concrete sequence occurs in quick succession.

So, for London clay, ultimate skin frictional resistance,

$$Q_s = 0.45 \times C_u \times A_s \tag{7.8}$$

For any other types of clay, the adhesion factors as shown in Figure 7.7 (by Weltman and Healy) may be adopted if no loading test is available.

End bearing resistance: The soil surrounding the pile base is not affected by this method of installation of piles. So, the end bearing resistance remains unaltered.

Hence, the ultimate end bearing resistance shall be calculated from the following equation:

$$Q_b = 9 \times C_u \times A_b \qquad \text{[see Eq. (7.5)]}$$

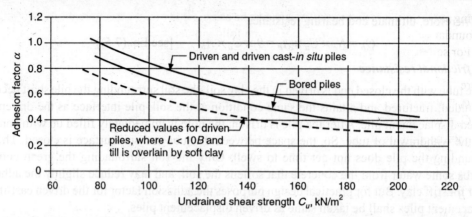

FIGURE 7.7   Curves comparing the adhesion factors for bored and driven cast-*in situ* piles relating to shear strengths of glacial till.

For London clay, total ultimate load carrying capacity

$$Q_u = 9 \times C_u \times A_b + 0.45 \times C_u \times A_s \tag{7.9}$$

7.11.4   Time Effect on the Load Carrying Capacity of Pile

In soft clays

Bjerrum [7.12] studied the load carrying capacity of pile with time after the installation of pile in soft clays. The behaviour of soil surrounding the pile shaft changes as the time passes. Long period of loading increases the effective skin friction and cohesion due to the consolidation of the clay. So, the factor of safety assumed for the design load carrying capacity of pile after short-term load test is on the conservative side when we consider the effect of time on the load carrying capacity of pile.

In stiff clays

Not sufficient study has been carried out on the load carrying capacity of pile when subjected to long-time loading. The driven piles causes the soil loosing contact to the upper part of pile shaft, and the radial fracture of soil mass surrounding the pile shaft allow the entry of water in the fractured zone, thus softening the clay and reducing the load carrying capacity of the pile.

Meyerhop and Murdock [7.13] studied the load tests of precast concrete piles in London clay and observed that for long-period of loading, a reduction of 10 to 20% of load carrying capacity occurred.

7.12   LOAD CARRYING CAPACITY OF PILE IN SOIL WITH MIXED PROPERTIES OF C_u AND ϕ'

7.12.1   Based on BS 8004: 1986

When a pile is installed in the fairly dense or stiff soil having the geotechnical properties of cohesion (C_u) and effective angle of shear resistance (ϕ'), say, clayey sand or sandy clay, the ultimate bearing stress of pile of square dimension may be calculated based on the three-dimensional loading on foundation suggested by Terzaghi with the following equation:

For square piles

$$q_u = 1.3 \times C_u \times N_c + \gamma \times z \times (N_q - 1) + 0.4 \times \gamma \times B \times N_y \qquad (7.10)$$

where

q_u = ultimate bearing stress of pile

C_u = undrained shear strength of soil

γ = net density of soil excluding pore water pressure = $\gamma_b - \gamma_w$

(where, γ_b = Dry density; γ_w = Density of water)

z = depth of soil below ground level

B = base dimension of square footing

N_c, N_q and N_y = Bearing capacity factors. These factors to be obtained from Figure 7.8.

For circular piles

$$q_u = 1.3 \times C_u \times N_c + \gamma \times z \times (N_q - 1) + 0.3 \times \gamma \times D \times N_y \qquad (7.11)$$

where

D = diameter of pile.

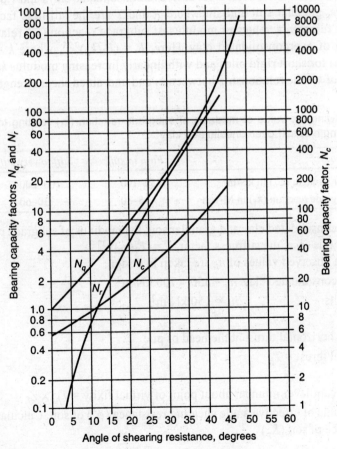

FIGURE 7.8 Terzaghi's bearing capacity factors for shallow foundation.

7.13 PILES SUBJECTED TO HORIZONTAL LOAD AT THE HEAD

When a pile is subjected to horizontal loads at the head in addition to vertical compressive load, the passive resistance of soil in contact with pile comes into play. The passive resistance offered by the soil depends on the geotechnical properties of soil. It is difficult to quantify the value of passive resistance. Peck, Hanson and Thornburn [7.14] suggested the following:

If the soil consists of sand , silt or clay having an N value greater than 5, a minimum horizontal load of 7 kN may be allowed which can be resisted by the passive resistance of soil. The extent of depth of pile from head that resists the passive force to be decided by the engineer on the type of soil encountered.

The simple method of calculating the lateral resistance of soil against the horizontal load at the head of pile at ground level as suggested by Broms [7.15], [7.16] is described as follows:

Determine the depth of pile from ground level to the point of virtual fixity (Z_f), where it is assumed that the ultimate passive resistance of soil above the point of rotation generates maximum ultimate bending moment where shear force is practically zero in the pile. The depth of virtual fixity may be taken for practical purposes equal to 1.5 m for compact granular soil or stiff clay, and 3 m for soft clay and silt. American Concrete Institute recommends that the point of virtual depth of fixity should be taken equal to $1.4 \times R$ for stiff, overconsolidated clays and $1.8 \times T$ for normally-consolidated clays, granular soil and silt where R and T are the stiffness factors, respectively corresponding to Terzaghi's values of modulus of subgrade reaction (k_1) relative to undrained shearing strength of overconsolidated clay. Here, $R = (E_1/k_B)^{0.25}$, where $k = k_1$ (modulus of subgrade reaction) for short rigid piles and with linearly increasing modulus k_1 should be taken on average value of k_1. The relationship between k_1 and undrained shear strength of clay is given in Table 7.4.

TABLE 7.4 Showing the value of modulus of subgrade reaction (k_1) relating to undrained shear strength of stiff overconsolidated clay

Consistency	Firm to stiff	Stiff to very stiff	Hard
Undrained shear strength (C_u) in kN/m^2	50–100	100–200	Over 200
Modulus of subgrade reaction (k_1) in MN/m^2	15–30	30–60	Over 60

For normally-consolidated clay and granular soil, the modulus of subgrade reaction increases with depth, and in this case, the stiffness factor, $T = (E_1/n_h)^{0.33}$

The following observed values of n_h are taken in design:

For normally-consolidated clay: $n_h = 350 - 700$ kN/m^2

For organic silts: $n_h = 150$ kN/m^2

Let

T_{hu} = ultimate horizontal thrust at the head of pile.

Safe horizontal thrust = T_h

Then

M_u = ultimate cantilever moment about point of virtual fixity = $T_{hu} \times Z_f$

Assume the value of effective angle shearing resistance (ϕ') of soil. Calculate the coefficient of passive resistance of soil (K_p)

Treat the pile as a long one with head restrained (pile cap behaving as fixed end).

Referring to Figure 7.9 (prepared by Broms) showing curves of ultimate moment resistance (M_u/C_uB^3) vs ultimate lateral resistance (H_u/C_uB^2):

Calculate the value of $M_u/(C_uB^3)$, where B = width or diameter of pile.

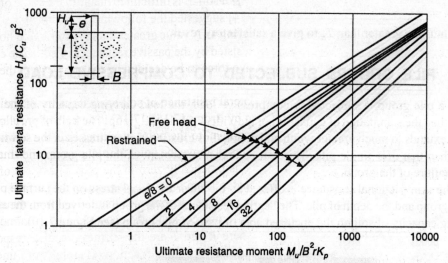

(a) Ultimate lateral resistance of long pile in cohesionless soil
related to ultimate resistance moment.

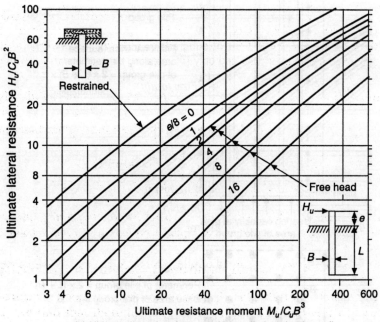

(b) Ultimate lateral resistance of long pile in cohesive soil
related to ultimate resistance moment.

FIGURE 7.9 Ultimate lateral resistance relating to ultimate moment for long pile.

Corresponding to the above, obtain the value of $H_u/(C_u B^2)$ from the curve. The value of H_u will give the value of ultimate lateral resistance of soil.

Assume a safety factor F. Therefore, safe lateral resistance of soil

$$H = \frac{H_u}{F}$$

So, H must be greater than T_h to give a satisfactory result.

7.14 PILE GROUPS SUBJECTED TO COMPRESSIVE LOAD

When a pile group is subjected to compressive load, the load carrying capacity of the group is lower than the summation of capacities of individual pile in the group. The bulb of pressure for the group extends to much greater width and depth, thus creating higher stresses in the soil to a wider zone than that of a single pile. This causes higher settlement of the pile group and thus results shear failure of the group.

The skin frictional resistance is offered by the shear frictional stress on the surface perimeter of the group and the depth of pile. The bearing resistance of the group is derived from the allowable bearing capacity of soil on the enclosed area of base of pile group (see Figure 7.10).

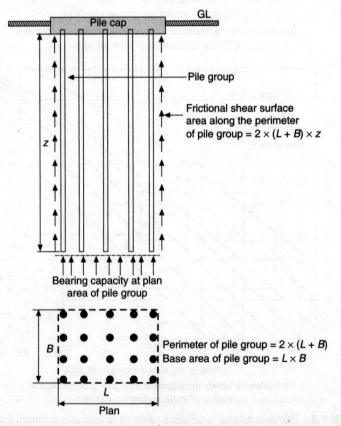

FIGURE 7.10 Piled foundation: Pile group subjected to compressive loads.

7.14.1 Load Carrying Capacity of Pile Groups Driven in Cohesive Soil

The ultimate load carrying capacity of pile group driven through soft clay, and to terminate in stiff clay is given by the following:

Ultimate skin frictional resistance:

$$Q_s = 2 \times (B + L) \times z \times \frac{C_u}{2} \qquad (7.12)$$

where

B = overall width of group enclosed by piles

L = overall length of group enclosed by piles

z = depth of penetration of pile

$\dfrac{C_u}{2}$ = average skin frictional stress.

(suggested by Peck, Hanson and Thornburn) [7.14]

Ultimate bearing resistance:

$$Q_b = 1.3 \times C_u \times s \times N_c \times B \times L \qquad (7.13)$$

where

s = shape factor dependent on length/width ratio of pile group. The value should be taken from curve shown in Figure 7.11.

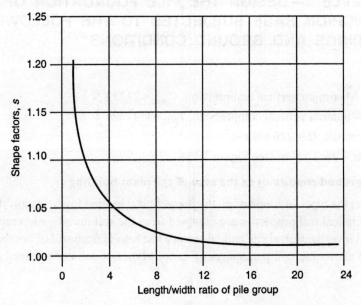

FIGURE 7.11   Curve showing shape factor vs Length/width ratio (*L/B*) of pile group (*Source:* Meyerhop and Skempton).

N_c = Bearing capacity factor. The value depends on depth to width ratio of the group, and may be taken from the curve shown in Figure 7.12.

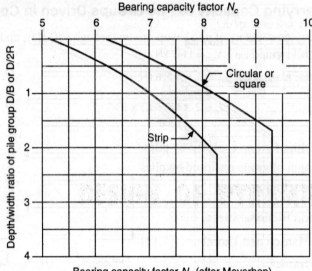

FIGURE 7.12   Curve showing relationship between N_c and depth/width ratio of pile group (*Source:* Meyerhop).

7.15   EXAMPLE 1—DESIGN THE PILE FOUNDATION OF A STANCHION BASE SUBJECTED TO THE FOLLOWING LOADINGS AND GROUND CONDITIONS

Loadings

Crane leg: Maximum vertical compression, V_{max} = 2133 kN ↓

Roof leg: Minimum vertical compression, V_{min} =1147 kN ↓

Horizontal thrust, H = 226 kN ←

Moment, M = 9662 kN m (see Figure 7.13)

Geotechnical ground conditions in the area of the plant building

Before we select the types of foundation, the geotechnical ground investigation should be carried out. The geotechnical soil properties are obtained from the soil investigation report prepared on the basis of soil investigation at site and laboratory test results from soil of borehole logs and site tests. Table 7.5 shows the soil parameters of various types of soil encountered at depths below ground level.

where

γ_b = bulk density of soil

ϕ' = effective angle of shear resistance of soil

δ = angle of skin friction between pile and soil in contact with pile.

The value of δ is dependent on the types of construction material (e.g., timber, steel, pre-cast and cast-*in situ* concrete), and the types of soil in contact specially the clay. The field measurements

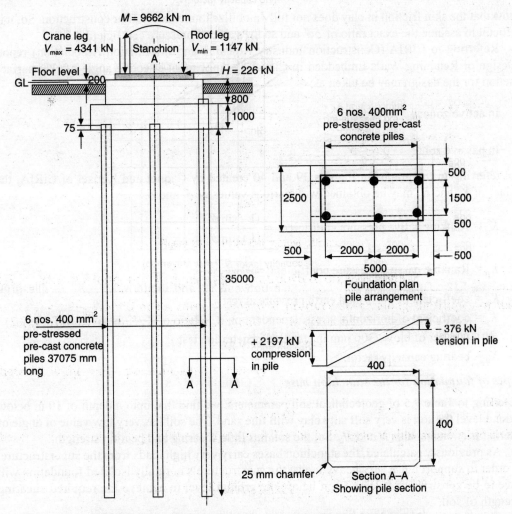

FIGURE 7.13 Piled foundation: pile loadings and arrangement.

TABLE 7.5 Showing soil characters of various types of soil at depths below ground level

Soil type	Depth below GL (in m)	γ_b (kN/m³)	ϕ' (in degrees)	δ (in degrees)	K_a	K_p	K_o	N	N_q
Top soil	0	16	0	0	0	0	0	0	0
Very soft silty clay with fine sand	2.5	18	12	0	0	0	0	4.0	4
Medium to stiff clayey fine sand	10	20	30	22.5	0.29	5.0	1.0	10.0	10–20
Dense to very dense grey sand	35	20	35	26.3	0.22	6.2	1.0	27.0	35–40
Stiff silty clay with fine sand	48 7	20	40	30	0.18	8.0	1.0	45.0	60–90

show that the skin friction in clay does not fully mobilize immediately after construction. So, it is difficult to assume the exact ratio of $\delta\phi'$ and so the value of pressure coefficients.

Referring to CIRIA (Construction Industry Research and Information Association) report 'Design of Retaining Walls Embedded in Clays', the maximum effective angle of skin surface friction for the design may be taken as:

In active zone: $\qquad \delta = \dfrac{2}{3}\phi'$

In passive zone: $\qquad \delta = \dfrac{1}{2}\phi'$

So, referring to the graphs in Figures 39 and 40 created by Caquot and Kerisel of CIRIA, the values of K_a and K_p may be obtained with various values of ϕ' and δ.

K_a = Rankine active pressure coefficient $= \dfrac{(1-\sin\phi')}{(1+\sin\phi')}$

K_p = Rankine passive pressure coefficient $= \dfrac{(1+\sin\phi')}{(1-\sin\phi')}$

K_o = coefficient of horizontal earth pressure at rest

K_s = coefficient of horizontal stress dependent on K_o (Ratio of K_s/K_o is given in Table 7.2)

N = number of blows/300 mm in standard penetration test

N_q = bearing capacity factor.

Types of foundation for the stanchion base

Referring to Table 7.5 of geotechnical soil parameters, we find that upto a depth of 10 m below ground level the soil is very soft silty clay with fine sand. The soil has very low value of angle of internal friction and also N and N_q. So, the soil has little shearing and bearing strength.

As previously calculated, the stanchion bases carry very high loads from the superstructure. In order to support these very heavy loads, the substructure's normally isolated foundation will have to be constructed at least 10 m below the ground level to achieve the required shearing strength of soil.

This type of construction is costly and uneconomical.

The alternative and economical way to solve the foundation problem is to adopt pile and to take them down to the soil stratum of adequate shearing and bearing strength to support the high loads at the base of the stanchion.

In our case, we shall adopt piled foundation consisting of a group of piles of sufficient depth to attain adequate load carrying capacity and with a pile cap to support the base of the stanchion that carry heavy loads and moments.

7.15.1 To Calculate the Safe Load Carrying Capacity of 400 mm² Pre-stressed Pre-cast Concrete Piles

Based on BS 8004: 1986

Before we design the piled foundation, we, firstly calculate the load carrying capacity of a single pile at various depths penetrating through soil of different properties. Let us consider the following criterion in our case.

The pile to be driven into the ground with geotechnical soil parameters, as given in the Table 7.5.
The size and type of pile: 400 mm^2 pre-cast pre-stressed concrete
Water table is at ground level in rainy season.

$$\tan \delta = \frac{3}{4} \phi' \quad \text{(assumed)}$$

- Cohesion $c = 0$ (by studying from the Table 7.5, soil is assumed cohesionless).
- Assume, $K_s = K_o = 1.0$; (referring to Table 7.2 showing the ratio K_s/K_o)

1. *To calculate the shear frictional stress at a depth z:*

   Let

   σ' = effective overburden pressure at a depth z from ground level = $(\gamma_b - \gamma_w) \times z$

   p = normal soil pressure on the pile surface at a depth $z = \sigma' \times K_s$

   Let

   s = shear frictional (skin) stress at a depth

   $$z = p \times \tan \delta = \sigma' \times K_s \times \tan \delta = (\gamma_b - \gamma_w) \times z \times K_s \times \tan \delta$$

   and

   $$(\gamma_b - \gamma_w) = \gamma$$

   Therefore,

   $$s = \gamma \times z \times K_s \times \tan \delta$$

   So, shear frictional stress in cohesionless soil at a depth z

   $$s_z = \gamma \times z \times K_s \times \tan \delta$$

   Therefore, at

   10 m depth, $s_{10} = \gamma \times z \times K_s \times \tan \delta = 8 \times 10 \times 1 \times \tan 22.5° = 33$ kN/m^2

   15 m depth, $s_{15} = 10 \times 15 \times \tan 22.5° = 62$ kN/m^2

   20 m depth, $s_{20} = 10 \times 20 \times \tan 22.5° = 83$ kN/m^2

   25 m depth, $s_{25} = 10 \times 25 \times \tan 22.5° = 104$ kN/m^2

   30 m depth, $s_{30} = 10 \times 30 \times \tan 22.5° = 124$ kN/m^2

   35 m depth, $s_{35} = 10 \times 35 \times \tan 26.5° = 173$ kN/m^2

   40 m depth, $s_{40} = 10 \times 40 \times \tan 26.3° = 198$ kN/m^2

   45 m depth, $s_{45} = 10 \times 45 \times \tan 26.3° = 222$ kN/m^2

   48 m depth, $s_{48} = 10 \times 48 \times \tan 30° = 277$ kN/m^2

   50 m depth, $s_{50} = 10 \times 50 \times \tan 30° = 289$ kN/m^2

2. *Ultimate shear frictional resistance:*

   $$Q_s = \frac{1}{2} \times \Sigma s_z \times z \times \text{perimeter}$$

   Therefore, at

   10 m depth, $Q_{s,\,10} = \frac{1}{2} \times s_{10} \times (10 - 2.5) \times 1.6 = 198$ kN

15 m depth, $Q_{s,\,15} = \dfrac{1}{2} \times (s_{10} + s_{15}) \times (z_{15} - z_{10}) \times 1.6 + Q_{s10} = 578$ kN

20 m depth, $Q_{s,\,20} = \dfrac{1}{2} \times (s_{15} + s_{20}) \times (z_{20} - z_{15}) \times 1.6 + Q_{s15} = 1158$ kN

25 m depth, $Q_{s,\,25} = \dfrac{1}{2} \times (s_{20} + s_{25}) \times (z_{25} - z_{20}) \times 1.6 + Q_{s20} = 1906$ kN

30 m depth, $Q_{s,\,30} = \dfrac{1}{2} \times (s_{25} + s_{30}) \times (z_{30} - z_{25}) \times 1.6 + Q_{s25} = 2818$ kN

35 m depth, $Q_{s,\,35} = \dfrac{1}{2} \times (s_{30} + s_{35}) \times (z_{35} - z_{30}) \times 1.6 + Q_{s30} = 4006$ kN

40 m depth, $Q_{s,\,40} = \dfrac{1}{2} \times (s_{35} + s_{40}) \times (z_{40} - z_{35}) \times 1.6 + Q_{s35} = 5490$ kN

45 m depth, $Q_{s,\,45} = \dfrac{1}{2} \times (s_{40} + s_{45}) \times (z_{45} - z_{40}) \times 1.6 + Q_{s40} = 7170$ kN

48 m depth, $Q_{s,\,48} = \dfrac{1}{2} \times (s_{45} + s_{48}) \times (z_{48} - z_{45}) \times 1.6 + Q_{s45} = 8368$ kN

50 m depth, $Q_{s,\,50} = \dfrac{1}{2} \times (s_{48} + s_{50}) \times (z_{50} - z_{48}) \times 1.6 + Q_{s48} = 9274$ kN

3. *Ultimate bearing resistance:* Ultimate bearing resistance at a depth

$$z = Q_b = \gamma \times z \times A_b \times N_q$$

where

A_b = base area of pile = $0.4^2 = 0.16$ m^2

N_q = 20, 40 and 60, respectively for $\phi' = 30°$, 35° and 40°

Therefore, at

10 m depth, $Q_{b,\,10} = 8 \times 10 \times 0.16 \times 20 \ = 256$ kN
15 m depth, $Q_{b,\,15} = 10 \times 15 \times 0.16 \times 20 = 480$ kN
20 m depth, $Q_{b,\,20} = 10 \times 20 \times 0.16 \times 20 = 640$ kN
25 m depth, $Q_{b,\,25} = 10 \times 25 \times 0.16 \times 20 = 800$ kN
30 m depth, $Q_{b,\,30} = 10 \times 30 \times 0.16 \times 20 = 960$ kN
35 m depth, $Q_{b,\,35} = 10 \times 35 \times 0.16 \times 20 = 1120$ kN
40 m depth, $Q_{b,\,40} = 10 \times 40 \times 0.16 \times 40 = 2560$ kN
45 m depth, $Q_{b,\,45} = 10 \times 45 \times 0.16 \times 40 = 2880$ kN
48 m depth, $Q_{b,\,48} = 10 \times 48 \times 0.16 \times 60 = 4608$ kN
50 m depth, $Q_{b,\,50} = 10 \times 50 \times 0.16 \times 60 = 4800$ kN

4. *Ultimate load carrying capacity:*   Ultimate capacity,

$$Q_u = Q_s + Q_b$$

Therefore, at

10 m depth, $Q_u = (198 + 256)$ kN $= 454$ kN
15 m depth, $Q_u = (578 + 480)$ kN $= 1058$ kN
20 m depth, $Q_u = (1158 + 640)$ kN $= 1798$ kN
25 m depth, $Q_u = (1906 + 800)$ kN $= 2708$ kN
30 m depth, $Q_u = (2818 + 960)$ kN $= 3778$ kN
35 m depth, $Q_u = (4006 + 1120)$ kN $= 5126$ kN
40 m depth, $Q_u = (5490 + 2560)$ kN $= 8050$ kN
45 m depth, $Q_u = (7170 + 2880)$ kN $= 10050$ kN
48 m depth, $Q_u = (8368 + 4608)$ kN $= 12976$ kN
50 m depth, $Q_u = (9274 + 4800)$ kN $= 14074$ kN

5. *Safe load carrying capacity of pile:*   Assuming a safety factor $= 2.5$, safe capacity

$$Q = \frac{Q_u}{2.5}$$

Therefore, at

10 m depth, $Q_{10} = \dfrac{454}{2.5} = 182$ kN

15 m depth, $Q_{15} = \dfrac{1058}{2.5} = 423$ kN

20 m depth, $Q_{20} = \dfrac{1798}{2.5} = 719$ kN

25 m depth, $Q_{25} = \dfrac{2708}{2.5} = 1083$ kN

30 m depth, $Q_{30} = \dfrac{3778}{2.5} = 1511$ kN

35 m depth, $Q_{35} = \dfrac{5126}{2.5} = 2050$ kN

40 m depth, $Q_{40} = \dfrac{8050}{2.5} = 3220$ kN

45 m depth, $Q_{45} = \dfrac{10050}{2.5} = 4020$ kN

48 m depth, $Q_{48} = \dfrac{12976}{2.5} = 5190$ kN

50 m depth, $Q_{50} = \dfrac{14074}{2.5} = 5630$ kN

With the above values at various depths, plot a curve. This curve will give the safe capacity of pile at any depth (see Figure 7.14).

Based on Eurocode 7: 2004

1. *End bearing resistance:* Referring to Annex D.4 (drained condition), characteristic bearing resistance may be calculated from the following expression:

$$Q_{bk} = [c' \times N_c \times b_c \times s_c \times i_c + q' \times N_q \times b_q \times s_q \times i_q + 0.5 \times \gamma' \times B' \times N_\gamma \times b_\gamma \times s_\gamma \times i_\gamma] \times A_b \qquad \text{See Eq. (D.2)}$$

where

c' = cohesion intercept in terms of effective stress = 0
　{from geotechnical soil parameter (Table 7.5)}

N_c, N_q and N_γ are the bearing capacity factors
b_c, b_q and b_γ are the inclination factors for the pile base
s_c, s_q and s_γ are the shape factors of pile base
i_c, i_q and i_γ are the shape factors for pile shape
B' = effective width or diameter of pile
A_b = base area of pile
q' = effective overburden pressure at pile base at a depth $z = \gamma' \times z$
γ' = effective density of soil = $(\gamma_b - \gamma_w)$;
　　(where, γ_b = bulk density; γ_w = water density)

Since $c' = 0$, the first term in the above expression is zero.
Since the diameter of pile is insignificant compared to the length of pile, B' may be regarded negligible, and the last term in the above expression is assumed zero.

Therefore,

$$Q_{bk} = q' \times N_q \times b_q \times s_q \times i_q \times A_b$$

At a depth 10 m below ground level

$$\phi' = 30°; \ \phi'_d \text{(design value of } \phi') = \frac{\phi'}{\gamma_{\phi'}} = \frac{30}{1.25} = 24°$$

(for partial factors for soil parameters, see Table A.2 in Eurocode 7)
At a depth 35 m below ground level

$$\phi' = 35°; \ \phi'_d = \frac{35}{1.25} = 28°$$

At a depth 48 m below ground level

$$\phi' = 40°; \ \phi'_d = \frac{40}{1.25} = 32°$$

So, at a depth or 10 m below ground level

$$N_q = e^{(\pi + \tan 24)} \times \tan^2 \left(45 + \frac{24}{2}\right) = 9.6$$

$$b_q = (1 - \alpha \times \tan 24) = 1,$$

where α = inclination of base. Assumed horizontal = 0)
Therefore, end bearing resistance for drained condition at:

10 m depth, $Q_{bk, 10}$ $= A_b \times (q' \times N_q \times b_q \times s_q \times i_q)$

$= 0.4^2 \times (8 \times 10 \times 9.6 \times 1 \times 1.4 \times 0.7 = 120$ kN

15 m depth, $Q_{bk, 15}$ $= 0.4^2 \times 10 \times 15 \times 9.6 \times 1 \times 1.4 \times 0.7 = 225$ kN

20 m depth, $Q_{bk, 20}$ $= 0.4^2 \times 10 \times 20 \times 9.6 \times 1 \times 1.4 \times 0.7 = 300$ kN

25 m depth, $Q_{bk, 25}$ $= 0.4^2 \times 10 \times 25 \times 9.6 \times 1 \times 1.4 \times 0.7 = 375$ kN

30 m depth, $Q_{bk, 30}$ $= 0.4^2 \times 10 \times 30 \times 9.6 \times 1 \times 1.4 \times 0.7 = 450$ kN

35 m depth, $Q_{bk, 35}$ $= 0.4^2 \times 10 \times 35 \times 14.7 \times 1 \times 1.47 \times 0.7 = 847$ kN

40 m depth, $Q_{bk, 40}$ $= 0.4^2 \times 10 \times 40 \times 14.7 \times 1 \times 1.47 \times 0.7 = 968$ kN

45 m depth, $Q_{bk, 45}$ $= 0.4^2 \times 10 \times 45 \times 14.7 \times 1 \times 1.47 \times 0.7 = 1089$ kN

48 m depth, $Q_{bk, 48}$ $= 0.4^2 \times 10 \times 48 \times 23.2 \times 1 \times 1.53 \times 0.7 = 1908$ kN

50 m depth, $Q_{bk, 50}$ $= 0.4^2 \times 10 \times 50 \times 23.2 \times 1 \times 1.53 \times 0.7 = 1988$ kN

2. *Characteristic frictional resistance of pile:* Referring to Eq. (7.2a),

$$Q_{sd} = \frac{1}{2} \times q' \times K_s \times \tan \delta \times A_s$$

Assume $K_s = 1$

$$\tan \delta = \tan \left(\frac{3}{4} \times \frac{\phi'}{\gamma_{\phi'}} \right); \quad \text{where } \gamma_{\phi'} = 1.25$$

A_s = surface peremeter $\times$ length considered = $4 \times 0.4 \times L = 1.6 \times L$
Neglect top 2 m soil having negligible frictional resistance.

At 10 m depth, $\phi' = 30$; $\tan \delta = \left(\frac{3}{4} \times \frac{30}{1.25} \right) = 18°$

At 35 m depth, $\phi' = 35$; $\tan \delta = \left(\frac{3}{4} \times \frac{35}{1.25} \right) = 21°$

At 48 m depth, $\phi' = 40$; $\tan \delta = \left(\frac{3}{4} \times \frac{40}{1.25} \right) = 24°$

Therefore, at

10 m depth, $Q_{sk, 10} = \frac{1}{2} \times (10 - 2.5) \times 8 \times 1 \times \tan 18 \times 1.6 \times 7.5 = 160$ kN

15 m depth, $Q_{sk, 15} = \frac{1}{2} \times (15 - 2.5) \times 10 \times 1 \times \tan 18 \times 1.6 \times 12.5 = 400$ kN

20 m depth, $Q_{sk, 20} = \frac{1}{2} \times (20 - 2.5) \times 10 \times \tan 18 \times 1.6 \times 17.5 = 780$ kN

25 m depth, $Q_{sk, 25} = \dfrac{1}{2} \times (25 - 2.5) \times 10 \times \tan 18 \times 1.6 \times 22.5 = 1316$ kN

30 m depth, $Q_{sk, 30} = \dfrac{1}{2} \times (30 - 2.5) \times 10 \times \tan 18 \times 1.6 \times 27.5 = 1966$ kN

35 m depth, $Q_{sk, 35} = \dfrac{1}{2} \times (35 - 2.5) \times 10 \times \tan 21 \times 1.6 \times 32.5 = 3244$ kN

40 m depth, $Q_{sk, 40} = \dfrac{1}{2} \times (40 - 2.5) \times 10 \times \tan 21 \times 1.6 \times 37.5 = 4318$ kN

45 m depth, $Q_{sk, 45} = \dfrac{1}{2} \times (45 - 2.5) \times 10 \times \tan 21 \times 1.6 \times 42.5 = 5547$ kN

48 m depth, $Q_{sd, 48} = \dfrac{1}{2} \times (48 - 2.5) \times 10 \times \tan 24 \times 1.6 \times 45.5 = 7374$ kN

50 m depth, $Q_{sk, 50} = \dfrac{1}{2} \times (50 - 2.5) \times 10 \times \tan 24 \times 1.6 \times 45.5 = 8036$ kN

Assuming a partial resistance factor for base, $\gamma_b = 1.3$
and a partial resistance factor for shaft friction, $\gamma_s = 1.3$
(see Table A.6 of Eurocode 7: 2004)
Hence, design load carrying capacity,

$$Q = \left(\frac{Q_{bk}}{1.3} + \frac{Q_{sk}}{1.3} \right)$$

At

10 m depth, $Q_{10} = \dfrac{120 + 160}{1.3} = \dfrac{280}{1.3} = 215$ kN

15 m depth, $Q_{15} = \dfrac{225 + 400}{1.3} = \dfrac{625}{1.3} = 481$ kN

20 m depth, $Q_{20} = \dfrac{300 + 780}{1.3} = \dfrac{1080}{1.3} = 831$ kN

25 m depth, $Q_{25} = \dfrac{375 + 1316}{1.3} = \dfrac{1691}{1.3} = 1300$ kN

30 m depth, $Q_{30} = \dfrac{450 + 1966}{1.3} = \dfrac{2416}{1.3} = 1858$ kN

35 m depth, $Q_{35} = \dfrac{847 + 3244}{1.3} = \dfrac{4091}{1.3} = 3147$ kN

40 m depth, $Q_{40} = \dfrac{968 + 4318}{1.3} = \dfrac{5216}{1.3} = 4012$ kN

at 45 m depth, $Q_{45} = \dfrac{1089 + 5547}{1.3} = \dfrac{6636}{1.3} = 5105$ kN

48 m depth, Q_{48} $= \dfrac{1908 + 7374}{1.3} = \dfrac{9282}{1.3} = 7140$ kN

50 m depth, Q_{50} $= \dfrac{1988 + 8036}{1.3} = \dfrac{10024}{1.3} = 7710$ kN

Alternately, let us calculate design frictional resistance based on shear frictional stress. Let

s_z = shear frictional stress at a depth $z = \gamma' \times z \times K_s \times \tan \delta$

Assume

$K_s = 1$

$$\tan \delta = \left(\frac{3}{4} \times \frac{\phi'}{\gamma_{\phi'}} \right) = \tan (0.6 \ \phi'), \qquad \text{where } \gamma_{\phi'} = 1.25$$

At

10 m depth, $\phi' = 30°$; $\tan \delta = 0.6 \times 30 = 18°$; $\gamma' = (18 - 10) = 8$ kN/m^3
35 m depth, $\phi' = 35°$; $\tan \delta = 0.6 \times 35 = 21°$; $\gamma' = (20 - 10) = 10$ kN/m^3
48 m depth, $\phi' = 40°$; $\tan \delta = 0.6 \times 40 = 24°$; $\gamma' = 10$ kN/m^3

Therefore, at

10 m depth, $s_{10} = 8 \times 10 \times \tan 18 = 26$ kN/m^2
15 m depth, $s_{15} = 10 \times 15 \times \tan 18 = 49$ kN/m^2
20 m depth, $s_{20} = 10 \times 20 \times \tan 18 = 65$ kN/m^2
25 m depth, $s_{25} = 10 \times 25 \times \tan 18 = 81$ kN/m^2
30 m depth, $s_{30} = 10 \times 30 \times \tan 18 = 97$ kN/m^2
35 m depth, $s_{35} = 10 \times 35 \times \tan 21 = 134$ kN/m^2
40 m depth, $s_{40} = 10 \times 40 \times \tan 21 = 154$ kN/m^2
45 m depth, $s_{45} = 10 \times 45 \times \tan 21 = 173$ kN/m^2
48 m depth, $s_{48} = 10 \times 48 \times \tan 24 = 214$ kN/m^2
50 m depth, $s_{50} = 10 \times 50 \times \tan 24 = 223$ kN/m^2

Next, to calculate design shear frictional stress at any depth z

$$Q_{sk} = \frac{1}{2} \times \Sigma s_z \times z \times \text{perimeter of pile} \ (0.4 \ \text{m}^2) = 0.8 \times \Sigma s_z \times z$$

Hence, at

10 m depth, $Q_{sk, 10} = 0.8 \times s_{10} \times (10 - 2.5) = 156$ kN
15 m depth, $Q_{sk, 15} = 0.8 \times (s_{10} + s_{15}) \times (z_{15} - z_{10}) + Q_{sd, 10} = 456$ kN
20 m depth, $Q_{sk, 20} = 0.8 \times (s_{15} + s_{20}) \times (z_{20} - z_{15}) + Q_{sd,15} = 912$ kN
25 m depth, $Q_{sk, 25} = 0.8 \times (s_{20} + s_{25}) \times (z_{25} - z_{20}) + Q_{sd, 20} = 1496$ kN
30 m depth, $Q_{sk, 30} = 0.8 \times (s_{25} + s_{30}) \times (z_{30} - z_{25}) + Q_{sd, 25} = 2208$ kN
35 m depth, $Q_{sk, 35} = 0.8 \times (s_{30} + s_{35}) \times (z_{35} - z_{30}) + Q_{sd, 30} = 3132$ kN
40 m depth, $Q_{sk, 40} = 0.8 \times (s_{35} + s_{40}) \times (z_{40} - z_{35}) + Q_{sd, 35} = 4284$ kN

45 m depth, $Q_{sk, 45} = 0.8 \times (s_{40} + s_{45}) \times (z_{45} - z_{40}) + Q_{sd, 40} = 5592$ kN
48 m depth, $Q_{sk, 48} = 0.8 \times (s_{45} + s_{48}) \times (z_{48} - z_{45}) + Q_{sd, 45} = 6521$ kN
50 m depth, $Q_{sk, 50} = 0.8 \times (s_{48} + s_{50}) \times (z_{50} - z_{48}) + Q_{sd, 48} = 7220$ kN

3. *Design load carrying capacity of pile:*

$$Q = \frac{Q_{bk}}{\gamma_b} + \frac{Q_{sk}}{\gamma_s}$$

where
γ_b = partial base resistance factor = 1.3
γ_s = partial shaft (compression) resistance factor = 1.3
(For resistance factors, see Table A.6 of Eurocode 7)
Therefore, at

10 m depth, $Q_{10} = \dfrac{\left(Q_{bk, 10} + Q_{sk, 10}\right)}{1.3} = \dfrac{(120 + 156)}{1.3} = \dfrac{276}{1.3} = 212$ kN

15 m depth, $Q_{15} = \dfrac{225 + 456}{1.3} = \dfrac{681}{1.3} = 524$ kN

20 m depth, $Q_{20} = \dfrac{300 + 912}{1.3} = \dfrac{1212}{1.3} = 932$ kN

25 m depth, $Q_{25} = \dfrac{375 + 1496}{1.3} = \dfrac{1971}{1.3} = 1516$ kN

30 m depth, $Q_{30} = \dfrac{450 + 2208}{1.3} = \dfrac{2658}{1.3} = 2045$ kN

35 m depth, $Q_{35} = \dfrac{847 + 3132}{1.3} = \dfrac{3979}{1.3} = 3060$ kN

40 m depth, $Q_{40} = \dfrac{968 + 4284}{1.3} = \dfrac{5252}{1.3} = 4040$ kN

45 m depth, $Q_{45} = \dfrac{1089 + 5592}{1.3} = \dfrac{6681}{1.3} = 5139$ kN

48 m depth, $Q_{48} = \dfrac{1908 + 6521}{1.3} = \dfrac{8429}{1.3} = 6484$ kN

50 m depth, $Q_{50} = \dfrac{1988 + 7220}{1.3} = \dfrac{9208}{1.3} = 7083$ kN

With the above values of design load carrying capacity of pile at various depths, a graph is drawn (see Figure 7.14).

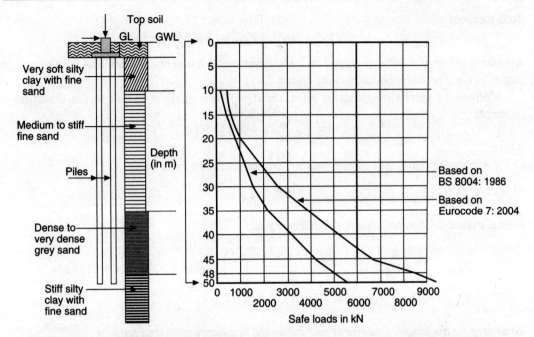

FIGURE 7.14   Curve showing relationship between pile safe capacity and depth below ground.

Thus, we find that based on Eurocode 7, the design load carrying capacity of pile is appreciably higher than the value calculated based on BS 8004.

7.15.2   Determination of Size, Number and Length of Pile of Piled Foundation

The determination of number and length of pile will be based on BS 8004: 1987 as the load carrying capacities of pile are low compared to the values calculated based on Eurocode 7: 2004.

Based on BS 8004: 1986

Thrust and tension on piled foundation due to vertical loads and moments: Referring to Figure 7.13 showing loadings (unfactored) on base of stanchion,
Vertical loads:

   Maximum load from crane leg = 4062 + 279 = 4341 kN

   Minimum load from roof leg = Σ DL + Σ LL = 661 + 486 = 1147 kN

Total vertical loads,

$$W = 4341 + 1147 = 5488 \text{ kN}$$

Moment:

   Due to wind from right to left = 2599 kN m

   Due to crane surge right to left = 3070 kN m

   Due to load eccentricity = 1.25 × (4341 − 1147) = 3993 kN m

Total moment:
$$M = (2599 + 3070 + 3993) = 9662 \text{ kN m}$$

Assume a group of 6 piles: arranged at 2 m centres along moment direction and 0.75 m at right angles to the direction of moment (see Figure 7.13).

Moment of inertia of group of piles about y–y axis at right angles to the direction of moment,
$$I_y = \Sigma A \times x^2 = 4 \times A \times 2^2 = 16 A$$
where

A = cross-sectional area of pile, and x = Distance of piles from y-axis

Z_y = section modulus of pile group = $\dfrac{16A}{2}$ = $8A$

Hence, maximum compression at the extreme pile,

$$P_{max} = A \times \left(\frac{W}{6A} + \frac{M}{Z_y} \right) = A \times \left(\frac{5488}{6A} + \frac{9662}{8A} \right) = (915 + 1208) \text{ kN} = 2197 \text{ kN}$$

$$P_{min} = (915 - 1208) \text{ kN} = -293 \text{ kN tension.}$$

To determine the length and size of pile subjected to compression and tension

1. For maximum compression in pile = 2197 kN

   Weight of pile cap (assumed) = $[5.0 \times 2.5 \times 1 \text{ (cap)} + 4 \times 1.5 \times 0.8 \text{ (pedestal)}] \times 24 = 415 \text{ kN}$

   Gross load on pile $= 2197 + \dfrac{415}{6} = 2266 \text{ kN}$

   Referring to the Figure 7.14 showing the safe load on pile based on BS 8004: 1986.
   With 37 m pile depth in the soil, safe capacity of pile = 2500 kN > 2266 kN (**Satisfactory**).
   Therefore, adopt: 400 mm^2 pre-stressed pre-cast concrete pile, 37 m long from side of cap.

2. For maximum tension in pile = 376 kN
   As the pile is in tension, the resistance offered by the soil is the skin friction without any assistance from bearing resistance. Referring to the previous calculations on ultimate capacity of piles, ultimate shear resistance of pile at 37 m depth,

   $$Q_s = (4006 + 5490) = 4748 \text{ kN}$$

   Since the pile is in tension, the ultimate frictional resistance should be divided by a higher factor of safety to obtain the safe capacity of pile subjected to tension. The factor of safety varies between 3 and 6 depending on the soil behaviour.
   In our case, we assume a factor of safety = 5 (average), to avoid any foundation failure. Hence,

   safe frictional resistance against uplift of pile = $\dfrac{4748}{5}$ = 950 kN

   And the tension in the pile = 376 kN << 950 kN (**Satisfactory**, see Figure 7.13).

To check the lateral resistance of soil subjected to shear (horizontal thrust) in pile at stanchion base level:

1. *Shear in pile:*   Referring to Figure 7.13.

   Shear due to horizontal crane surge = 122.8 kN

   Shear due to wind = 103.5 kN

   Therefore,

   Total shear H = 226 kN

   Number of piles resisting the shear = 6

   And shear/pile = $\dfrac{226}{6}$ = 37.7 kN (unfactored)

   To obtain ultimate shear:

   Since wind and crane surge are acting simultaneously, the partial safety factor may be assumed $\gamma_f = 1.2$ (refer to BS 5950: part 1: 2000).

   Therefore, ultimate shear on each pile = 1.2×37.7 = 45.3 kN

2. *To estimate the point of virtual fixity of pile below ground level and moment:*   Referring to Table 7.5 (showing geotechnical soil parameters at various depths), we find that the top 10 m of soil has got very low value of effective angle of shear resistance $\phi' = 12°$. So, the passive resistance offered by the soil is also very low. It is difficult to determine quantitatively the value of passive resistance offered by the soil and the point of virtual fixity of pile below the ground level. It may be assumed that the point of virtual fixity occurs at a depth 10 m from the ground level. Therefore, ultimate cantilever moment in the pile due to horizontal shear

$$M_u = 45.3 \times 10 = 453 \text{ kN m}$$

3. *To calculate the ultimate lateral resistance of long pile in cohesionless soil:*   With $\phi' = 12°$, coefficient of passive resistance,

$$K_p = \frac{1 + \sin \phi'}{1 - \sin \phi'} = 1.53$$

(the value of δ, i.e. the value of angle of skin friction between pile and soil is neglected)

$$\frac{M_u}{B^4 \times \gamma \times K_p} = \frac{45.3}{0.4^4 \times (18 - 10) \times 1.53} = 1446 \text{ kN m}$$

where

   B = width of pile = 0.4 m

   γ = submersed density of soil = $(18 - 10) = 8 \text{ kN/m}^3$

Referring to Figure 7.9 (a) curves of ultimate lateral resistance moment/ultimate lateral resistance with restrained head due to stiff pile cap in cohesionless soil.

$$\frac{H_u}{K_p \times B^3 \times \gamma} = 450$$

(where H_u = ultimate lateral resistance of soil)

Therefore,

$$H_u = \frac{450}{1.53 \times 0.4^3 \times 8} = 574 \text{ kN}$$

Assuming a safety factor = 5 for the low shearing strength of soil, safe lateral resistance of soil

$$\frac{H_u}{5} = \frac{575}{5} = 115 \text{ kN} \gg 37.7 \text{ kN} \qquad \textbf{(Satisfactory)}.$$

7.15.3 Structural Design of Pre-stressed Pre-cast Concrete Piles 400 mm² and 37 m Long

Based on BS 8110: part 1: 1997 [7.19]

Design considerations: The pile shall be lifted and pitched by clings placed at a distance of 20% of length of the pile from each end, to secure the maximum safety against overstressing of concrete and breakdown of member. The pile should be driven by diesel hammer or any other equipment. The pile shall be designed in accordance with BS 8110: part 1: 1997.

- The characteristic cube strength of concrete at 28 days shall be $f_{cu} = 50$ N/mm².
- Minimum uniform pre-stress in concrete in pile driven by diesel hammer shall be 5 N/mm² in accordance with BS 8004: 1986.
- The characteristic strength of prestressing tendons are given in the appropriate British Standards (BS 5896 and BS 4757) and reinforcement in BS 8110.
- The jacking force should not normally exceed 70% of characteristic strength of tendon.
- *Serviceability classification:* The amount of flexural tensile stress allowed under service load may be classified as follows:

Class 1: No flexural tensile stress

Class 2: Flexural stress but no visible cracking (Grade 50 concrete tensile stress = 3.2 N/mm²

Class 3: Surface crack width not exceeding 0.2 mm but not exceeding 0.1 mm in severe environments (for grade 50 concrete design tensile stress with 0.2 mm crack = 5.8 N/mm²)

TABLE 7.6 Showing mechanical properties of strands

Nominal diameter of strands (in mm)	Nominal area of steel (in mm²)	Specified characteristic load (in kN)	Specified characteristic strength (f_{pu}) in N/mm²	BS No.
7-wire 9.3	52.3	92	1760	5896 (7-wire standard strand)
7-wire 11	71	125	1760	5896 (7-wire standard strand)
7-wire 12.5	94.2	165	1752	5896 (7-wire standard strand)
7-wire 15.2	138.7	232	1670	5896 (7-wire standard strand)
19-wire 18	210	370	1760	4757 (19-wire strand)
19-wire 25.4	423	659	1560	4757 (19-wire strand)
19-wire 28.6	535	823	1540	4757 (19-wire strand)
19-wire 31.8	660	979	1480	4757 (19-wire strand)

Design: Refer to Figure 7.15 as follows:

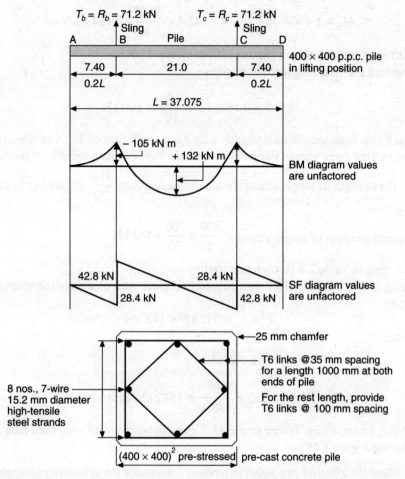

FIGURE 7.15 Design details of 400 mm² pre-stressed pre-cast concrete piles.

1. *To determine the number and size of high-tensile steel strands:* Consider the piles to be classified as class 3 category. No loss in pre-stress is assumed. Let us consider the pile in lifting position with slings held at 20% of length from each end.

Size of pile is 400 mm² *c*

Cross-section of pile = A_c = 0.4² = 0.16 mm²

Length of pile, L = 37075 mm

With density of concrete = 24 kN/m³, weight of pile

$$W = 0.16 \times 37.075 \times 24 = 142.4 \text{ m}^2$$

With a partial safety factor, γ_f = 1.4

Ultimate maximum + moment at mid span

$$M_u = 1.4 \times W \times \frac{L^2}{40} = 1.4 \times 142.4 \times \frac{37.075}{40} = 184.8 \text{ kN m}$$

With a minimum uniform pre-stress in concrete = 5 N/mm²
Required pre-stressing force in tendons

$$A_c \times 5 = 0.16 \times 10^6 \times \frac{5}{10^3} = 800 \text{ kN}$$

Try, 8 nos. high-tensile steel strands with 3 nos. each face of 400 mm² concrete pile.
The jacking force should normally not exceed 70% of characteristic strength of tendon.

So, the strength of single strand should not be less than $\frac{100}{70}$ of jacking force.

Therefore,

required strength of single strand = $\frac{800}{8} \times \frac{100}{70} = 143 \text{ kN}$

Referring to Table 7.6 (shown previously).
Using 7-wire strand of 15.2 mm diameter nominal size, characteristic strength of single
strand

$$A_{ps} \times f_{pu} = 232 \text{ kN} < 143 \text{ kN}$$

where

$$A_{ps} = 138.7 \text{ mm}^2$$

$$f_{pu} = 232 \times \frac{10^6}{138.7} = 1670 \text{ kN/mm}^2$$

Hence, adopt: 8 nos. 7-wire strand 15.2 mm diameter with 3 nos. each face of 400 mm²
pile (see Figure 7.15).

2. *To check the effective pre-stress in tendon:* To check the effective pre-stress in tendons
   to maintain 5 N/mm² pre-stress in concrete:
   Total compressive force in the cross-section

$$C = c \times A_c = 5 \times 400^2 = 800000 \text{ N}$$

where

c = Uniform pre-stress = 5 N/mm²;
area of 8 nos. 7-wire strand = 8 × 138.7 = 1110 mm²
Therefore, design effective pre-stress in tendon

$$f_{pe} = \frac{800000}{1110} = 721 \text{ N/mm}^2 << 1670 \text{ N/mm}^2 \textbf{ (OK)}$$

3. *To check the resisting moment of section in flexure:* (ultimate limit state method): The
   resisting moment of section

$$M_{ru} = f_{pb} \times a_{ps} \times (d - d_n)$$

where

d = effective depth to the centroid of the steel area

$= 400 - 40$ (cover) $- 6$ (strip diameter) $- 6$ (1/2 bar diameter)

x = neutral axis depth

d_n = depth to the centroid of compression zone = $0.45x$

f_{pb} = design tensile stress in tendon

f_{pu} = specified characteristic strength of high-tensile steel = 1670 N/mm^2

f_{pe} = design effective pre-stress in tendon = 721 N/mm^2 (calculated previously)

A_{ps} = area of pre-stressing tendon in tension zone = 38138.7 = 416.1 mm^2

f_{cu} = concrete cube strength in 28 days = 50 N/mm^2.

For bonded tendons, the values of f_{pb} and x may be obtained from Table 4.4, BS 8110: 1997. With

$$\frac{f_{pu} \times A_{ps}}{f_{cu} \times b \times d} = \frac{1670 \times 416.1}{50 \times 400 \times 348} = 0.1$$

and

$$\frac{f_{pe}}{f_{pu}} = \frac{721}{1670} = 0.43$$

From Table: $f_{pb}/0.95 p_u = 1.00$

Hence,

$$f_{pb} = 0.95 \times 1670 = 1587 \text{ N/mm}^2$$

Again, with $f_{pe}/f_{pu} = 0.43$

$$f_{pu} \times \frac{A_{ps}}{(f_{cu} \times b \times d)} = 0.1$$

From Table : $\dfrac{x}{d} = 0.23$

Hence,

$$x = 0.23 \times 348 = 80 \text{ mm}$$

and

$$d_n = 0.45 \times x = 0.45 \times 80 = 36 \text{ mm}$$

Therefore, moment of resistance of section,

$$M_{ru} = f_{pb} \times A_{ps} \times (d - d_n) = 1587 \times 416.1 \times (348 - 36) = 206 \text{ kN m} > 184.8 \text{ kN m (OK)}$$

4. *To check the limit-state of serviceability of section:*

Allowable compressive stress in concrete at transfer = $0.4 \times f_{cu} = 0.4 \times 50 = 20$ N/mm^2

(with uniform or near uniform distribution of pre-stress)

Allowable compressive stress in bending = $0.33 \times f_{cu} = 0.33 \times 50 = 16.7$ N/mm^2

Allowable flexural tensile stress for class 3 member = 6.3 N/mm^2

(Refer to Table 4.2; BS8110: part 1: 1997; pre-tensioned tendons distributed in the tensile zone)

The elastic analysis was carried out as follows:

$$\text{Maximum compressive stress} = p + \frac{M}{Z}$$

where

M = service moment (with partial safety factor $\gamma_f = 1$)

$$= \frac{184.8 \ (\text{previosly calculated})}{1.4} = 132 \ \text{kN m}$$

Z = section modulus of concrete section = $b \times \dfrac{D^2}{6}$ = $400 \times \dfrac{400^2}{6}$ = $106.7 \times 10^5 \ \text{mm}^3$

Therefore, maximum compressive stress in concrete,

$$f_{cb} = \frac{5 + 132 \times 10^6}{106.7 \times 10^5} = 5 + 12.4 = 17.4 \ \text{N/mm}^2$$

(Since the lifting of pile is carried out with slings attached at 0.2 L from each end, the maximum moment is calculated with the assumption as a continuous beam. In this case the allowable compressive stress may be increased from 0.33 f_{cu} to 0.4 f_{cu}).
So, maximum allowable compressive stress in bending

$$f_{cb} = 0.4 \times 50 = 20 \ \text{N/mm}^2 < 17.4 \ \text{N/mm}^2 \quad \textbf{(OK)}$$

And maximum tensile stress in concrete,

$$f_{tb} = 5 - 12.4 = 7.4 > 6.3 \ (\text{with limiting crack width} = 0.1 \ \text{mm})$$
$$\text{and} > 7.3 \ (\text{with limiting crack width} = 0.2 \ \text{mm})$$

(But may be accepted)

5. *To check the shear stress in the member:*   We are to check the shear stress at a section cracked in flexure as a class 3 member. Referring to BM and SF diagram in Figure 7.15, consider the section at the sling position (i.e. 0.2 × L from each end of the pile)
Ultimate bending moment at the sling support,

$$M_u = \frac{3.84 \times 7.4^2}{2 \times 1.4} = 105 \times 1.4 = 147 \ \text{kN m}$$

Ultimate design shear at the sling support,

$$V_u = \frac{3.84 \times 22.275}{2 \times 1.4} = 42.8 \times 1.4 = 59.9 \ \text{kN}$$

M_0 = moment necessary to produce zero stress in the concrete at the extreme tension fibre.

In this calculation, only 0.8 of the stress due to pre-stress should be taken into account.
Let

p = stress in concrete due to 0.8 × pre-stressing in concrete = $0.8 \times 5 = 4 \ \text{N/mm}^2$

Z = modulus of section of 400 × 400 concrete pile = $106.7 \times 10^5 \ \text{mm}^3$

Hence, moment necessary to produce zero stress in extreme fibre in concrete,

$$M_0 = p \times Z = \frac{4 \times 106.7 \times 10^5}{10^6} = 42.7 \text{ kN m}$$

Design ultimate shear resistance of a section cracked in flexure,

$$V_{cr} = \left(1 - 0.55 \times \frac{f_{pc}}{f_{pu}}\right) \times v_c \times b_v \times d + M_o \times \frac{V_u}{M_u}$$

where

$f_{pc} = 721 \text{ N/mm}^2$

$f_{pu} = 1670 \text{ N/mm}^2$

v_c = design concrete shear stress

b_v = width of section = 400 mm

d = effective depth of section.

$$\% \text{ of steel} = 100 \times \frac{A_{ps}}{b_v \times d} = \frac{100 \times 416.1}{400 \times 348} = 0.3$$

Referring to Table 3.8 (BS 8110: 1997) with effective depth, $d = 348$ mm

$$V_c = 0.42 \text{ N/mm}^2$$

Therefore,

$$V_{cr} = \frac{\left[\left(1 - 0.55 \times \dfrac{721}{1670}\right) \times 0.42 \times 400 \times 348\right]}{10^3 + 42.7 \times \dfrac{59.9}{147}} = 44.58 + 17.4 = 62 \text{ kN}$$

But the value of V_{cr} should not be less than

$$0.1 \times b_v \times d \times f_{cu}^{0.5} = 0.1 \times 400 \times 348 \times \frac{50^{0.5}}{10^3} = 98.43 \text{ kN} \gg V_u \ (59.9 \text{ kN})$$

So, theoretically no shear reinforcement is required. Therefore, provide nominal shear reinforcement.

6. *Design of lateral reinforcement:*

Assume 6 mm link; length of link $= 4 \times (400 - 2 \times 40 - 6) = 1256$ mm

Volume of pile per m run $= 400^2 \times 10^3 = 16 \times 10^7 \text{ mm}^3$;

Volume/link $= a \times 1256 \text{ mm}^3$ (where a = area)

Referring to BS 8004: Minimum % of links required at ends of pile = 0.6% concrete volume

Area of links required per m $= \dfrac{0.006 \times 6 \times 10^7}{1256} = 764 \text{ mm}^2$

Using 6 mm links area $= 28.3 \text{ mm}^2$

Spacing of links required $= \dfrac{1000}{764} \times 28.3 = 37$ mm

Adopt: 6 mm links @ 35 mm c/c for 1 m at both ends and the rest length @ 100 mm c/c.

7.15.4 Design of Reinforced Concrete Pile Cap and Pedestal

Refer to Figure 7.16.

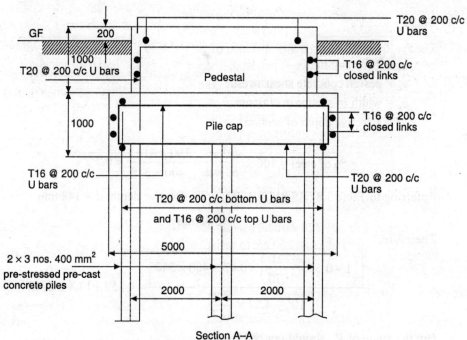

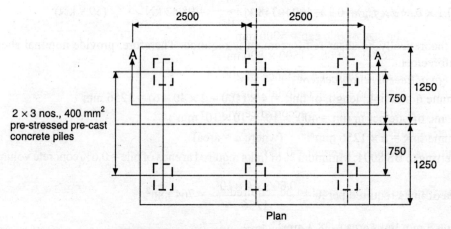

FIGURE 7.16 Piled foundation: RC details of pile cap.

7.15.5 Based on BS 8110: Part 1: 1997

Design of pile cap

1. *Loadings:* Maximum unfactored vertical compression on end pile = 2197 kN (previously calculated)

   With partial safety factor $\gamma_f = 1.2$
   Maximum design ultimate compression on end pile = 1.2 × 2197 = 2636 kN

2. *Ultimate design moment:* Consider the size of pile cap = 2500 × 5000 × 1000 mm thick
   And the size of pedestal = 1500 × 4000 × 800 mm depth
   The end piles are placed at a distance of 2000 mm from the centre of pedestal. So, the centre of pile is at the edge of pedestal. Therefore, no moment is developed in the pile cap.

3. *Design of section:* As no moment is developed, theoretically no reinforcement is required.
   In accordance with BS 8110: 1997
   Minimum % of steel = 0.13 of gross concrete area.
   Hence, area of tensile reinforcement to be provided = 0.0013 × 1000 × 1000 = 1300 mm^2
   Provide: T20 @ 200 c/c bottom both ways and T16 @ 200 c/c top both ways (see Figure 7.16).

4. *Check for shear:* As the edge of pedestal is along the centre line of pile, theoretically the cap is not subjected to shear. So, no shear reinforcement is required. Provide: T16 horizontal closed ties @ 200 c/c to resist bursting force.

5. *Pedestal:* Provide T20 vertical bars @ 200 c/c along the periphery of pedestal, and T16 horizontal closed links @ 200 c/c to resist bursting force.

Based on Eurocode 7: 2004

Design of reinforced concrete pile cap

1. *Loadings:* From previous calculations:
   Maximum unfactored compression on pile = 2197 kN
   Assume, average partial safety factor = $(\gamma_{gk} + \gamma_{qk}) = (1.35 + 1.5) = 1.43$

   Ultimate compression = 1.43 × 2197 = 3142 kN.

2. *Moment:* The size of pile cap = 5000 mm × 2500 mm × 1000 mm thick
   The size of pedestal = 4000 × 1500 × 800 mm thick

   The end piles are placed at a distance of 2000 mm from the centre of pedestal. So, the centre of pile is at the edge of pedestal. Therefore, no moment is developed in the pile cap.

3. *Design of reinforcement:* In accordance with Eurocode 7:
   With $f_{ck} = 30$ N/mm^2,
   Minimum % of reinforcement = 0.15%
   Therefore,
   area of tensile reinforcement to be required = $0.0015 \times B \times d = 0.0015 \times 1000 \times 915$
   $$= 1373 \text{ mm}^2$$
   Provided: T20 @ 200 c/c bottom both ways and T16 @ 200 c/c top both ways (see Figure 7.16).

4. *Check for shear:* As the edge of pedestal is along the centre line of pile, theoretically the cap is not subjected to shear. So, provide nominal shear reinforcement T16 horizontal closed ties @ 200 c/c to resist any bursting force.

5. *Reinforcement in pedestal:* Provide T20 vertical bars @ 200 c/c along the periphery of pedestal and T16 horizontal closed links @ 200 c/c to resist bursting force.

7.16 EXAMPLE 2—DESIGN OF LOAD CARRYING CAPACITY OF A PILE GROUP

Refer to Figure 7.17.

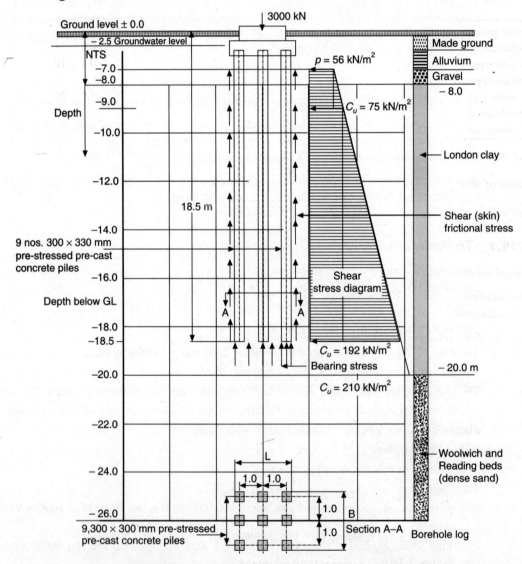

FIGURE 7.17 Safe pile capacity acting as a group.

A pile group has to be designed to carry a compressive load of 3000 kN

Total nos. of piles in the group = grouped 3 nos. in each row of 3

Size of pile = 300 mm^2 pre-stressed pre-cast concrete

The piles are to be driven into clay to a depth 18.5 m from ground level.

Design pile capacity of single one when acting individually, and total capacity. Also, design the pile capacity when acting in a group. The geotechnical soil properties of the ground are given in Table 7.7.

TABLE 7.7 Geotechnical soil properties in London clay

Soil type	Depth below GL (m)	γ_b (kN/m^3)	C_u (kN/m^2)	ϕ' (degrees)	δ (degrees)	K_a	K_p	K_o	N	N_q
Made ground	0.0	18	20	25	16.7	0.36	3.2	0.6	0–4	12
Alluvium	4.0	18	20	25	16.7	0.36	3.2	0.6	4–10	12
Gravel river terrace deposits	7.0	20	0	35	23.3	0.27	3.7	0.5	10–15	45
London clay	9.0	19	55–210	20	14	0.44	2.7	1.0	20–60	8
Woolwich and Reading beds	20.0	20	150	29	19.3	0.35	2.9	0.5	60–80	23

For values of N_q relating to ϕ', refer to Figure 7.8 (Terzaghi's bearing capacity factors)

Value of $\delta = \frac{2}{3} \times \phi'$ (assumed)

For values of C_u with depth in London clay, refer to Figure 2.1 from borehole results.

7.16.1 To Calculate the Load Carrying Capacity of Pile

Based on BS 8004: 1986

To calculate the capacity of individual pile: Ignore the skin frictional resistance of made ground and alluvium.

1. *Frictional stress:* Firstly, consider, the frictional stress of cohesionless soil at a depth z

$$s = \gamma \times z \times K_s \times \tan \delta$$

and skin frictional stress in cohesive soil at a depth z

$$s = \alpha \times C_u$$

where

$$\gamma = (\gamma_b - \gamma_w); \ (\gamma_b = \text{bulk density}, \ \gamma_w = \text{water density} = 10 \ \text{kN/m}^3)$$

$$\frac{K_s}{K_o} = 2 \ \text{for large displacement driven piles (see Table 7.2)}$$

$$\frac{K_s}{0.5} = 2; \ K_s = 1, \text{ where } K_o = 0.5 \text{ (assumed for gravel)}$$

$$\alpha = \text{adhesion factor} = 0.45 \text{ (assumed for London clay)}$$

From Figure 2.1: C_u at 9.0 m = 75 kN/m^2

C_u at 20 m = 210 kN/m^2 (maximum allowed) at 20 m depth

At

7 m depth, in gravel, $s_7 = \gamma \times z \times K_s \times \tan \delta = 8 \times 7 \times = 24$ kN/m^2

9 m depth, in gravel, $s_9 = \gamma \times z \times K_s \times \tan \delta = 10 \times 9 \times \tan 23.3 = 39$ kN/m^2

9 m depth, in clay, $s_9 = \alpha \times C_u = 0.45 \times 75 = 34$ kN/m^2

18.5 m depth in clay, $s_{18.5} = \alpha \times C_u = 0.45 \times 192 = 86$ kN/m^2

2. *Ultimate frictional resistance:*

$$Q_s = \frac{1}{2} \times \Sigma \, s_z \times z \times \text{perimeter}$$

(Perimeter of 300 mm^2 pile = $p_r = 4 \times 0.3 = 1.2$ m)

Therefore, at

7 m depth, $Q_{s,7} = \dfrac{1}{2} \times s_7 \times z_7 \times p_r = \dfrac{1}{2} \times 24 \times 7 \times 1.2 = 101$ kN

9 m depth, $Q_{s,9} = \dfrac{1}{2} \times (24 + 39) \times 2 \times 1.2 + Q_7 = 76$ kN + 101 kN = 177 kN

18.5 m depth, $Q_{s,18.5} = \dfrac{1}{2} \times (s_9 + s_{18.5}) \times (z_{18.5} - z_9) \times 1.2 + Q_{s,9}$

$$= \frac{1}{2} \times (34 + 86) \times 9.5 \times 1.2 + 177 = 861 \text{ kN}$$

3. *Ultimate bearing resistance:*   Ultimate bearing resistance in cohesionless soil at a depth

$$z = Q_b = \gamma \times z \times A_b \times N_q$$

Ultimate bearing resistance in cohesive soil at a depth,

$$z = Q_b = C_u \times A_b \times N_c$$

where

     A_b = Base area = $0.3^2 = 0.09$ m^2

Values of N_q at 7, 9 and 18.5 m depth with $\phi' = 25°$, 35°, and 20° are 12, 45, and 8, respectively.

C_u at 9 m depth = 75 kN/m^2;

At 18.5 m depth,

$$C_u = 75 + (210 - 75) \times \frac{9.5}{11} = 192 \text{ kN/m}^2$$

Value of N_c in clay = 9 (assumed)

Therefore, at

7 m depth in gravel, $Q_b = \gamma \times z \times A_b \times N_q = 8 \times 7 \times 0.09 \times 45 = 227$ kN

9 m depth in clay, $Q_b = C_u \times A_b \times N_c = 75 \times 0.09 \times 9 = 61$ kN

18.5 m depth in clay, $Q_b = C_u \times A_b \times N_c = 192 \times 0.09 \times 9 = 156$ kN

4. *Ultimate load carrying capacity:* Ultimate capacity

$$Q_u = Q_s + Q_b$$

Therefore, at

7 m depth, $Q_u = 101 + 227 = 328$ kN

9 m depth, $Q_u = 177 + 61 = 238$ kN

18.5 m depth, $Q_u = 861 + 156 = 1017$ kN

5. *Safe capacity of pile:* With a safety factor = 2.5, safe capacity

$$Q = \frac{Q_u}{2.5}$$

Therefore, at

7 m depth, $Q_7 = \dfrac{328}{2.5} = 131$ kN

9 m depth, $Q_9 = \dfrac{238}{2.5} = 95$ kN

18.5 m depth, $Q_{18.5} = \dfrac{1017}{2.5} = 407$ kN

Assumed 9 piles to support the load of 3000 kN

Therefore,

Total safe capacity of 9 piles = $9 \times 407 = 3663$ kN > 3000 kN (**Satisfactory**)

To calculate safe capacity of 9 piles when acting as group: (Refer to Figure 7.17)

1. *To calculate the ultimate frictional resistance:* Ultimate frictional resistance,

$$Q_s = \frac{1}{2} \times \Sigma s_z \times z \times \text{perimeter}$$

Perimeter of group

$$p_r = 2 \times (L \times B) = 2 \times (2.3 + 2.3) = 9.2 \text{ m (3 rows of 3 piles in a row)}.$$

where

$$L = 2 (1.0 + 0.15) = 2.3$$

(spacing of pile = 1.0 m; pile size = 0.3×0.3; $L = B$)

Therefore, at 7 m depth in gravel,

$$Q_{s,7} = \frac{1}{2} \times s_7 \times (z_7 - z_4) \times p_r = \frac{1}{2} \times 24 \times 3 \times 9.2 = 331 \text{ kN}$$

Values of frictional stresses (s) are calculated before (neglect the made-up ground)

At 9 m depth in clay,

$$Q_{s,9} = \frac{1}{2} \times (s_7 + s_9) \times (z_9 - z_7) \times p_r + Q_{s,7}$$

$$= \frac{1}{2} \times (24 + 39) \times (9 \times 7) \times 9.2 + 331 = 911 \text{ kN}$$

At 18.5 m depth in clay,

$$Q_{s, 18.5} = \frac{1}{2} \times (s_9 + s_{18}) \times (z_{18.5} - z_9) \times p_r + Q_{s, 9}$$

$$= \frac{1}{2} \times (34 + 86) \times (18.5 - 9) \times 9.2 + Q_{s, 9} = 6155 \text{ kN}$$

2. *To calculate the ultimate bearing resistance:*   Ultimate bearing resistance in cohesionless soil at a depth,

$$z = Q_b = \gamma \times z \times A_b \times N_q$$

Ultimate bearing resistance in cohesive soil at a depth,

$$z = Q_b = C_u \times A_b \times N_c \times s$$

where

A_b = base area of group = $L \times B = 2.3 \times 2.3 = 5.29 \text{ m}^2$

Values of N_q at 7, 9, and 18.5 m depth with $\phi' = 25°$, $35°$, and $20°$ are 12, 45 and 8, respectively.

C_u at 9 m depth = 75 kN/m^2

At 18.5 m depth,

$$C_u = 75 + (210 + 75) \times \frac{9.5}{11} = 192 \text{ kN/m}^2$$

(Value of N_c depends on the ratio of depth/width of pile group)
Referring to Figure 7.12:

$$\text{Depth} = 18.5, \text{ width} = 2.3; \quad \frac{D}{B} = \frac{18.5}{2.3} = 8; N_c = 9.4$$

At 7 m depth,

$$\frac{D}{B} = \frac{7}{2.3} = 3; \quad N_c = 9.4$$

s = shape factor depends on the dimension of L and B
From Figure 7.11, (with $L/B = 1$) $s = 1.15$
Therefore, at
7 m depth in gravel, $Q_b = \gamma \times z \times A_b \times N_q = 8 \times 3 \times 5.29 \times 45 = 5713 \text{ kN}$
9 m depth in clay, $Q_b = C_u \times A_b \times N_c = 75 \times 5.29 \times 9.4 = 3729 \text{ kN}$
18.5 m depth in clay, $Q_b = 192 \times 5.29 \times 9.4 = 9547 \text{ kN}$

3. *Ultimate load carrying capacity:*   Ultimate capacity

$$Q_u = Q_s + Q_b$$

Therefore, at
7 m depth, $Q_{u, 7} = 331 + 5713 = 6044 \text{ kN}$

9 m depth, $Q_{u, 9} = 911 + 3729 = 4640$ kN

18.5 m depth, $Q_{u, 18.5} = 6155 + 9547 = 15702$ kN

4. *Safe capacity of pile group:*   With a safety factor = 2.5, safe capacity of pile group,

$$Q = \frac{15702}{2.5} = 6281 \text{ kN}$$

Applied compressive load = 3000 kN << 6281 kN (**Satisfactory**).

Based on Eurocode 7: 2004

From previous calculation results, it was found that the safe capacity of a group of piles is higher than the value obtained by the calculations based on BS 8004.

REFERENCES

[7.1] Kulhawy, F.H. Limiting tip and side resistance, fact or fallacy, symposium on analyses and design of pile foundations, *Proceedings of American Society of Civil Engineers*, San Francisco, pp. 80–98, 1984.

[7.2] Berezantsev, V.G. et al, Load bearing capacity and deformation of piled foundations, *Proceedings of the 5th International Conference*, ISSMFE, Paris, Vol.12, pp.11-12, 1961.

[7.3] Fleming, A.W. and Z. Sliwinski, The use and influence of bentonite in bored piled construction, Construction Industry Research and Information Association (CIRIA) Report, p. 3, 1977.

[7.4] Peck, R.B., W. E. Hansen, and T.H. Thornburn, *Foundation Engineering*, Asia Publishing House, New Delhi, 1962.

[7.5] Tomlinson, M.J., The adhesion of piles in stiff clay, Construction Industry Research and Information Association (CIRIA), Research report No. 26, London, 1970.

[7.6] Burland, J.B., Shaft friction of piles in clay, *Ground Engineering*, Vol. 6, No. 3, pp. 30-42 May 1973.

[7.7] Clerk, J.I. and G.G. Meyerhop, The behaviour of Piles in clay, Canadian Geotechnical Journal, Vol. 10, No. 1, pp. 86–102, 1973.

[7.8] Tomlinson, M.J., The adhesion of piles driven in clay soils, *Proceedings of 5th. International Conference*, ISSMFE, London, Vol. 2, pp. 66–71, 1957.

[7.9] Tomlinson, M.J., Some effects of pile driving on skin friction, *Proceedings of the Conference on the Behaviour of Piles*, Institution of Civil Engineers, London, pp. 104-114, 1971.

[7.10] Weltman, A.J. and P.R. Healy, Piling on boulder clay and other glacial tills, Construction Industry Research and Information Association (CIRIA) Report, p. 5, 1978.

[7.11] Skempton, A.W., Cast-*in situ* bored piles in London clay, *Geotechnique*, Vol. 9, No. 4, pp. 153–173, 1959.

[7.12] Bjerrum, L., Problems of soil machanics and construction in soft clay, *Proceedings of the 8th International Conference*, ISSMFE, Moscow, Vol. 3, pp.150–157, 1973.

[7.13] Meyerhop, G.G. and L.J. Murdock, An investigation of the bearing capacity of some bored and driven piles in London clay, *Geotechnique*, Vol. 3, no. 7, pp. 267-282, 1953.

[7.14] Peck, R.B., W.E. Hansen, and T.H. Thornburn, Foundation Engineering, Asia Publishing House, New Delhi, 1962.

[7.15] Broms, B., The lateral resistance of piles in cohesive soils, Journal of the Soil Mechanics Division, American Society of Civil Engineers, Vol. 90, No. SM2, pp. 27-63, March 1964.

[7.16] Broms, B., The lateral resistance of piles in cohesionless soils, Journal of the Soil Mechanics Division, American Society of Civil engineers, Vol. 90, No. SM3, pp. 123-156, May 1964.

[7.17] BS 8004: 1986:   British Standard Code of Practice for Foundations

[7.18] Eurocode 7:2004: Geotechnical Design, Part 1: General Rules

[7.19] BS 8110: 1997:   Structural Use of Concrete, Part 1: Code of Practice for Design and Construction.

Chapter 8

Diaphragm Wall Foundation

8.0 DESCRIPTION

The diaphragm wall foundation may be classified as bored cast-*in situ* continuous piles used in the construction of highway and railway tunnels and multi-storey basement and underground metro stations. The diaphragm walls act to carry vertical loads and also as a retaining wall to resist earth and water pressures. The section of diaphragm wall is generally cast in panels of 3 to 5 m long and 0.6 to 1.5 m thick depending on the design requirement and with designed reinforcement. Each panel is cast with ends having groves so that when the panels are cast side by side they form continuous wall with watertight joints.

Secant piles are also used in diaphragm wall construction. The commonly used diameters are 300, 450, 600 and 750 mm, and in some deep wall constructions of 25 m or more, upto 1200 mm diameter piles are used. They are generally bored piles installed very close (almost touching each other). After the excavation, the exposed surface of wall is lined with concrete to make the wall watertight and also aesthetically pleasing.

Contiguous piles are of special type of diaphragm wall construction where high degree of continuity of rigity of structure is needed. In contiguous piled diaphragm wall construction two types of piles are used, one is male pile and the other one is female piles, alternately placed and overlapping each other. The male piles are reinforced and the females are unreinforced.

Since the female piles are unreinforced, the strength of male pile is calculated considering the load taken by the male pile equal to twice the diameter of pile. The method of construction is described in Section 8.1.1. (Refer to the Proceedings of the Conference on Diaphragm Walls and Anchorage, ICE, London, 1974 [8.1]).

8.1 METHOD OF CONSTRUCTION OF DIAPHRAGM WALL

The following are the sequence of construction of diaphragm wall (Tomlinson, M.J. [8.2]):

Step 1: Excavate and construct continuous guide walls about a metre deep on either side of the excavation trench to guide the rig and concrete pouring equipment.

Step 2: Excavate by means of grab type rig or any equipment to the size of a panel (say 5 m long and 1 m in width).

Step 3: Fill the excavated hole with bentonite slurry. Special equipment is installed at the site to get the continuous supply of bentonite slurry of required consistency, and to remove any impurities. The bentonite slurry (gravity 1.04) retains the excavated face in position.

Step 4: The reinforcement cage of adequate concrete covering arrangement is gradually lowered in the excavated rectangular slit.

Step 5: The concrete is placed gradually inside the hole. As the concrete is filled in, the excess of bentonite slurry is pumped out. The process goes on until the panel is complete with concrete.

Step 6: The pumped out bentonite slurry is filtered and re-circulated for reuse in the next operation.

Step 7: The next panel length is left, and the third one is excavated and concreted in the same procedure as mentioned above. Then the second one is completed. The sequence goes on.

8.1.1 Method of Construction of Contiguous Piled Diaphragm Wall

Step 1: By continuous-flight auger method, boreholes are made for the two female piles upto the designed depth and keeping a space slightly lower than the diameter of the male pile, thus overlapping each other ensuring a considerable degree of watertightness and maintaining continuous rigidity of wall. The overlapping on each side varies from 150 to 250 mm (depending on the assumed clear cover of reinforcement of male piles). The bentinite may be needed in case of permeable soil.

Step 2: Concrete is poured in the two female unreinforced piles with minimal vibration.

Step 3: The bore hole of diameter of the male pile (same diamer as female pile) is made, thus cutting side of partially green concrete of female pile.

Step 4: The reinforcement cage is inserted in the whole of male pile.

Step 5: Concrete is poured in the whole of male pile.

Step 6: The sequence of construction will go on till the construction is complete.

8.2 GEOTECHNICAL ASPECTS OF SOIL BEHAVIOUR ON THE DIAPHRAGM WALL

Before we start to analyze the diaphragm wall, we shall investigate the geotechnical aspects of soil behaviour on the diaphragm wall embedded in the soil. It has got certain influence on the structural behaviour on the diaphragm wall and on the method of construction of the wall.

The diaphragm wall is generally embedded in the ground with varying soil characteristics at different depths. When the wall is embedded in clay type of soil, particularly the stiff clay, its behaviour on the wall is highly complex (soil-structure interaction). CIRIA (Construction Industry Research and Information Association) Publication Report 104 (Design of Retaining Walls in Stiff Clays) [8.3] throws some light on the soil-structure interaction of clays. The report describes the characteristics of clay soil and its effect on the embedded structure and retaining walls.

8.3 TO CALCULATE THE SAFE CAPACITY OF DIAPHRAGM WALL SUBJECTED TO VERTICAL LOAD

8.3.1 Based on BS 8004: 1986 Foundations [8.4]

Safe capacity of diaphragm wall to resist vertical load,

$$Q = \frac{(Q_s + Q_b)}{2.5}$$

where

Q_s = ultimate shear (skin) frictional resistance of wall in clay = $\alpha \times C_u \times A_s$

Q_s = ultimate shear (skin) frictional resistance of wall in cohesionless soil

$$= \frac{1}{2} \times \Sigma \gamma \times z \times K_s \times \tan \delta \times A_s$$

and

α = adhesion factor (the value varies, dependant on the type of cohesive soil)

C_u = undrained shear strength of cohesive soil

A_s = surface area of pile in contact with soil/m depth

$\gamma = (\gamma_b - \gamma_w)$ = Net weight of soil; (γ_b = Bulk density of soil; γ_w = Water density)

z = depth of overburden pressure;

σ = horizontal shear stress = $\gamma \times z \times K_s$ (where, K_s = Coefficient dependent on the value of K_o and type and density of soil)

$\tan \delta$ = coefficient of wall friction = $\frac{2}{3} \times \phi'$ (assumed)

Factor of safety is assumed as 2.5

Q_b = ultimate bearing resistance in cohesive soil = $C_u \times A_b \times N_c$

Q_b = ultimate bearing resistance in cohesionless soil = $\gamma \times z \times A_b \times N_q$

(where, A_b = Bearing area of wall; N_c and N_q = Bearing capacity factors).

8.3.2 Based on Eurocode 7: 2004 [8.5]

Characteristic bearing resistance of diaphragm wall

Consider 1 m length of wall

1. *Referring to Annex D.3 Undrained conditions:* The characteristic bearing resistance of diaphragm wall may be calculated from the following expressions:

   Q_b = Characteristic bearing resistance of diaphragm wall

   $$\left[(\pi + 2) \times \frac{C_u}{\gamma_{C_u}} \times b_c \times s_c \times i_c \times q \right] \times A_b \qquad \text{[see Eq. (D.1)]}$$

   where

   C_u = Undrained shear strength of soil

γ_{C_u} = Partial safety factor for soil parameter = 1.4 (see Table A.2)

b_c = Inclination factor for base = $\dfrac{1-2\alpha}{\pi+2}$ (where α = base inclination = 0°) = 1

s_c = Shape of foundation base = $1+ 0.2 \times \left(\dfrac{B'}{L'}\right)$ for rectangular shape

(where, B' = Effective thickness = B; L' = Effective length = L = 1 m)

i_c = Inclination of load caused by a horizontal thrust

$$i_c = \frac{1}{2} \times \left[1 + \sqrt{1 - \left(\frac{H}{A' \times C_u}\right)} \right]$$

(assumed, no horizontal thrust acts on the base, $H = 0$) = $\dfrac{1}{2}$ [1 + 1] = 1

q = Overburden soil pressure at foundation base.

2. *Referring to Annex D.4 Drained conditions:*

$$Q_b = [c' \times N_c \times b_c \times s_c \times i_c + q' \times N_q \times b_q \times s_q \times i_q + \\ 0.5 \times \gamma' \times B' \times N_\gamma \times b_\gamma \times s_\gamma \times i_\gamma] \times A_b \qquad \text{[see Eq. (D.2)]}$$

where, N_q, N_c, and N_γ are the bearing capacity factors.

$$N_q = e^{\left[\pi \times \tan\left(\frac{\phi'}{\gamma_{\phi'}}\right)\right]} \times \tan^2\left[45° + \left(\frac{\phi'}{\gamma_{\phi'}}\right)^2\right]$$

$$N_c = (N_q - 1) \times \cot\left(\frac{\phi'}{\gamma_{\phi'}}\right)$$

$$N_\gamma = 2 \times (N_q - 1) \times \tan\left(\frac{\phi'}{\gamma_{\phi'}}\right)$$

(where, $\gamma_{\phi'}$ = Partial factor for angle of shearing resistance = 1.25 (see Table A.2) b_c, b_q, and b_γ are the base inclination factors).

$$b_c = b_q - \frac{1 - b_q}{N_q \times \tan\left(\dfrac{\phi'}{\gamma_{\phi'}}\right)}$$

$$b_q = b_\gamma = \left[1 - \alpha \times \tan\left(\frac{\phi'}{\gamma_{\phi'}}\right)\right]^2$$

since $\alpha = 0$; $b_q = b_\gamma = b_c = 1$

s_c, s_q, and s_γ are the foundation shape factors

$$s_q = 1 + \left(\frac{B'}{L'}\right) \times \sin\left(\frac{\phi'}{\gamma_{\phi'}}\right), \text{ for a rectangular shape}$$

$$s_\gamma = 1 - 0.3 \times \left(\frac{B'}{L'}\right), \text{ for a rectangular shape}$$

$$s_c = \frac{s_q \times N_q - 1}{N_q - 1}, \text{ for a rectangular shape.}$$

where, B' and L' are effective thickness and length of wall.

(Assume, $B' = B$ and $L' = L$ since no eccentricity developed on the section.)

i_c, i_q, i_γ are the inclination of load factors caused by thrust H

$$i_c = i_q - \frac{(1 - i_q)}{\left[N_c \times \tan\left(\frac{\phi'}{\gamma_{\phi'}}\right)\right]}$$

$$i_q = \left[1 - \frac{H}{\left[V + A' \times c' \times \cot\left(\frac{\phi'}{\gamma_{\phi'}}\right)\right]}\right]^m$$

$$i_\gamma = \left[1 - \frac{H}{\left[V + A' \times c' \times \cot\left(\frac{\phi'}{\gamma_{\phi'}}\right)\right]}\right]^{(m+1)}$$

Assume, no horizontal thrust H acts on base.

So, $i_c = i_q = i_\gamma = 1$

where m is a factor depending on the direction of H towards B' or L'

$$m = m_B \frac{[2 + (B'/L')]}{[1 + (B'/L')]} \text{ when } H \text{ acts in the direction of } B'$$

$$m = m_L \frac{[2 + (L'/B')]}{[1 + (L'/B')]} \text{ when } H \text{ acts in the direction of } L'$$

B' and L' are effective width and length of foundation base.

Characteristic frictional resistance of diaphragm wall

1. *In cohesive soil*

   Q_s = Characteristic frictional resistance of wall in clay = $\alpha \times C_u/\gamma_{C_u} \times A_s$

   where

   α = Adhesion factor, the value of which depends on the type of cohesive soil.

   C_u = Undrained shear strength of soil

   γ_{C_u} = Partial factor for undrained shear strength of soil = 1.4 (see Table A.2)

   A_s = Surface area of wall in contact with soil

2. *In cohesionless soil:*

Q_s = Characteristic frictional resistance of wall in cohesionless soil

$$= \frac{1}{2} \times \Sigma q' \times K_s \times \tan \delta \times A_s$$

where q' = Effective overburden pressure at a depth $z = \gamma' \times z$
(where γ' = Effective soil density).

$\tan \delta$ = Coefficient of wall friction in soil $= \tan\left[\frac{2}{3} \times \left(\frac{\phi'}{\gamma_{\phi'}}\right)\right]$ assumed.

where

ϕ' = Effective angle of shearing resistance of soil.
$\gamma_{\phi'}$ = Partial factor of angle of shearing resistance for soil parameter.
K_s = coefficient dependant on the value of K_o and type and density of soil.
A_s = surface area of wall in contact with soil.

Total design resistance of diaphragm wall

Q = Total design carrying capacity (resistance) of wall in soil $= \dfrac{Q_b}{\gamma_b} + \dfrac{Q_s}{\gamma_s}$

where, γ_b and γ_s are partial resistance factors of base and shaft for driven and bored piles (see Tables A.6 and A.7 given in Eurocode EC 7, Annex A).

γ_b = partial resistance factor at base
    = 1.3 for driven piles; 1.6 for bored piles
γ_s = partial resistance factor for shaft compression
    = 1.3 for both driven and bored piles.

8.4 DESIGN EXAMPLE 1

An underground (cut and cover) highway tunnel of reinforced concrete is constructed of diaphragm walls to resist the vertical loads from roof slab and the base slab carrying the highway traffic, and also the soil pressure on the exterior sides of walls. The details of tunnel is shown in the Figure 8.1.

8.4.1 Design Data

1. The depth of diaphragm wall from top of roof slab = 16.0 m
2. Thickness of diaphragm wall = 1.0 m
3. Each panel length = 5.0 m
4. Thickness of roof slab = 120 m
5. Thickness of base slab = 1.0 m
6. 2.5 m soil overburden pressure on roof slab = 50 kN/m²
7. Developer load on tunnel roof = 50 kN/m²
8. Road construction loads on base slab = 32 kN/m²
9. HA loading on base slab = 31 kN/m²
10. Maximum water table from ground level = 2.5 m

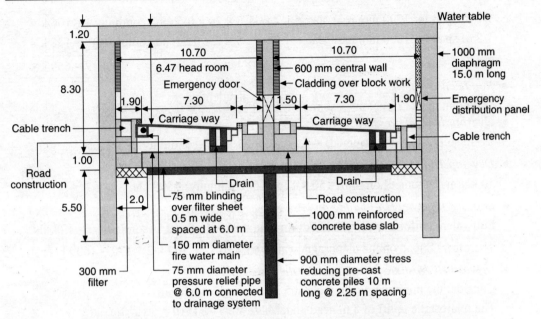

FIGURE 8.1 Diaphragm wall foundation: cut and cover highway tunnel.

TABLE 8.1 Geotechnical soil properties in London clay

Soil type	Depth below GL (m)	γ_b (kN/m³)	C_u (kN/m²)	ϕ' (degrees)	δ (degrees)	K_a	K_p	K_o	N	N_q
Made ground	0.0	18	20	25	16.7	0.36	3.2	0.6	0–4	12
Alluvium	4.0	18	20	25	16.7	0.36	3.2	0.6	4–10	12
Gravel river terrace deposits	7.0	20	0	35	23.3	0.27	3.7	0.5	10–15	45
London clay	9.0	19	55–210	20	14	0.44	2.7	1.0	20–60	8
Woolwich and Reading beds	20.0	20	150	29	19.3	0.35	2.9	0.5	60–80	23

For values of N_q relating to ϕ', refer to Figure 7.8 (Terzaghi's bearing capacity factors)

Value of $\delta = \frac{2}{3} \times \phi'$ (Assumed from CIRIA report)

For values of C_u with depth in London clay, refer to Figure 2.1 from borehole log results. We are to design the diaphragm walls and describe the method of construction of tunnel.

8.4.2 To Calculate the Loads Supported by Each Diaphragm Wall/m run

The roof and base slab are assumed continuous over central support. Refer to Figure 8.1:

- *Dead loads:*
  Self-weight of 1000 mm diaphragm wall 14.8 m depth $= 1 \times 14.8 \times 24 = 355$ kN

1/2 of span for 1200 mm roof slab = $1.2 \times 11.5 \times 24 \times 0.5$ (end continuity) = 166 kN
1/2 of span for 1000 mm base slab = $1.0 \times 11.5 \times 2 \times 0.5$ (end continuity) = 138 kN

Total   = 659 kN

- *Road construction:*
  1400 mm thick (23 kN/m^3 assumed) = $1.4 \times 10.7 \times 23 \times 0.5 = 172$ kN
- *Overburden soil pressure on roof:*
  2.5 m soil (20 kN/m^3 assumed) = $2.5 \times 12 \times 20 \times 0.5$ (continuity) = 300 kN
- *Developer load (future building construction):*
  50 kN/m^2 (assumed) on roof = $50 \times 12 \times 0.5$ (continuity) = 300 kN
- *Imposed highway HA loading on base slab carriage way:*
  Equivalent uniform load = 31 kN/m^2/m lane = $31 \times 11.5 \times 0.5$ (continuity) = 178 kN
  Therefore, Σ load on the diaphragm wall = $659 + 172 + 300 \times 2 + 178 = 1609$ kN
- *Upward Hydrostatic pressure under the base slab:*
  Consider the minimum water table at 5 m below ground level.
  The hydrostatic uplift of 8 m head under base slab = $8 \times 10 = 80$ kN/m
  Assuming the slab continuous over central support and assumed fixed at the diaphragm wall, the upward reaction end on the diaphragm wall = $0.5 \times 80 \times 11.5 = 460$ kN
  Therefore, net downward load on the diaphragm wall = $(1609 - 460) = 1149$ kN.

8.4.3   To Check the Safe Load Carrying Capacity of Diaphragm Wall/m Run

Based on BS Code 8004: 1986

1. *Frictional stress:*   Firstly, consider the shear frictional of cohesionless soil at a depth

$$z = s_z = \gamma \times z \times K_s \times \tan \delta$$

and the skin frictional stress in cohesive soil at a depth

$$z = s_z = \alpha \times C_u$$

where

    $\gamma = \gamma_b - \gamma_w$; γ_b = Bulk density of soil;
    γ_w = Density of water
    $K_s/K_o = 1$ for bored and cast-*in situ* piles (see Table 7.2)
    $K_o = 1$ in overconsolidated sand

Therefore,

    $K_s = 1$
    $\tan \delta = \tan 23.3°$
    α = Adhesion factor; for overconsolidated London clay = 0.45 (assumed)
C_u at 9 m depth from $G_L = 75$ kN/m^2
C_u at 20 m depth from $G_L = 210$ kN/m^2 (maximum)

Hence, C_u at 18.5 m depth from G_L = 192 kN/m²;
at 13 m C_u = 124 kN/m² (see Figure 8.2)

2. *Ultimate frictional resistance:*
Ultimate frictional resistance,

$$Q_S = \frac{1}{2} \times \Sigma s_z \times z \times p_r \qquad \text{(where } p_r = \text{perimeter/m)}$$

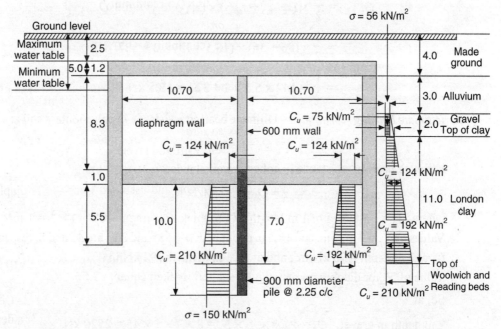

FIGURE 8.2 Diaphragm wall foundation; shear stresses in diaphragm walls and central piles.

Perimeter, p_r upto 13 m depth = 1.0 m (only external soil–pile contact surface)

Perimeter, p_r from 13 m to 18.5 m depth = 2×1 m (both external and internal soil–pile contact surfaces below base slab)

So, at 7 m depth,

$$Q_{s,7} = \frac{1}{2} \times 24 \times 7 \times 1 = 84 \text{ kN}$$

(perimeter = only external soil contact surface)
At 9 m depth,

$$Q_{s,9} = \frac{1}{2} \times (s_{z,9} + s_{z,7}) \times (z_9 - z_7) \times p_r + Q_{s,7}$$

$$= \frac{1}{2} \times (39 + 24) \times (9 - 7) \times 1 + 84 = 147 \text{ kN}$$

At 13 m depth,

$$Q_{s,13} = \frac{1}{2} \times (s_{z,13} + s_{z,9}) \times (z_{13} - z_9) \times p_r + Q_{s,9}$$

$$= \frac{1}{2} \times 90 \times 4 \times 1 + 147 = 327 \text{ kN}$$

At 18.5 m depth,

$$Q_{s,18.5} = \frac{1}{2} \times (s_{z,18.5} + s_{z,13}) \times (z_{18.5} - z_{13}) \times p_r + Q_{s,13}$$

$$= \frac{1}{2} \times (86 + 56) \times (18.5 - 13) \times 2 + 327$$

$$= \frac{1}{2} \times 142 \times 5.5 \times 2 + 327 = 1108 \text{ kN}$$

3. *Ultimate bearing resistance:*   Ultimate bearing resistance in cohesionless soil at a depth,

$$z = Q_b = \gamma \times z \times A_b \times N_q$$

Ultimate bearing resistance in cohesive soil at a depth,

$$z = Q_b = C_u \times A_b \times N_c$$

where, A_b = Base area of 1 m length of 1 m thick diaphragm wall = $1 \times 1 = 1 \text{ m}^2$
Values of N_q at 7 m, 9 m, and 18.5 m depth with $\phi' = 35°$ and $20°$, are 45 and 8, respectively.
C_u at 7 m depth = 75 kN/m², and at 18.5 m depth = 192 kN/m²
Value of N_c for diaphragm rectangular section is taken equal to 7.5.
So, at

7 m depth in gravel, $Q_b = \gamma \times z \times A_b \times N_q = 8 \times 7 \times 1 \times 45 = 2520$ kN
9 m depth in clay, $Q_b = C_u \times A_b \times N_c = 75 \times 1 \times 7.5 = 563$ kN
18.5 m depth in clay, $Q_b = C_u \times A_b \times N_c = 192 \times 1 \times 7.5 = 1440$ kN

4. *Ultimate load carrying capacity/m run of diaphragm wall:*   Ultimate capacity,

$$Q_u = Q_s + Q_b$$

So, at
7 m depth, $Q_{u,7} = Q_{s,7} + Q_{b,7} = 84 + 2520 = 2604$ kN
9 m depth, $Q_{u,9} = Q_{s,9} + Q_{b,9} = 147 + 563 = 710$ kN
18.5 m depth, $Q_{u,18.5} = Q_{s,18.5} + Q_{b,18.5} = 1108 + 1440 = 2548$ kN

5. *Safe capacity of wall/run · m length of wall:*   With a safety factor = 2.5, safe capacity of diaphragm wall/m run,

$$Q = \frac{Q_u}{2.5}$$

Therefore, at
7 m depth, $Q_7 = \dfrac{2604}{2.5} = 1042$ kN

9 m depth, $\qquad Q_9 = \dfrac{710}{2.5} = 284$ kN

18.5 m depth, $Q_{18.5} = \dfrac{2548}{2.5} = 1019$ kN

When the water table on the exterior side of diaphragm wall is at the minimum (5 m below ground level), then the vertical downward load on the diaphragm wall = 1149 kN (calculated before), and the safe capacity of diaphragm wall/m run = 1019 kN < 1149 kN (though slightly less but can be accepted).

When the water table is below the base slab and the drainage system under the base slab is working with 70% effective in permanent condition, the loadings on the base slab will be supported by the soil underneath.

As the base slab is continuous over central support and fixed at ends to the diaphragm walls, the intensity of loading on the soil,

(Dead load of slab + Construction load + Highway HA loading)

$$= (1 \times 24 + 1.4 \times 23 + 31) = 87.2 \text{ kN/m}^2$$

If we take into account the ultimate bearing capacity of clay at a depth 13 m below ground level, and referring to Eq. (2.5) by Terzaghi in Chapter 2, then

$$q_u = 5.7 \times C_u$$

(where $N_c = 5.7$ from Figure 2.5 in Chapter 2)

At a depth 13 m the value of $C_u = 124$ kN/m^2

Hence, $q_u = 5.7 \times 124 = 707$ kN/m^2 (with a factor of 2.5)

Safe bearing capacity of clay,

$$q = \frac{707}{2.5} = 283 \text{ kN/m}^2 \gg 87 \text{ kN/m}^2$$

As the end of base slab is assumed fixed to the diaphragm wall, we may consider certain length slab from the diaphragm wall to act a cantilever member in conjunction with the diaphragm wall to support the vertical load on the wall.

Let us assume 1/4 of span = $\dfrac{1}{4} \times 10.7 = 2.68$ (say 2.5 m to act as cantilever).

Therefore,

$\qquad\qquad\qquad\qquad$ net safe carrying capacity of slab = (283 – 87) 2.5 = 490 kN

$\qquad\qquad$ total safe capacity of (diaphragm wall + cantilever slab) = (1019 + 490) = 1509 kN

In this case, the vertical downward load on the diaphragm wall

$\qquad$ = (weight of diaphragm wall + weight of roof slab + 2.5 m soil overburden on roof + 50 kN/m^2 developer load)

$\qquad$ = (355 + 166 + 300 + 300) = 1121 kN < 1509 kN $\qquad$ **(Satisfactory)**

Therefore, the diaphragm wall 18.5 m depth below ground level has satisfactory safe capacity.

Based on Eurocode 7: 2004

Characteristic shear frictional resistance:

1. The shear frictional stress in cohesionless soil at a depth,

$$z = s_z = \gamma' \times z \times K_s \times \tan \delta = \gamma' \times z \times K_s \times \tan \left(\frac{2}{3} \times \frac{\phi'}{\gamma_{\phi'}} \right)$$

and shear frictional stress in cohesive soil at a depth,

$$z = s_z = \alpha \times \frac{C_u}{\gamma_{C_u}}$$

where

γ' = effective density of soil

$\gamma_{\phi'}$ = partial factor of angle of shear resistance of soil = 1.25 (see Table A.2)

γ_{C_u} = partial factor for undrained shear strength of soil = 1.4 (see Table A.2)

K_s/K_o = 1 for bored and *in situ* piles (wall) (see Table 7.2)

(where K_o = 1 for overconsolidated sand; hence K_s = 1)

α = adhesion factor; for overconsolidated London clay, α = 0.45 (assumed)

Therefore, at

7 m depth, $\quad \tan \delta = \dfrac{2}{3} \times \dfrac{35}{1.25} = 18.7°$

9 m depth, $\quad \tan \delta = \dfrac{2}{3} \times \dfrac{20}{1.25} = 10.7°$

20 m depth, $\quad \tan \delta = \dfrac{2}{3} \times \dfrac{29}{1.25} = 15.5°$

C_u/γ_{C_u} at

9 m depth from $\quad$ GL $= \dfrac{75}{1.4} = 54$ kN/m^2

20 m depth from $\quad$ GL $= \dfrac{210}{1.4} = 150$ kN/m^2

18.5 m depth from GL $= \dfrac{192}{1.4} = 137$ kN/m^2

13 m depth from $\quad$ GL $= \dfrac{124}{1.4} = 89$ kN/m^2

So, at

7 m depth in gravel, $\qquad s_7 = \gamma' \times z \times K_s \times \tan 18.7 = 8 \times 7 \times \tan 18.7 = 19$ kN/m^2

9 m depth in gravel, $\qquad s_9 = 10 \times 9 \times \tan 18.7 = 30$ kN/m^2

9 m depth in London clay, $\qquad s_9 = \alpha \times C_u/\gamma_{C_u} = 0.45 \times 54 = 24$ kN/m^2

13 m depth in London clay, $s_{13} = 0.45 \times 89 = 40 \, \text{kN/m}^2$

18.5 m depth in London clay, $s_{18.5} = 0.45 \times 137 = 62 \, \text{kN/m}^2$

20.0 m depth in woolwich bed, $s_{20} = \gamma \times z \times K_s \times \tan 15.5 = 10 \times 20 \times \tan 15.5 = 55 \, \text{kN/m}^2$
(see Figure 8.3).

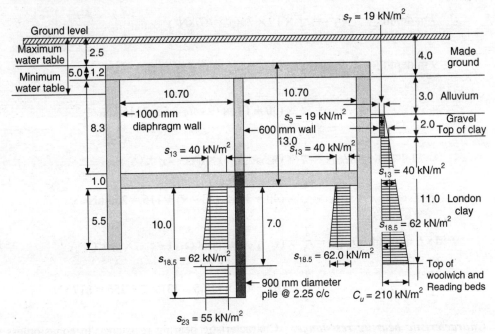

Notes:
1. In cohesionless soil: shear frictional stress in kN/m^2 at a depth z below ground level

$$= s_z = \gamma' \times z \times \tan \left(\frac{2}{3} \times \frac{\phi'}{\gamma_{\phi'}} \right)$$

2. In cohesive soil: shear frictional stress at a depth z below ground level

$$= s_z = \alpha \times \left(\frac{C_u}{\gamma_{C_u}} \right) \quad \text{where } \gamma' = \text{effective soil density (kN/m}^3)$$

$\phi' = $ Effective angle of shearing resistance
$\gamma_{\phi'} = $ Partial factor for soil parameter = 1.25
$\alpha = $ Adhesion factor = 0.45
$C_u = $ Undrained shear strength of clay

$\gamma_{C_u} = $ Partial factor for clay soil parameter = 1.4

FIGURE 8.3   Diaphragm wall foundation; shear stresses in diaphragm walls and central piles (based on Eurocode 7).

2. *Characteristic frictional resistance/m run of diaphragm wall:* Characteristic frictional resistance,

$$Q_s = \frac{1}{2} \times \Sigma s_z \times z \times p_r$$

where, p_r = perimeter.

The perimeter upto 13 m depth = 1 m (only external soil–wall contact surface)

The perimeter from 13 m to 18.5 m depth = $2 \times 1 = 2$ m (both external and internal soil–wall contact surfaces below the base slab). Therefore, at

7 m depth, $\qquad Q_{s,\,7} = \dfrac{1}{2} \times 19 \times 7 \times 1 = 67$ kN

9 m depth, $\qquad Q_{s,\,9} = \dfrac{1}{2} \times [s_{z,\,9} + s_{z,\,7} \times (z_9 - z_7) + Q_{s,\,7}$

$\qquad\qquad\qquad = \dfrac{1}{2} \times (30 + 19) \times (9 - 7) + 67 = 116$ kN

13 m depth, $\quad Q_{s,\,13} = \dfrac{1}{2} \times (s_{z,\,13} + s_{z,\,9}) \times (z_{13} - z_9) + Q_{s,\,9}$

$\qquad\qquad\qquad = \dfrac{1}{2} \times (40 + 30) \times (13 - 9) + 116 = 256$ kN

18.5 m depth $\quad Q_{s,\,18.5} = \dfrac{1}{2} \times (s_{z,\,18.5} + s_{z,\,13}) \times (z_{18.5} - z_{13}) \times p_r + Q_{s,\,13}$

$\qquad\qquad\qquad = \dfrac{1}{2} \times (62 + 40) \times (18.5 - 13) \times 2 + 256 = 817$ kN

Characteristic bearing resistance: Characteristic bearing resistance in cohesionless soil at a depth,

$$z = Q_b = [\gamma' \times z \times N_q \times b_q \times s_q \times i_q] \times A_b \qquad \text{[see Eq. (D.4)]}$$

Characteristic bearing resistance in cohesive undrained soil at a depth,

$$= Q_b = \left[(\pi + 2) \times \frac{C_u}{\gamma_{C_u}} \times b_c \times s_c \times i_c + q \right] A_b \qquad \text{[see Eq. (D.1)]}$$

At 18.5 m, the wall bears on cohesive London clay. So, we shall calculate the bearing resistance of London clay, where

$\dfrac{C_u}{\gamma_{C_u}}$ at 18.5 m depth = 137 kN/m² (calculated before)

$\dfrac{1}{2} b_c = 1 - 2 \times \dfrac{\alpha}{(\pi + 2)};$ $\qquad$ since $\alpha = 0$ and $b_c = 1$

$s_c = 1 + 0.2 \times \left(\dfrac{B'}{L'} \right);$ $\qquad$ since $B' = B = 1$ m and $L' = L = 1$ m; $s_c = 1.2$

$$i_c = \frac{1}{2} \times \left[1 + \frac{(1-H)}{A' \times \dfrac{C_u}{\gamma_{C_u}}} \right]^{0.5}, \quad \text{since } H = 0, \ i_c = 1$$

q = overburden at 18.5 m depth = $20 \times 18 = 360$

A_b = base area = $1 \times 1 = 1$

Therefore, Q_b at 18.5 m depth,

$$[(\pi + 2) \times 137 \times 1 \times 1.2 \times 1 + 360] \times 1 = (845 + 360) = 1205 \text{ kN}$$

Design capacity of diaphragm wall:

Design capacity of diaphragm wall/m run

$$Q = \frac{Q_s}{\gamma_s} + \frac{Q_b}{\gamma_b}$$

where γ_s and γ_b are the partial resistance factors for bored diaphragm wall. (Referring to Table A.7 of Eurocode 7).

$$\gamma_s = 1.3 \text{ and } \gamma_b = 1.6$$

Hence,

$$Q = \frac{817}{1.3} + \frac{1205}{1.6} = 628 + 753 = 1381 \text{ kN}$$

Thus, based on Eurocode 7:2004, we find that design capacity of diaphragm wall is higher than the value (1019 kN) calculated using BS 8004: 1986.

8.4.4 Method of Construction of Tunnel in Relation to Diaphragm Wall

Before we start to analyze the diaphragm walls for bending moments and shear forces developed due to the retaining of soil on the exterior faces of tunnel, we should study the structural behaviour of wall during and after the construction of tunnel. Various stages of construction with soil and water pressures behind the diaphragm walls will generate varying bending moments and shear forces and the maximum value will be taken for the structural design of walls.

As the tunnel is situated in a highly populated suburban area, careful considerations shall be given in the construction of tunnel so that minimum disturbances in the traffic flow occur during the construction period. Generally, two methods of construction are followed, namely (1) top down construction method, and (2) bottom up construction method.

In the *top down construction method*, the construction starts from top, firstly with construction of top roof slab of tunnel, and then excavating down below the roof slab upto the bottom of excavation to reach the bottom of base slab level. During the excavation period proper intermediate shoring (propping) arrangement should be provided in order to prevent the collapse of excavated surfaces. In this method, minimum disturbance of traffic or traffic flow is observed, since the constructed roof slab may be used for traffic. This method is used in underground tunnel construction, particularly where heavy traffic is encountered.

In the *bottom up construction method*, the excavation starts from top and gradually goes to the bottom excavation level. The bottom slab is then cast during this excavation period. Adequate shoring arrangements at different levels should be provided to avoid any collapse of vertical excavated sides. The slabs at intermediate levels from bottom up are constructed gradually with simultaneous removal of props. Finally, the top slab is constructed. This method is generally applied in multistoried underground car parks, offices and underground metro stations. Before the start of excavation by adopting either of the above methods, we should analyze the wall with soil and water pressures at different stages of excavation and to find out that the wall section is structurally adequate.

In our case, we shall adopt the top down construction method as shown in Figure 8.4.

8.4.5   Analysis of Diaphragm Wall Subjected to Soil Pressure

Analytical concept

It is already described that the soil-structure interaction on diaphragm wall is highly complex. The soil behaves in certain ways depending on the following points:

- Type of soil in particular, the clay and the overconsolidated London clay
- Position of water table
- The stiffness of member in contact with soil
- Method of construction.

1. In cohesionless soil, the active pressure exerted on the wall is dependant on the value of effective angle of shear resistance (ϕ') and the angle skin friction (δ) soil and the contact surface of wall. The effectiveness of pressure is almost immediate after the soil is placed with consolidation on the back of the wall or when the excavation is carried out in front of wall.

2. In cohesive soil, the temporary construction stage just after the excavation are:

   - *Behind the wall*: The active pressure exerted on the wall depends mainly on the value of cohesion of soil and the moisture content particularly in overconsolidated London clay. In London clay, just after the excavation the upper part moves inwards, whether propped or not. The retained mass of soil undergoes quick softening and experiences tension cracks in short term. So, the wall pressure exerted behind the wall is lower than the original value. Even we may find a gap between wall and clay mass upto some depth from top when the water table is low. Gradually, the pressure increases on the wall due to the release of pore water within clay mass, and this process takes place for a long period of time when the full extent of pressure is experienced.

   - *In front of wall:*   The passive pressure exerted in front of the wall in passive zone below the formation level (below base slab level of tunnel) depends on the condition of soil specially for the London clay. Due to the presence of negative excess pore pressure, the clay soil possesses original undrained shear strength in short term. The upper part of clay soil looses the original shear strength to some extent due to the softening effect during the period of excavation. It is very difficult to ascertain the value of reduction. CIRIA report (104) recommends a reduction between 20% and 30%.

In our case, it is reasonable to adopt a reduction of 30% of original value.

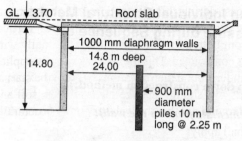

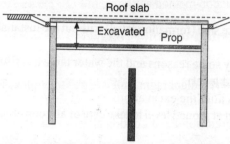

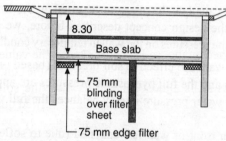

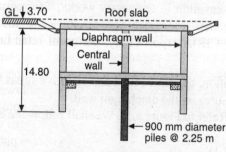

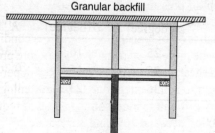

Top down method

Step 1: Construct external diaphragm walls. Install central stress reducing piles at the bottom of floor slab. Fill the bores of pile trench to ground level with compacted sand.

Step 2: Excavate upto the soffit level of roof slab.

Step 3: Construct the roof slab on ground over blinding. The roof slab shall span over the diaphragm walls.

Step 4: Excavate underneath the roof slab upto a depth half way between the roof slab and the bottom slab. Install horizontal props.

Step 5: (a) Excavate upto the bottom of base slab.

(b) Place 75 mm blinding over filtram (filter) plastic sheet 0.5 m wide @ 6 m spacing.

(c) Cast the base slab (with connections to the diaphragm walls) over the blinding layer within 7 days after the completion of excavation (to reduce the effect of heave of clay soil under the base slab).

Step 6: Remove the intermediate prop.

Step 7: Construct 14 days the central wall upto the soffit of roof slab to reduce the effect of ground heave of clay soil below the base slab.

Step 8: Backfill over the roof slab with self-compacting granular soil.

Step 9: The sequence shall continue for every 15 m long segment of tunnel.

FIGURE 8.4 Diaphragm wall foundation; construction sequence.

8.4.6 Analysis of Diaphragm Wall as an Individual Structural Member Subjected to Soil and Water Pressure during Sequence of Construction of Tunnel

Based on BS code of practice 8004: 1986 (In top down construction method:)

Case 1: *Temporary condition (without any intermediate prop on the wall):*

1. *Conditions:*   The following conditions shall apply:

- The top slab is cast.
- The excavation is completed upto the base slab (formation level) without the installation of any intermediate prop.
- The pumping has temporarily stopped by some reasons and the water table has risen to the maximum level (2.5 m below ground level).
- The base slab will be cast within 7 days after the excavation.
- A surcharge of 10 kN/m² is assumed to act at ground level to take care of any construction traffic.

With the above conditions, firstly, we shall calculate the pressures exerted on the wall.

2. *Pressure calculations:*   Bearing in mind the design concept described before, we shall consider the following theory in calculating the pressures on the wall in temporary condition:

- *In effective stress theory:*   Behind the wall, the effective soil pressure (based on the value of soil properties of ϕ', δ and K_a) and the full hydrostatic pressures are applied (tension crack created by negative pore water pressure in clay balances the full water pressure in the crack).
- *In total stress theory:*   The clay soil in front of wall is weakened (due to softening effect) in shear strength after the excavation in temporary works. The reduction of undrained shear strength of London clay is assumed between 20% and 30% of the original value as stated before (see CIRIA report (104); design of retaining walls embedded in stiff clay) [8.3].

In our case, as this is a temporary condition, the mixed total and effective stress theory shall be followed to determine the pressures on the diaphragm wall.

3. *Active soil pressures behind the wall:* (Refer to Figure 8.5). We shall follow the effective stress analysis:

Properties of soil: (Referring to Table 8.1)

Soil type	γ_b (kN/m³)	ϕ' (degree)	δ (degree)	K_a
For made ground	18	25	16.7	0.36
For alluvium	18	25	16.7	0.36
For gravel	20	36	23.3	0.27

Undrained shear strength (C_u) in London clay:

C_u at 9 m from ground level (top of clay) = 75 kN/m²

C_u at 13 m from ground level (excavation depth) = 124 kN/m^2

C_u at 18.5 m from ground level (bottom of wall) = 192 kN/m^2

Therefore, active soil pressures behind the wall (water table 2.5 m below ground level) based on effective stress analysis:

In made ground:

At 2.5 m depth below ground level,

$$p_{a,1} = K_a \times \gamma \times z_1 = 0.36 \times 18 \times 2.5 = 16 \text{ kN/m}^2$$

At 4.0 m depth below ground level,

$$p_{a,2} = K_a \times \gamma \times (z_2 - z_1) = 0.36 \times 8 \times 1.5 = 20 \text{ kN/m}^2$$

In alluvium:

At 7 m depth below ground level,

$$p_{a,3} = p_{a,2} + K_a \times \gamma \times (z_3 - z_2) = 20 + 0.36 \times 8 \times 3 = 29 \text{ kN/m}^2$$

In gravel:

At 9 m depth below ground level,

$$p_{a,4} = p_{a,3} + K_a \times \gamma \times (z_4 - z_3) = 29 + 0.27 \times 10 \times 2 = 34 \text{ kN/m}^2$$

In clay:

At 9 m depth (top of clay) below ground level,

$$p_{a,5} = K_a \times [\gamma \times z_1 + \gamma \times z_2 + \gamma \times z_3 + \gamma \times z_4]$$
$$= 0.44 \times [18 \times 2.5 + 8 \times 1.5 + 8 \times 3 + 10 \times 2] = 44 \text{ kN/m}^2$$

At 18.5 m depth below ground level,

$$p_{a,6} = p_{a,5} + K_a \times [\gamma \times (z_5 - z_4)] = 44 + 0.44 \times 9 \times (18.5 - 9) = 82 \text{ kN/m}^2$$

Due to surcharge, $w_s = 10$ kN/m^2 at ground level, pressure behind the wall:

In alluvium:

$$p_s = K_a \times w_s = 0.36 \times 10 = 3.6 \text{ kN/m}^2;$$

In clay:

$$0.44 \times 10 = 4.4 \text{ kN/m}^2$$

Average pressure due to surcharge = 4 kN/m^2

Water pressure at 18.5 m depth from maximum water level,

$p_w = 16 \times 10 = 160$ kN/m^2

(where, $\gamma = \gamma_b - \gamma_w$; z = depth below ground level; p_a = active pressure).

The active pressure diagram behind the wall is shown in Figure 8.5.

Passive pressure in front of the wall based on total stress analysis: As discussed before, the reduced shear strength in clay is assumed 70% original strength.

Therefore, at

13 m depth below ground level, $C_{u,1} = 0.7 \times 124 = 87$ kN/m^2

14 m depth below ground level, $\quad C_{u,2} = 0.7 \times 136 + \gamma \times z = 95 \ kN/m^2$

18.5 m depth below ground level, $C_{u,3} = 0.7 \times 192 = 134 \ kN/m^2$

Due to the softening effect of top portion of clay just after excavation, the shear strength of clay is assumed to be equal to zero at the top of excavation (at formation level), and at about 1 m depth (assumed) the clay regains its shear strength in value.

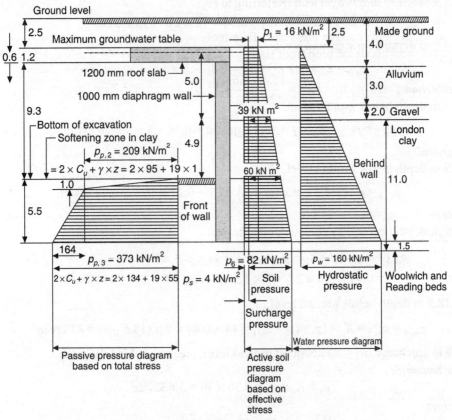

Mixed total and effective stress analysis of diaphragm
wall without prop in temporary condition
Case 1

FIGURE 8.5 Soil and water pressure diagram on diaphragm wall.

Using the expression for the pressure coefficient for cohesion

$$K_{pc} = 2 \times \left(1 + \frac{c_w}{C_u}\right)^{0.5}$$

where, $\quad c_w$ = wall adhesion (assuming $c_w = 0$; $K_{pc} = 2$)

Hence, passive pressure at 1 m below formation level,

$$p_{p,2} = K_{pc} \times C_{u,2} + \gamma \times z = 2 \times 95 + 19 \times 1 = 209 \text{ kN/m}^2$$

and passive pressure at 18.5 m below ground level,

$$p_{p,3} = K_{pc} \times C_{u,3} + \gamma \times z = 2 \times 134 + 19 \times 4.5 = 354 \text{ kN/m}^2$$

The passive pressure diagram in front of wall below formation level is shown in Figure 8.4.

    4. *Stability of diaphragm wall:* Referring to Figure 8.5, assume that the only prop of the wall is the roof slab (already cast) about which the wall may rotate due to the resultant action of active and passive pressures. Take moments of all the forces of active and passive pressures about the prop (roof slab).

$$M\text{(active)} = \left[16 \times 15.4 \times \frac{15.4}{2} + \frac{66}{2} \times 15.4 \times \frac{2}{3} \times 15.4 \right] \quad \text{(soil pressure)}$$

$$+ 4 \times 15.4 \times \frac{15.4}{2} \quad \text{(surcharge)}$$

$$+ \frac{160}{2} \times 15.4 \times \frac{2}{3} \times 15.4 \quad \text{(hydrostatic pressure)}$$

$$= 20191 \text{ kN m} \quad \text{(clockwise moment)}$$

$$M\text{(passive)} = \left[\frac{209}{2} \times \left(\frac{2}{3} + 9.9 \right) + 209 \times 4.5 \times \left(\frac{4.5}{2} + 10.9 \right) + \frac{164}{2} \times 4.5 \times \left(4.5 \times \frac{2}{3} + 10.9 \right) \right]$$

$$= 18601 \text{ kN m} \quad \text{(anticlockwise moment)}$$

From the above calculations we find that the moment due to active pressure is much higher than the moment due to passive pressure. The resulting effect is that the wall moves inwards, and the wall collapses. So, we cannot excavate upto the formation level without the intermediate prop on the wall.

Case 2: *Temporary condition (with intermediate prop on the wall):* Refer to Figure 8.6.

    1. *Conditions:*   The following conditions shall apply:

- The top slab is cast.
- The excavation is completed upto the formation level with the installation of prop half way between the roof slab and the formation level.
- The pumping has stopped temporarily and the water table has risen upto the maximum level of 2.5 m below ground level.
- The base slab is waiting to be cast within approximately 7 days after the excavation is complete.
- A surcharge of 10 kN/m² is allowed at the ground level to cater for the expected traffic.

With the above conditions, we calculate the pressures on the wall.

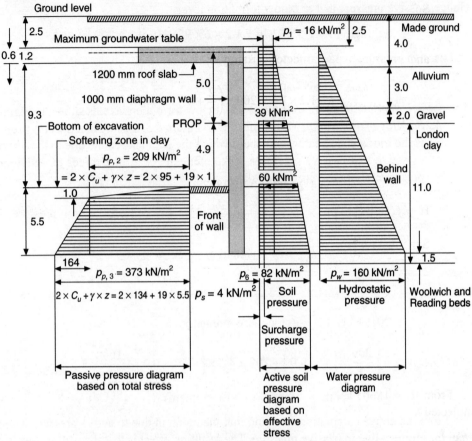

FIGURE 8.6 Soil and water pressure diagrams on diaphragm wall.

2. *Pressure calculations:* Same as in case 1 (see Figure 8.6).

Stability of diaphragm wall: Take moments about the intermediate prop:

$$M \text{ (active, clockwise)} = \left(39 \times \frac{10.4^2}{2} + 43 \times \frac{10.4^2}{3} + 4 \times \frac{10.4^2}{2} \right)$$

$$\text{soil pressure} + \left(56 \times \frac{10.4^2}{2} + 104 \times \frac{10.4^2}{3} \right)$$

water pressure $= 3876 + 6778 = 10654$ kN m

In ultimate design analysis, assume partial safety factors, $\gamma_f = 1.5$ for soil and water pressures respectively (refer to Table 5 of CIRIA Report 104).

So, ultimate moment at prop,

$$M_u \text{ (active)} = 1.5 \times 3876 + 1.2 \times 6778 = 13948 \text{ kN m (clockwise)}$$

and assuming a partial factor of safety, $\gamma_f = 1.2$, for passive resistance

$$M_u \text{ (passive)} = 1.2 \times \left[\frac{1}{2} \times 209 \times \left(\frac{2}{3} + 4.9 \right) + 209 \times 4.5 \times \left(5.9 + \frac{4.5}{2} \right) \right.$$

$$\left. + \frac{1}{2} \times 164 \times 4.5 \times \left(5.9 + \frac{2}{3} \times 4.5 \right) \right]$$

$$= 1.2 \times 11530 = 13837 \text{ kN m (anticlockwise)}$$

Hence,

net ultimate moment at prop $= 13948 - 13837 = 110$ kN m

Safe load on prop:

$$P_w = \frac{1}{2} \times (39 + 82) \times 10.4 + \frac{1}{2} \times 2.5 \times (28 + 39) + 4 \times 13$$

$$+ \frac{1}{2} \times 13.3 \times (25 + 160) - \frac{1}{2} \times 209 \times (5.5 + 4.5)$$

$$- \frac{1}{2} \times 4.5 \times 164 = 2014 - 414 = 600 \text{ kN}$$

From the above results, we conclude that in temporary condition the intermediate prop is subjected to a working load of 600 kN.

Case 3: *Temporary condition with intermediate prop (long-term say 1 year):*   Refer to Figure 8.7.

1. *Conditions:*   The following conditions shall apply:

   - The top slab is cast.
   - The excavation is completed upto the formation level with the installation of intermediate prop during excavation.
   - After the excavation is complete, the contractor has stopped working for a long period (say about 1 year) due to some contractual disagreement.
   - The pumping has stopped and the water table has risen to the maximum level of 2.5 m below the ground level.
   - The surcharge of 10 kN/m² at the ground level may be taken into account.

   With the above points in mind, we shall analyze the wall with pressures on both sides.

2. *Pressure calculations:*   As the bottom slab was not cast for a long period, the London clay in front of wall below formation level gradually loses its undrained shear strength (C_u) due to the release of pore water pressure, and the soil reduces to effective cohesive strength (c'). So, in this case we shall analyze the wall based on effective stress theory. It is assumed that the pressure in clay below the formation level starts reducing to zero at the toe of wall.

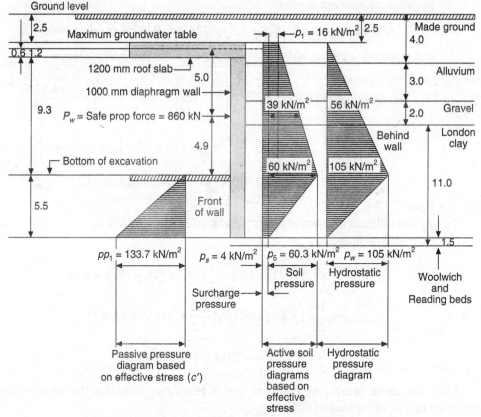

Effective stress analysis of diaphragm wall with intermediate
prop in temporary condition
Case 3: Long-term

FIGURE 8.7 Soil and water pressure diagrams on diaphragm wall.

Therefore, Active soil pressures behind the wall are as follows: (see Figure 8.7):
At 2.5 m depth, (z_1) below ground level

$$p_1 = K_a \times \gamma \times z_1 = 0.36 \times 18 \times 2.5 = 16 \text{ kN/m}^2$$

At 4 m depth,

$$p_2 = K_a \times \gamma \times (z_2 - z_1) + p_1 = 0.36 \times 8 \times 1.5 + 16 = 20 \text{ kN/m}^2$$

At 7 m depth,

$$p_3 = K_a \times \gamma \times (z_3 - z_2) + p_2 = 0.36 \times 8 \times 3 + 20 = 29 \text{ kN/m}^2$$

At 8.1 m depth (prop level),

$$p_4 = K_a \times \gamma \times (z_4 - z_3) + p_3 = 0.27 \times 10 \times 1.1 + 29 = 32 \text{ kN/m}^2$$

At 9 m depth,

$$p_5 = K_a \times \gamma \times (z_5 - z_4) + p_4 = 0.44 \times 10 \times 0.9 + 32 = 34 \text{ kN/m}^2$$

At 13 m depth,

$$p_6 = K_a \times \gamma \times z = 0.44 \times (2.5 \times 18 + 1.5 \times 8 + 3 \times 8 + 2 \times 10 + 4 \times 9 = 60 \text{ kN/m}^2$$

Below 13 m (formation level) it is assumed that the pressure starts reducing and becomes zero at the toe level.
Pressure due to surcharge of 10 kN/m^2 = $p_{s,1}$ = 4 kN/m^2

Water pressure behind the wall are as follows:
At 8.1 m depth below ground level,

$$p_{w,1} = 10 \times 5.6 = 56 \text{ kN/m}^2$$

At 13 m depth,

$$p_{w,2} = 10 \times 10.5 = 105 \text{ kN/m}^2$$

Below 13 m depth, water pressure on both sides of wall balances. So, the water pressures at toe on both sides of wall below formation level is assumed to be zero.

3. *Ultimate moment in wall at prop:* Take moment about prop, the cantilever moments in wall

$$M_u \text{ (active)} = 1.5 \times \left[39 \times 4.9^2 + 21 \times \frac{4.9^2}{3} + \frac{1}{2} \times 60 \times 5.5 \times \left(4.9 + \frac{5.5}{3} \right) \right.$$

$$+ 10.4 \times 4 \times \frac{10.4}{2} \right] + 1.2 \times \left[56 \times \frac{4.9^2}{2} + 49 \times \frac{4.9^2}{3} \right.$$

$$+ \frac{105}{2} \times 5.5 \times \left(4.9 + \frac{1}{3} \times 5.5 \right) \right]$$

$$= 1.5 \times 1964 + 1.2 \times 3009 = 6557 \text{ kN m (clockwise)}$$

$$M_u \text{ (passive)} = 1.5 \left[\frac{133.7}{2} \times 5.5 \times \left(4.9 + \frac{2}{3} \times 5.5 \right) \right]$$

$$= 1.5 (3150) = 4725 \text{ kN m (anticlockwise)}$$

Therefore,

$$\text{net } M_u \text{ in wall at prop} = (6557 - 4725) \text{ kN m} = 1832 \text{ kN m}$$

4. *Safe (working) force in prop:* Reaction on prop due to active pressures behind the wall

$$= \left[(39 + 60) \times \frac{4.9}{2} + \frac{60}{2} \times 5.5 + \frac{1}{2} \times (29 + 39) \times 2.5 + 4 \times 12.9 \right]$$

$$+ \frac{1}{2} \times \left[(56 + 105) \times 4.9 + \frac{1}{2} \times 105 \times 5.5 \right]$$

$$= (545 + 683) \text{ kN} = 1228 \text{ kN}$$

Reaction on prop due to passive pressures in front of wall,

$$\frac{1}{2} \times 5.58133.7 = 368 \text{ kN}$$

Therefore,
net reaction (safe force) on the prop = (1228 − 368) kN = 860 kN

Case 4: *Analysis of diaphragm wall in permanent condition when base slab is constructed:*

1. *Design considerations:* The following are the design considerations:

   - Assume the bottom slab is finally cast.
   - The intermediate prop has been removed.
   - 2.5 m soil overburden has been placed over the roof.
   - The developer load of 50 kN/m^2 has been considered.
   - The pumping system is finally withdrawn.
   - The water table has reached to the maximum level to 2.5 m below ground level.
   - The effective stress analysis of soil pressure shall be carried out with the assumption that the strength of clay has been reduced to cohesion (c') from undrained shear strength (C_u) in front of the wall (below the formation level) due to the release of pore water pressure. The value of c' is assumed to be zero at the centre of base slab and reaches its maximum value at the toe level.
   - In active pressure calculations behind the wall, the coefficient of earth pressure at rest (K_0) shall be considered.
   - It is assumed that the active pressure reaches the maximum value at the centre of base slab, and gradually reduces to zero at the toe level.
   - Below the formation level, the water pressure behind the wall shall be considered constant because the water pressure in front of wall behind the formation level balances the extra increase of water pressure behind the wall.
   - The central load bearing wall has been constructed to take up the loads from the roof slab.
   - The roof slab is assumed continuous over the central wall and the ends of slab is assumed fixed to the diaphragm wall.

2. *Pressure calculations:* Refer to Figure 8.8.

   - Soil pressures behind the wall at:
   3.1 m (centre of slab) below GL,

   $$p_1 = K_o \times \gamma \times z_1 = 0.6 \times 18 \times 3.1 = 33 \text{ kN/m}^2$$

   13 m (centre of base slab),

   $$p_2 = K_o \times \gamma \times z_2 = 1 \times [18 \times 2.5 + 8 \times 1.5 + 8 \times 3 + 10 \times 2 + 9 \times 4] = 137 \text{ kN/m}^2$$

   18.5 m below GL, $p_o = 0$

   - Soil pressure behind the wall due to surcharge of 10 kN/m^2 at:
   12.5 m depth below GL,

   $$p_{s,1} = K_o \times s = 1 \times 10 = 10 \text{ kN/m}^2$$

Assumed constant for the whole depth of wall at:

18.5 m below GL, $p_2 = 10$ kN/m^2

- Water pressures behind the wall at:
  3.1 m below GL, $p_{w,1} = \gamma_w \times z_1 = 10 \times 0.6 = 6$ kN/m^2
  13 m below GL, $p_{w,2} = 10 \times 10.5 = 105$ kN/m^2
  18.5 m below GL, $p_{w,3} = 105$ kN/m^2

- Soil pressure in front of the wall at:

  13 m below GL $= 0$
  18.5 m below GL $= 133.7$ kN/m^2

3. *Moment calculations:* Refer to the loadings on diaphragm wall, as shown in Figure 8.8. Assuming the diaphragm wall fixed with the roof slab at A, continuous over base slab at B, and cantilevered below base slab as BC,

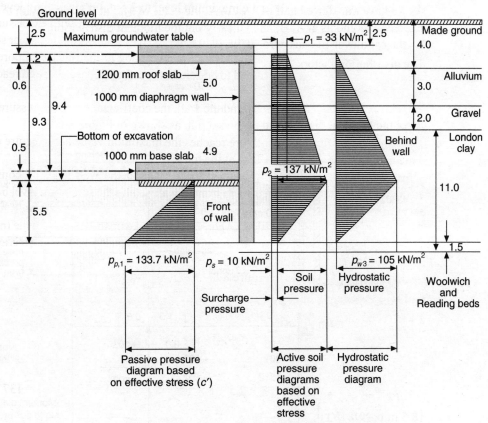

Effective stress analysis of diaphragm wall in permanent
condition when base slab is constructed
Case 4: Permanent condition

FIGURE 8.8   Soil and water pressure diagrams on diaphragm wall.

- Consider the soil pressure only:
  Then, for cantilever BC, moment

$$M_{bc} = 10 \times \frac{6^2}{2} + \frac{1}{2} \times 137 \times 6 \times \frac{1}{3} \times 6 - \frac{1}{2} \times 133.7 \times 6 \times \frac{2}{3} \times 6 = 602 \text{ kNm}$$

For span AB: Considering the wall fixed at A and free at B assuming 3/4 of original stiffness, half of fixed end moment at B is transferred to A
Therefore,

$$M_{fba} = \left(43 \times \frac{9.4^2}{12} + \frac{1}{2} \times 104 \times \frac{9.4^2}{10} \right) = 776 \text{ kN m}$$

$$M_{fab} = \left(43 \times \frac{9.4^2}{12} + \frac{1}{2} \times 104 \times \frac{9.4^2}{15} \right) + \frac{1}{2} \times M_{fba} = 623 + \frac{776}{2} = 1011 \text{ kN m}$$

As we have transferred half of M_{fba} to A, the value of M_{fba} at B is zero. With the above fixed end moments at A, B, and C, carry out the moment distribution.
As the cantilever BC has zero stiffness,
The distribution factors,

$$D_{fbc} = 0$$
$$D_{fba} = 1$$

After the moment distribution is carried out, as shown in Figure 8.9.

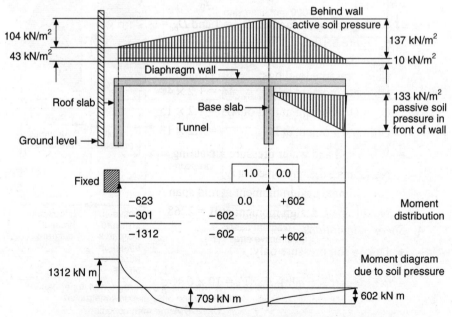

Analysis of diaphragm wall in permanent condition with soil pressures

FIGURE 8.9   Diaphragm wall; moment distribution and moment diagram due to soil pressure.

Free mid span moment in

$$AB = 43 \times \frac{9.4^2}{8} + \frac{1}{2} \times 104 \times 9.4^2 \times 0.128 = 1063 \text{ kN m}$$

With a partial safety factor, $\gamma_f = 1.5$, for soil pressure:

Final ultimate moment at A $\qquad = -1.5 \times 1312 = -1968 \text{ kN m}$

Final ultimate moment at B $\qquad = 1.5 \times 602 = +903 \text{ kN m}$

Final ultimate moment at mid span AB $= 1.5 \times 709 = +1064 \text{ kN m}$

- Next, consider water pressure only:

$$M_{fbc} = 105 \times \frac{6^2}{2} = 1890 \text{ kN m}$$

$$M_{fba} = \frac{1}{2} \times 105 \times \frac{9.4^2}{10} = 464 \text{ kN m}$$

$$M_{fab} = \frac{1}{2} \times 105 \times \frac{9.4^2}{15} = 309 \text{ kN m}$$

Considering 3/4 of actual stiffness of BA with AB, simply supported at B $M_{fba} = 0$

$$M_{fab} = 309 + \frac{1}{2} \times 464 = 541 \text{ kN m}$$

With distribution factors, $D_{ba} = 1$ and $D_{bc} = 0$, carry out moment distribution, as shown in Figure 8.10.

From the results of moment distribution, and with a partial safety factor $\gamma_f = 1.2$ for water pressure loadings:

Ultimate moment at A, $\qquad M_u = 1.2 \times 404 = 485 \text{ kN m}$

Ultimate moment at mid of AB $= 1.2 \times 150 = 180 \text{ kN m}$

Ultimate moment at B $\qquad = 1.2 \times 1890 = 2268 \text{ kN m}$

- When soil and water pressure are acting simultaneously:

Net ultimate design moment at A $\qquad = 1968 - 485 = 1483 \text{ kN m (anticlockwise)}$

Net ultimate design moment at mid span AB $\quad = 1064 - 180 = 884 \text{ kN m}$

Net ultimate design moment at B $= 2268 - 903 = 1365 \text{ kN m (clockwise)}$

4. *Shear calculations:*

- Due to soil pressure only:

At support B (right), $\qquad V_b = 10 \times 6 + \frac{1}{2} \times 137 \times 6 - \frac{1}{2} \times 133.7 \times 6 = 70 \text{ kN}$

At support B (left), $V_b \text{ (left)} = 43 \times \frac{9.4}{2} + \frac{1}{2} \times 104 \times 9.4 \times \frac{2}{3} = 528 \text{ kN}$

At support A, $\qquad V_a = 43 \times \frac{9.4}{2} + \frac{1}{2} \times 104 \times 9.4 \times \frac{1}{3} = 365 \text{ kN}$

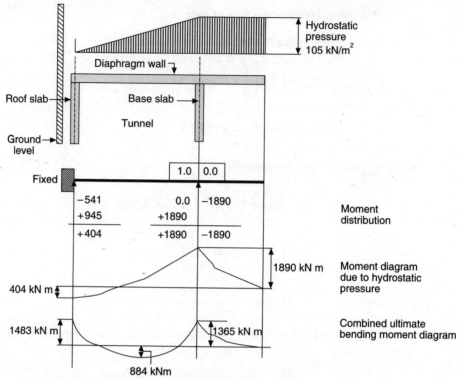

Analysis of diaphragm wall in permanent condition with hydrostatic
pressures and combined soil and hydrostatic pressures

FIGURE 8.10   Diaphragm wall; moment distribution and combined moment diagram.

- Due to water pressure only:

At support B (right), $V_b = 105 \times 6 = 630$ kN

$$\text{At support B (left)} \quad = \frac{1}{2} \times 105 \times 9.4 \times \frac{2}{3} = 329 \text{ kN}$$

$$\text{At support A} \quad = \frac{1}{2} \times 105 \times \frac{9.4}{3} = 165 \text{ kN}$$

- When soil and water pressure are acting simultaneously:

With a partial safety factor $\gamma_f = 1.5$ for soil pressures and 1.2 for water pressures
Ultimate shear at B (right), $V_b \text{(right)} = 1.5 \times 70 + 1.2 \times 630 = 861$ kN
Ultimate shear at B (left), $V_b \text{(left)} = 1.5 \times 528 + 1.2 \times 329 = 1187$ kN
Ultimate shear at A, $V_a = 1.5 \times 365 + 1.2 \times 165 = 746$ kN

- Calculations for depth and reinforcement: BS 8110:1997 [8.6]

For reinforcement calculations, the moment at the face of support is to be considered.
Consider the cantilever portion of wall at the face of base slab.

Active soil pressure at the face of base slab $= 137 \times \dfrac{5.5}{6} = 126 \text{ kN/m}^2$

Ultimate moment due to soil,

$$M_{us} = 1.5 \times \left[\frac{1}{2} \times 126 \times 5.5 \times \frac{1}{3} \times 5.5 + 10 \times \frac{5.5^2}{2} \right.$$

$$\left. - \frac{1}{2} \times 133.7 \times 5.5 \times \frac{2}{3} \times 5.5 \right] = -842 \text{ kN m}$$

Ultimate moment due to water,

$$M_{uw} = 1.2 \left[105 \times 5.5 \times \frac{5.5}{2} \right] = 1906$$

Therefore, ultimate net moment at the face of base slab $= 1906 - 842 = 1064$ kN m
Next, consider moment at the face of roof slab.
Active soil pressure at the face of roof slab,

$$33 + 104 \times \frac{0.6}{9.4} = 33 + 7 = 40 \text{ kN/m}^2$$

Active water pressure at the face of roof slab,

$105 \times \dfrac{0.6}{9.4} = 7 \text{ kN/m}^2$

Therefore, ultimate moment at the face of roof slab,

1483 (already calculated before) $- 746 \times 0.6 + 1.5$

$$\times \left[43 \times \frac{0.6^2}{2} + \frac{1}{2} \times 7 \times 0.6 \times \frac{1}{3} \times 0.6 \right]$$

$$+ 1.2 \times \left[\frac{1}{2} \times 7 \times 0.6 \times \frac{1}{3} \times 0.6 \right]$$

$$= 1483 - 448 + 12 + 1 = 1048 \text{ kN m} < 1064$$

So, the section of wall at the face of base slab is subjected to an ultimate moment,

$$M_u = 1064 \text{ kN m}$$

And in Case 3: Ultimate moment at prop support = 1832 kN m (previously calculated) > 1064 kN m. So, adopt the ultimate moment for Case 3.
Therefore, ultimate design moment,

$$M_u = 1832 \text{ kN m}$$

and ultimate design axial load,

$$N_u = 1.2 \times 1121 \text{ kN} = 1345 \text{ kN}$$

(already calculated for wall safe capacity).

With partial safety factor for combination of dead and developer loads, $\gamma_f = 1.2$

Assumed depth of diaphragm wall, $D = 1000$ mm

Effective depth,

$$d = 1000 - 40 \text{ (cover)} - 20 \text{ (half main bar diameter)} - 20 \text{ (distribution bar)} = 920 \text{ mm}$$

Assumed,

$$f_{cu} = 40 \text{ N/mm}^2; f_y = 460 \text{ N/mm}^2 \text{ and } d/D = \frac{920}{1000} = 0.9$$

Referring to Chart 39 of BS 8110: part 3: 1985:

$$\frac{M_u}{b \times D^2} = \frac{1832 \times 10^6}{1000 \times 1000^2} = 1.83$$

$$\frac{N_u}{b \times D} = \frac{1345 \times 1000}{1000 \times 1000} = 1.35$$

$$\frac{100 \times A_{sc}}{b \times D} = 0.7$$

Therefore,

$$A_{sc} = 0.7 \times 1000 \times \frac{1000}{100} = 7000 \text{ mm}^2; \qquad \text{each face} = \frac{A_{sc}}{2} = 3500 \text{ mm}^2$$

Adopt: T40 @ 150 c/c both faces ($A_{sc}/2$ provided = 8378 mm^2)

- Check for shear:

Ultimate shear at left of support (base slab) = 1187 kN (already calculated)

Hence, ultimate shear at a distance d from face of base slab (1.4 m from centre of base slab),

$$V_u = 1187 - 1.5\left[\frac{1}{2} \times (132 + 147) \times 1.4\right] - 1.2\left[\frac{1}{2} \times (89 + 105) \times 1.4\right] = 731 \text{ kN}$$

shear stress,

$$v_u = \frac{V_u}{(b \times d)} = \frac{731 \times 10^3}{1000 \times 920} = 0.79 \text{ N/mm}^2$$

Allowable shear stress,

$$v_c = \frac{0.79}{\gamma_m} \times \left(\frac{1008 \times A_s}{b \times d}\right)^{1/3} \times \left(\frac{f_{cu}}{25}\right)^{1/3}$$

$$= \frac{0.79}{1.25} \times \left(\frac{100 \times 8378}{1000 \times 920}\right)^{1/3} \times \left(\frac{40}{25}\right)^{1/3} = 0.72 \text{ N/mm}^2 < v_u$$

But the shear stress may be enhanced when the section considered is less than $2d$ from the face of support.

Therefore, the effective allowable shear stress

$$v_{ce} = v_c \times \frac{2d}{a_v} = 0.72 \times 2 \times \frac{920}{1000} = 1.32 \text{ N/mm}^2 > v_u \text{ (Satisfactory)}.$$

Therefore, theoretically no shear reinforcement is required.

Provide: T16 stirrups @ 500 mm, 4 legged (area of shear steel provided = 804 mm^2)

Distribution bars: Provide T16 @ 125 c/c each face (see Figures 8.11 and 8.12)

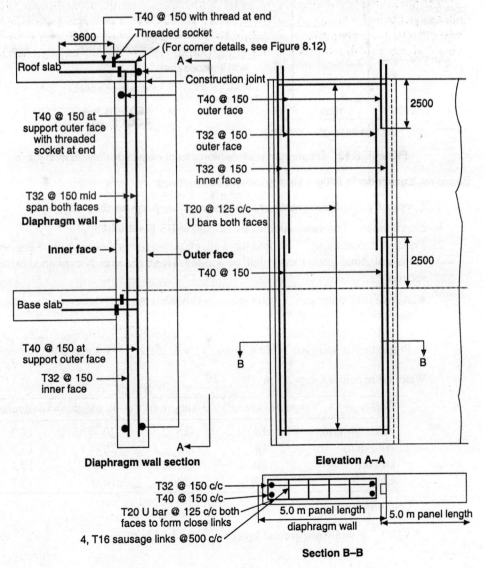

FIGURE 8.11 Diaphragm wall; reinforcement details.

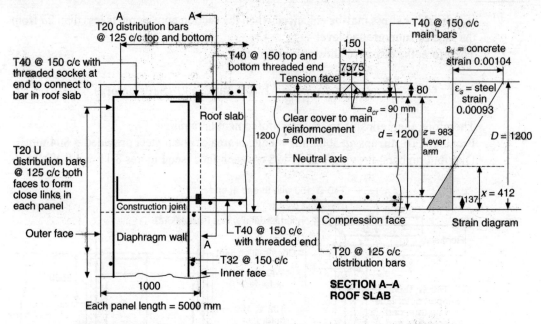

FIGURE 8.12 Diaphragm wall; reinforcement details at construction joints.

Based on Eurocode 7: 2004 (in top down construction)

Case 1: Temporary condition (without any intermediate prop on the wall):

1. *Conditions:* The same conditions as used in BS 8004 will apply.
2. *Pressure calculations:* Behind the wall, effective stress theory shall be applied. In front of the wall, total stress theory shall be applied. These are already explained in the previous section.

   • Active (soil pressures + water pressures) behind the wall (based on the effective stress analysis):

   Properties of soil (see Table 8.1) and $\gamma_{\phi'} = 1.25$; $\gamma_{C_u} = 1.4$ and $\delta = \dfrac{2}{3} \times \dfrac{\phi'}{\gamma_{\phi'}}$

Water table below GL = 2.5 m

Soil type	density (kN/m³)	ϕ' (degree)	$\phi'/\gamma_{\phi'}$ (degree)	δ (degree)	K_a
Made ground	18	25	20	13.3	0.43
Alluvium	18	25	20	13.3	0.43
Gravel	20	36	28.8	19.2	0.30
Clay	19	20	16.0	10.7	0.50

London clay:

$$C_u/\gamma_{C_u} \text{ at 9 m from ground level} = \frac{75}{1.4} = 53.6 \text{ kN/m}^2$$

$$\text{at 13 m from ground level} = \frac{124}{1.4} = 88.6 \text{ kN/m}^2$$

at 18.5 m from ground level $= \dfrac{192}{1.4} = 137 \text{ kN/m}^2$

where, ϕ' and C_u are characteristic soil properties

$$\left(\frac{\phi'}{\gamma_{\phi'}}\right) = \phi'_d \text{ and } \left(\frac{C_u}{\gamma_{C_u}}\right) = C_{ud}$$

are the design values of ϕ' and C_u

Due to soil pressure at:
2.5 m below GL,

$$p_{a,\,2.5} = K_a \times \gamma' \times z_1 = 0.43 \times 18 \times 2.5 = 19 \text{ kN/m}^2$$

4 m below GL,

$$p_{a,\,4} = K_a \times \gamma' \times (z_4 - z_{2.5}) + p_{a,\,2.5} = 0.43 \times 8 \times 1.5 + 19 = 24 \text{ kN/m}^2$$

7 m below GL,

$$p_{a,\,7} = 0.3 \times 8 \times 3 + 24 = 30 \text{ kN/m}^2$$

9 m in clay below GL,

$$p_{a,\,9} = 0.5 \times (18 \times 2.5 + 8 \times 1.5 + 8 \times 3 + 10 \times 2) = 51 \text{ kN/m}^2$$

18.5 m in clay below GL,

$$p_{a,\,18.5} = p_{a,\,9} + K_a \times \gamma' \times (z_{18.5} - z_9) = 51 + 0.5 \times 9 \times 9.5 = 94 \text{ kN/m}^2$$

Due to surcharge :10 kN/m^2,

$$p_s = K_a \times 10 = \frac{\text{Ave.}\,(0.5 + 0.43 \times 2 + 0.3)}{4 \times 10} = 4 \text{ kN/m}^2$$

Due to water pressure: At 18.5 m depth

$$p_{w,\,18.5} = (18.5 - 2.5) \times 10 = 160 \text{ kN/m}^2 \qquad \text{[see Figure 8.5 (a)]}$$

- Passive soil pressure in front of wall: Assumed 30% reduced undrained shear strength of London clay due to the immediate effect of stress relief just after the excavation. Due to the softening effect of the top portion of clay just after excavation, the shear strength of clay is assumed equal to zero at the top of excavation, and at about 1 m depth below formation level the clay regains its shear strength to its full value. Using the expression for the pressure coefficient for cohesion,

$$K_{pc} = 2 \times \left(1 + \frac{c_w}{C_u}\right)^{0.5}$$

where c_w = wall adhesion (assuming $c_w = 0$; $K_{pc} = 2.0$)

So, at 13 m below ground level,

$$C_{u,\,1} = 0$$

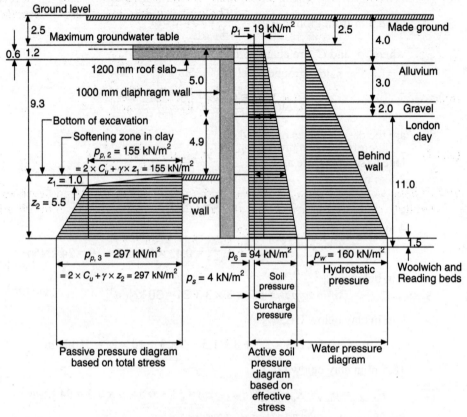

Mixed total and effective stress analysis of diaphragm
wall without prop in temporary condition
Case 1
(In accordance with Eurocode 7)

Notes: Refer Eurocode 7: 2004

1. Effective stress analysis behind the wall: Active soil pressure at a depth $z_a = p_a = K_a \times \gamma' \times z_a$

2. Total stress analysis in front of wall: Passive soil pressure at a depth $z_p = p_p = 2 \times \dfrac{C_u}{\gamma_{C_u}} \times \gamma \times z_p$

   (where γ_{C_u} = Partial soil parameter factor = 1.4),

where

$$K_a = \frac{1 - \sin\left(\dfrac{\phi'}{\gamma_{\phi'}}\right)}{1 + \sin\left(\dfrac{\phi'}{\gamma_{\phi'}}\right)}$$

(where, $\gamma_{\phi'}$ = Partial soil parameter factor = 1.25)
γ' = Effective soil density; γ = bulk density; z_a = depth below GL; z_p = depth below formation level.

FIGURE 8.5(a)   Soil and water pressure diagrams on diaphragm wall.

At 14 m below ground level,

$$C_{u,2} = 0.7 \times \frac{C_{u,14}}{\gamma_{C_u}} = 0.7 \times \frac{136}{1.4} = 68 \text{ kN/m}^2$$

At 18.5 m below ground level,

$$C_{u,3} = 0.7 \times \frac{C_{u,18.5}}{\gamma_{C_u}} = 0.7 \times \frac{192}{1.4} = 96 \text{ kN/m}^2$$

Therefore, passive pressure at 13 m below ground level,

$$p_{p,1} = 0 \text{ kN/m}^2$$

Passive pressure at 14 m below ground level,

$$p_{p,2} = C_{u,2} \times K_{pc} + \gamma \times z = 68 \times 2 + 19 \times 1 = 155 \text{ kN/m}^2$$

Passive pressure at 18.5 m below ground level,

$$p_{p,3} = C_{u,3} \times K_{pc} + \gamma \times z = 96 \times 2 + 19 \times 5.5 = 297 \text{ kN/m}^2 \qquad \text{[see Figure 8.5(a)]}$$

3. *Stability of diaphragm wall:* Assume the only prop of the wall is the roof slab, already cast, about which the wall rotate due to the actions of active and passive pressures on the vertical sides of wall. Take moments of all the active pressures on the wall about the centre of top roof slab.

$$M_{active} = 19 \times 16 \times 15.4 + \frac{1}{2} \times 75 \times 16 \times \frac{2}{3} \times 15.4 + 4 \times 16 \times \frac{15.4}{2}$$

$$+ \frac{1}{2} \times 160 \times 16 \times \frac{2}{3} \times 15.4 = 24572 \text{ kN m}$$

$$M_{passive} = \frac{1}{2} \times 155 \times 13.67 + 4.5 \times 155 \times 16.25$$

$$+ \frac{1}{2} \times 4.5 \times 122 \times 17 = 17060 \text{ kN m}$$

From the above, we conclude that the moment created by active pressures is much higher than the moment resisted by the passive pressures. The resulting effect is that the wall moves inwards and the wall may collapse. Thus, we cannot excavate upto the formation level without the intermediate prop to the wall.

Case 2: *Temporary condition (with intermediate prop to the wall):* [Refer to Figure 8.6(a)]

1. *The following conditions shall apply:*
   - The top slab is cast.
   - The excavation is completed upto the formation level with the installation of prop halfway between the roof slab and the formation level.
   - The pumping has stopped temporarily and the water table has risen upto the maximum level of 2.5 m below ground level.
   - The base slab is waiting to be cast within approximately 7 days after the excavation is complete.

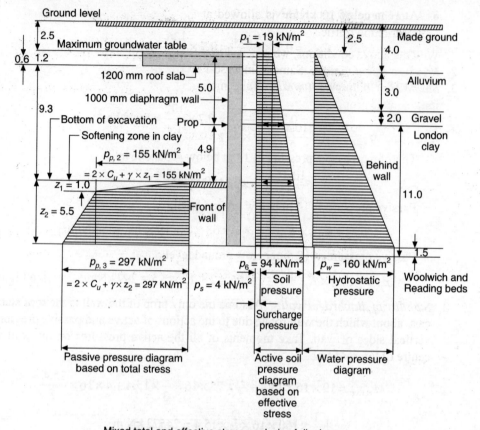

Mixed total and effective stress analysis of diaphragm
wall without prop in temporary condition
Case 2 Short-term
Temporary prop, base slab not cast (In accordance with Eurocode 7)

Notes: Refer Eurocode 7: 2004

1. Effective stress analysis behind the wall: Active soil pressure at a depth $z_a = p_a = K_a \times \gamma' \times z_a$

2. Total stress analysis in front of wall: Passive soil pressure at a depth $z_p = p_p = 2 \times \dfrac{C_u}{\gamma_{C_u}} \times \gamma \times z_p$

(where γ_{C_u} = Partial soil parameter factor = 1.4)

where

$$K_a = \frac{1 - \sin\left(\dfrac{\phi'}{\gamma_{\phi'}}\right)}{1 + \sin\left(\dfrac{\phi'}{\gamma_{\phi'}}\right)}$$

(where, $\gamma_{\phi'}$ = Partial soil parameter factor = 1.25)
γ' = effective soil density; γ = bulk density; z_a = depth below GL; z_p = depth below formation level.

FIGURE 8.6(a) Soil and water pressure diagrams on diaphragm wall.

- A surcharge of 10 kN/m^2 is allowed at the ground level to cater for the expected construction traffic.

With the above conditions, we proceed to calculate the pressures on the wall.

2. *Pressure calculations:*   Same as in Case 1 [see Figure 8.5(a)]
3. *Stability of diaphragm wall:*   Take moments of all the active pressures about the intermediate prop,

$$M_{active} = 4 \times \frac{10.4^2}{2} + \frac{1}{2} \times 49 \times 10.4^2 \times \frac{2}{3} + 4 \times \frac{10.4^2}{2} \text{ (soil)}$$

$$+ 56 \times \frac{10.4^2}{2} + \frac{1}{2} \times 104 \times 10.4^2 \times \frac{2}{3} \text{ (water)}$$

$$= (4417 + 6778) = 11195 \text{ kN m}$$

Take moments of all passive pressures about the intermediate prop

$$M_{passive} = \frac{1}{2} \times 155 \times 5.57 + 175 \times 4.5 \times 9.15 + \frac{1}{2} \times 122 \times 4.5 \times 7.9 = 9806 \text{ kN m}$$

Referring to CIRIA Report 104 (Table 5), in calculating ultimate design moments by strength factor method in temporary condition:

- In effective stress analysis on active pressures: The moments due to soil and water pressures to be multiplied by a factor, $\gamma_f = 1.5$ and 1.2, respectively.
- In total stress analysis on passive pressures: The moments due to soil pressures to be multiplied by a factor $\gamma_f = 1.5$.

Therefore, ultimate design moment due to active pressure,

$$M_{u,\ active} = 1.5 \times 4417 + 1.2 \times 6778 = 14759 \text{ kN m}$$

and ultimate design moment due to passive pressure,

$$M_{u,\ passive} = 1.5 \times 9806 = 14709 \text{ kN m}$$

Therefore, net ultimate moment at prop = 14759 − 14709 = 50 kN m
Safe load on prop:

- Due to active pressure

$$p_a = \frac{1}{2} \times 10.4 \times (45 + 94) + 19 \times \frac{5}{2} + \frac{1}{2} \times 26 \times 5 \times \frac{2}{3} + 4 \times \left(10.4 + \frac{5}{2}\right)$$

$$+ \frac{1}{2} \times 10.4 \times (56 + 160) + \frac{1}{2} \times 56 \times 5 \times \frac{2}{3} = 2081 \text{ kN}$$

- Due to passive pressure

$$p_p = \frac{1}{2} \times 155 \times 95.5 + 4.5 + \frac{1}{2} \times 122 \times 4.5 = 1050 \text{ kN}$$

Therefore, net safe load on prop

$$p = 2081 - 1050 = 1031 \text{ k N [see Figure 8.5(a)]}$$

Case 3: Long-term temporary condition: In this, the excavation is complete, but due to unavoidable conditions the base slab is left not cast for a long time. As this case occurs very rarely, we may omit this condition.

Case 4: Permanent condition when the base slab is constructed:

1. *Conditions:* The following conditions may apply:

   - The base slab is constructed.
   - The intermediate prop has been removed.
   - 2.5 m of soil overburden has been placed over the roof.
   - The developer load of 50 kN/m² has been considered.
   - The pumping system to keep the water table down has been withdrawn.
   - The water table has reached to the maximum 2.5 m below ground level.
   - The effective stress analysis on both sides of the wall shall be carried out with the assumption that the strength of clay has been reduced to cohesion intercept in terms of effective stress (c') from the undrained shear strength (C_u) in front of the wall to the release of more water pressure.
   - In active pressure calculations behind the wall, the coefficient of earth pressure (K_o) shall be considered.
   - In passive pressure calculations in front of the wall, the coefficient of earth pressure (K_p) shall be considered.
   - It is assumed that the active pressure reaches the maximum value at the centre of base slab and then gradually reduces to zero at the toe of the wall.
   - Below the formation level, the water pressure behind the wall shall be considered to be of constant value because the water pressure in front of the wall and below the formation level balances the extra increase of water pressure behind the wall.
   - The central load bearing wall has been constructed to take up the loads from the roof slab.
   - The roof slab is assumed to be continuous over the central wall and the ends of roof slab is assumed to be fixed to the diaphragm wall.

2. *Pressure calculations:* Refer to Figure 8.8(a).

   - Soil pressures behind the wall: In calculating the value of K_o:

   In made ground and Alluvium:

$$K_o = 1 - \sin\left(\frac{\phi'}{\gamma_{\phi'}}\right) = 1 - \sin\left(\frac{25}{1.25}\right) = 0.65$$

   In gravel:

$$K_o = 1 - \sin\left(\frac{\phi'}{\gamma_{\phi'}}\right) = 1 - \sin\left(\frac{35}{1.25}\right) = 0.53$$

   In clay:

$$K_o = 1 - \sin\left(\frac{\phi'}{\gamma_{\phi'}}\right) = 1 - \sin\left(\frac{20}{1.25}\right) = 0.72$$

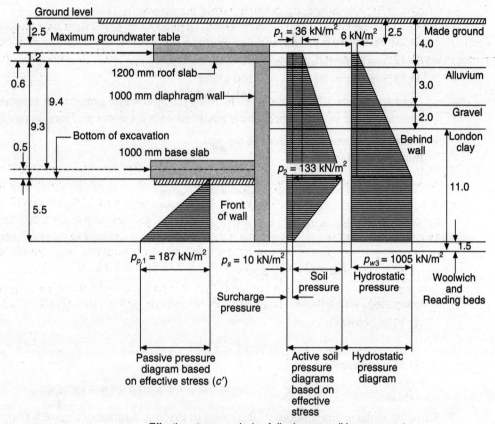

FIGURE 8.8(a) Soil and water pressure diagrams on diaphragm wall.

But in London clay $K_o = 1.0$ (assumed)

At 3.1 m (centre of roof slab) below GL,

$$p_{a,\,3.1} = K_o \times \gamma' \times z_1 = 0.65 \times 18 \times 3.1 = 36 \text{ kN/m}^3$$

At 12.5 m (centre of base slab) below GL,

$$p_{a,\,12.5} = K_o \times \Sigma \gamma' \times z$$

$$= 1 \times (18 \times 2.5 + 8 \times 4.5 + 10 \times 2 + 9 \times 3.5) = 133 \text{ kN/m}^2$$

At 18.5 m below GL = 0,

(assumed that the soil pressure reduces to zero at toe of wall)

- Soil pressures behind the wall due to surcharge of 10 kN/m²

  At 18.5 m below GL,

  $$p_{s,\,18.5} = K_o \times s_w = 1 \times 10 = 10 \text{ kN/m}^2$$

- Water pressures behind the wall:

  At 3.1 m below GL, $p_{w,3.1} = \gamma_w \times z_{3.1} = 10 \times 0.6 = 6$ kN/m^2

  At 12.5 m below GL, $p_{w,12.5} = 10 \times 10 = 100$ kN/m^2

  At 18.5 m below GL, $p_{w,18.5} = 100$ kN/m^2

  (between levels 12.5 m and 18.5 m from GL, the water pressure is assumed to be constant as the increased pressure is balanced with the water pressure on passive side)

- Passive soil pressures in front of the wall:

  In clay design value of ϕ'

  $$\phi'_d = \frac{\phi'}{\gamma_{\phi'}} = \frac{20}{1.25} = 16°$$

  $K_p = 2.5$ (see Figure 40 of CIRIA Report 104)

  $$K_{pc} = 2\left[K_p \times \left(1 + \frac{c_w}{c'}\right)\right]^{0.5} = 2\,(2.5)^{0.5} = 3.16$$

  (assuming, wall adhesion, $c_w = 0$)

  At 13 m below GL,

  $$p_{p,13} = 0 \text{ kN/m}^2$$

  At 18.5 m below GL,

  $$p_{p,18.5} = K_p \times \gamma' \times z + K_{pc} \times c' = 2.5 \times 9 \times 5.5 + 3.16 \times 20 = 187 \text{ kN/m}^2$$

3. *Ultimate moment calculations:* Referring to loading diagram of Figure 8.8(a): Assume that the diaphragm wall is fixed at the roof slab at A and continuous over the base slab at B. Assume that the partial safety factors γ_f for soil pressure and water pressure = 1.5 (see Table A.1 of Eurocode).

   Consider the actions of active and passive soil pressures and the water pressures.

   Cantilever moment M_{fu} for BC

$$1.5 \times \left[\frac{1}{2} \times 133 \times 6 \times \frac{6}{3} + 10 \times 6 \times \frac{6}{2} + 100 \times 6 \times \frac{6}{2} - \frac{1}{2} \times 187 \times 6 \times \frac{2}{3} \times 6\right] = 784 \text{ kN m}$$

$$M_{fu,\,AB} \text{ at A} = 1.5\left[46 \times \frac{9.4^2}{12} + \frac{1}{2} \times 97 \times 9.4 \times 0.067 \times 9.4 + \frac{1}{2} \times 94 \times 9.4\right.$$

$$\times 0.067 \times 9.4 + \frac{9.4^2}{2}\right] + 1.5 \times \frac{1}{2}\left[46 \times \frac{9.4^2}{12} + \frac{1}{2} \times 97 \times 9.4\right.$$

$$\times 0.1 \times 9.4 + \frac{1}{2} \times 94 \times 9.4 \times 9.4 \times 0.1 + 6 \times \frac{9.4^2}{2}\right]$$

$$= 1754 + 1086 = 2840 \text{ kN m}$$

With the above fixed end moments, moment distribution was carried out.
Distribution factor for member BA = 1 [see Figure 8.10(a)].

After moment distribution,

Final moment at A, M_{ua} = 2448 kNm

Final moment at C, M_{ub} = 784 kNm

Final moment at mid span

$$M_{bc} = 1.5\left[46 \times \frac{9.4^2}{8} + \frac{1}{2} \times 97 \times 9.4 \times \frac{9.4}{7.81} + 6 \times \frac{9.4^2}{8} + \frac{1}{2} \times 94 \times 9.4 \times \frac{9.4}{7.81}\right]$$

$$- \left(\frac{2448 + 784}{2}\right)$$

$$= -2482 - 1616 = 866 \text{ kN m}$$

Final ultimate moment diagram is drawn as shown in Figure 8.10(a)

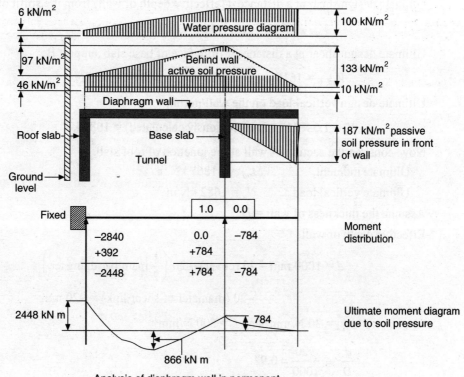

Analysis of diaphragm wall in permanent
condition with soil pressures
(Based on Eurocode 7)

FIGURE 8.10(a)   Ultimate moment diagram; Eurocode 7.

4. *Design of depth and reinforcement:*   Ultimate reaction at A (centre of roof slab),

$$R_a = 1.5\left[46 \times \frac{9.4}{2} + \frac{1}{2} \times 9.4 \times \frac{97}{3} + 6 \times \frac{9.4}{2} + \frac{1}{2} \times 9.4 \times \frac{9.4}{3}\right] + \left(2448 - \frac{784}{9.4}\right) = 992 \text{ kN}$$

Ultimate reaction at B (centre of base slab)

$$R_b = 1.5\left[46 \times \frac{9.4}{2} + \frac{1}{2} \times 9.4 \times 97 \times \frac{2}{3} + 6 \times \frac{9.4}{2} + \frac{1}{2} \times 9.4 \times 94 \times \frac{2}{3} + 10 \times 6 + \frac{1}{28} \times\right.$$

$$\left. 133 \times 6 + 100 \times 6 - \frac{1}{2} \times 6 \times 187\right] - \left(\frac{2448 - 784}{9.4}\right) = 1616 \text{ kN}$$

Ultimate design moment at the face of soffit of roof slab

$$M_{ud} = 992 \times 0.6 - 2448 - 1.5 \times (46 + 6) \times 0.6 \times \frac{0.6}{2} = -1867 \text{ kN m}$$

Ultimate design shear at a distance d (effective depth of wall) from the soffit of roof slab

$$V_{ud, A} = 992 - 1.5 \times (46 + 6) \times 1.5 = 875 \text{ kN}$$

Ultimate design shear at a distance d from face of base slab support B

$$V_{ud, B} = 1616 - 1.5 \times 1.4 \times (143 + 100) = 1106 \text{ kN}$$

Ultimate design vertical load on the wall/m run,

$$N_u = 1.5 \times 1121 \text{ kN (previously calculated)} = 1682 \text{ kN}$$

Now, consider the section of wall at the junction of roof slab.

Ultimate moment, $M_{ud} = -1867 \text{ kN m}$

Ultimate vertical load, $N_u = 1682 \text{ kN m}$

Assume the thickness of wall $= D$

Effective depth of wall

$$d = 1000 \text{ mm} - 40 \text{ (cover)} - 20 \left(\frac{1}{2} \text{ main bar diameter}\right)$$

$$-20 \text{ (diameter of shear link)} = 920 \text{ mm}$$

$f_{ck} = 30 \text{ N/mm}^2 \text{ and } f_y = 500 \text{ N/mm}^2$

$$\frac{d}{D} = \frac{920}{1000} = 0.92$$

$$\frac{N_u}{(b \times D \times f_{ck})} = \frac{1682 \times 10^3}{(1000 \times 1000 \times 30)} = 0.06$$

$$\frac{M_u}{(b \times D^2 \times f_{ck})} = \frac{1867 \times 10^6}{(1000 \times 1000^3 \times 30)} = 0.06$$

Referring to Chart no. 9 of Eurocode 2: 2004:

$$A_s \times \frac{f_{yk}}{b_h \, f_{ck}} = 0.1$$

$$A_s = 0.1 \times 1000 \times 1000 \times \frac{30}{500} = 6000 \text{ mm}^2$$

On each face $= \dfrac{6000}{2} = 3000 \text{ mm}^2$

Adopt: T40 @ 150 c/c soil face (area provided = 8378 mm²) (see Figure 8.11).

Next, consider the section at mid span:

$M_u = 866$ kN m

$N_u = 1682$ kN m

$$\frac{N_u}{(b \times D \times f_{ck})} = 0.06$$

$$\frac{M_u}{(b \times D^2 \times f_{ck})} = \frac{866 \times 10^6}{(1000 \times 1000^2 \times 30)} = 0.05$$

Referring to Chart 9 of Eurocode 7:

$$A_s = 0.05 \times 1000 \times 1000 \times \frac{30}{500} = 3000 \text{ mm}^2$$

On each face $\dfrac{3000}{2} = 1500 \text{ mm}^2$

Adopt: T32 @ 150 c/c inside tunnel face (area provided = 5362 mm²)

5. *Check for shear:* Ultimate shear at a distance d from face of base slab at support B,

$$V_u = 1106 \text{ kN}$$

Shear stress,

$$v_u = \frac{V_u}{(0.9 \times b \times d)} = \frac{1106 \times 10^3}{(0.9 \times 1000 \times 920)} = 1.34 \text{ N/mm}^2 < 3.64 \text{ N/mm}^2$$

$$\rho = \frac{A_s}{(b \times d)} = \frac{5362}{(1000 \times 920)} = 0.0058$$

Allowable shear stress,

$$v_{rd} = 0.12 \times k \times (100 \times \rho \times f_{ck})^{0.33}$$

$$= 0.12 \times 1.47 \times (100 \times 0.0058 \times 30)^{0.33} = 0.45 < v_u$$

$$\left[\text{where } k = 1 + \left(\frac{200}{d}\right)^{0.5} = 1 + \left(\frac{200}{920}\right)^{0.5} = 1.47 \right]$$

So, shear reinforcement is required.
Using a spacing $s = 125$ mm,
area of shear reinforcement required

$$A_s = v_u \times b_w \times \frac{s}{(0.9 \times f_{ywd})} = 1.34 \times 1000 \times \frac{125}{0.9 \times 500} = 372 \text{ mm}^2 = 372 \text{ mm}^2$$

Use, T16 shear links @ 125 c/c 4 legged/m length, A_s provided $= 804 \text{ mm}^2 > 372 \text{ mm}^2$ (see Figure 8.11).

REFERENCES

[8.1]   *Proceedings of the Conference on Diaphragm Walls and Anchorages*, Institution of Civil Engineers, London, 1974.

[8.2]   Tomlinson, M.J., *Foundation Design and Construction*, Pitman Books Ltd., London, 1985.

[8.3]   *Construction Industry Research and Information Association (CIRIA)* publication report 104.

[8.4]   BS 8004: 1986: British Standard Code of Practice for Foundations.

[8.5]   Eurocode 7: 2004: Geotechnical design. Part 1: General rules.

[8.6]   BS 8110: 1997: Structural use of concrete. Part 1. Code of practice for design and construction.

Chapter 9

Sheet Piling Foundation

9.0 DESCRIPTION

The sheet piling foundation is the substructure that retains soil, and is subjected to soil pressure. The sheet piling is used in the construction of temporary and permanent works. Steel sheet piling is generally applied in both types of constructions. The sheet piling may act as cantilever wall and also as anchored bulkhead when the wall is held near the top by a tie-bar, anchored back into the stable volume of soil behind the plane of rapture. The anchored sheet-pile wall is only used when the retained material height exceeds 6 m.

9.1 TYPES OF EMBEDMENT SOIL

(a) *Cohesionless soils:*   Granular materials such as sand, gravel, hardcore, rockfilling, etc.
(b) *Cohesive soils:*   Clays and silts.
(c) *Mixed soils:*   Combinations of groups (a) and (b).

9.2 EARTH PRESSURE CALCULATIONS AGAINST A SHEET PILING WALL

The earth pressures to a vertical wall with ground surfaces horizontal are calculated as follows:
Active pressure

$$p_a = \gamma \times z \times \tan^2\left(45 - \frac{\phi}{2}\right) - 2 \times C_u \times \tan\left(45 - \frac{\phi}{2}\right) \qquad (9.1)$$

Passive pressure

$$p_p = \gamma \times z \times \tan^2\left(45 + \frac{\phi}{2}\right) + 2 \times C_u \times \tan\left(45 + \frac{\phi}{2}\right) \qquad (9.2)$$

where,

ϕ = angle of internal friction of soil in degrees

γ_b = bulk density of soil in kN/m^3

γ_w = water density in kN/m^2 = 10 kN/m^3

$\gamma = (\gamma_b - \gamma_w)$ = submersed density of soil

C_u = cohesion of soil (undrained shear strength of clay)

z = height of soil above any level under consideration.

The terms $\tan^2\left(45 - \dfrac{\phi}{2}\right)$ and $\tan^2\left(45 + \dfrac{\phi}{2}\right)$ may be expressed as

K_a = coefficient of active earth pressure

K_p = coefficient of passive earth pressure.

Hence,

$$p_a = \gamma \times z \times K_a - 2 \times C_u \times \sqrt{K_a} \tag{9.3}$$

and

$$p_p = \gamma \times z \times K_p + 2 \times C_u \times \sqrt{K_p} \tag{9.4}$$

9.3 EARTH PRESSURE IN COHESIONLESS SOIL

Cohesionless soils are free-draining. So, the excess pore water pressures generated during construction dissipates quite quickly. Therefore, the 'effective' stress condition exists both in short- and long-term. Hence, ϕ' (angle of shearing resistance of soil in degrees) in effective stress parameter shall be used in all the calculations.

The effect of wall friction (δ) on active pressure in cohesionless soil is insignificant and may be ignored. Then, Eq. (9.3) (active earth pressure at a depth z)

$$p_a = \gamma \times z \times K_a \tag{9.5}$$

and Eq. (9.4) (passive earth pressure at a depth z)

$$p_p = \gamma \times z \times K_p \tag{9.6}$$

Thus, for a cohesionless soil with $\phi' = 35°$ and $K_a = 0.27$.
Therefore, active pressure

$$p_a = 0.27 \times \gamma \times z$$

The effect of wall friction (δ) on passive pressure shall be taken into account. The value of the coefficient of wall friction, $\tan \delta$, may be assumed to be equal to 1/2 of $\tan \phi$. It is sufficiently accurate enough to take $\delta = 1/2$ of ϕ (Refer CIRIA report 104) [9.1].

Thus, for a cohesionless soil having $\phi' = 35°$ and referring to Figure 40 of CIRIA report 104

$$K_a = 7.$$

Therefore, passive pressure

$$p_p = 7 \times \gamma \times z.$$

9.4 EARTH PRESSURE IN COHESIVE SOIL

The strength of cohesive soil changes significantly over a period of time due to the changes of pore water pressure caused by the construction of retaining wall. The initial undrained shear strength (C_u) defined in 'total stress' condition changes to 'effective stress' condition due to the changes in pore water pressure when the water from the pores of soil is gradually squeezed out over a period of time, thus reducing the undrained shear strength (C_u) to cohesion (c') but increasing the values of effective angle of internal friction (ϕ') of soil.

The pressures on the wall can be considered in terms of total stress. With the relevant soil strength parameter for $\phi' = 0$ and $K_a = K_p = 1$, Eqs. (9.3) and (9.4) are given as total stresses by:

$$p_a = \gamma \times z - 2 \times C_u \qquad (9.7)$$

$$p_p = \gamma \times z + 2 \times C_u \qquad (9.8)$$

9.5 EARTH PRESSURE IN COHESIVE AND MIXED SOILS

In Eqs. (9.3) and (9.4), if we replace the terms $2\sqrt{K_a}$ and $2\sqrt{K_p}$ by K_{ac} and K_{pc}, then the above equations become

$$p_a = \gamma \times z \times K_a - C_u \times K_{ac} \qquad (9.9)$$

$$p_p = \gamma \times z \times K_p + C_u \times K_{pc} \qquad (9.10)$$

In total stress analysis the effects of wall friction (δ) and adhesion (c_w) are taken into account. The following maximum values of wall adhesion may be used in practice:

In active zones: $c_w = 0.5\ C_u$ but not greater than 50 kN/m²

In passive zones: $c_w = 0.5\ C_u$ but not greater than 25 kN/m²

The value of C_w should be taken equal to zero in total stress analysis because of possibility of developing tension crack. The values of δ should be assumed as the following:

In active zones: $\delta = \dfrac{2}{3} \times \phi$

In passive zone: $\delta = \dfrac{1}{2} \times \phi'$

With different ratios of δ/ϕ', the corresponding values of coefficients K_a and K_p are obtained from the Figures 39 and 40 in CIRIA Report 104. The values of K_{ac} and K_{pc} are obtained from the following expressions:

In active zones, $K_{ac} = 2\sqrt{\left[K_a\left(1 + \dfrac{c_w}{C_u}\right)\right]} = 2\sqrt{K_a}$

In passive zones, $K_{ac} = 2\sqrt{\left[K_p\left(1 + \dfrac{c_w}{C_u}\right)\right]} = 2\sqrt{K_p}$

(Since $c_w = 0$ (assumed); and $c_w/C_u = 0$)

Then, the active pressure

$$p_a = \gamma \times z \times K_a - C_u \times K_{ac}$$

and passive pressure

$$p_p = \gamma \times z \times K_p + C_u \times K_{pc}$$

9.6 METHOD OF ANALYSIS

For permanent structures

The following methods may be followed:

1. *In normally consolidated clays:*   Analysis is normally carried out using total stress parameters. It should be checked with effective stress values.
2. *In overconsolidated clays:*   Effective stress analysis shall usually be carried out. But a check should be made with total stress analysis.

For temporary structures

If the structure lifespan is not more than 3 months, it is advisable to analyze the structure with total stress parameters, but with a lifespan more than 3 months, effective stress analysis should be carried out. Referring to CIRIA report 104 (design of retaining wall embedded in stiff clay), a mixed total and effective stress analysis is recommended.

9.7 ANALYSIS OF CANTILEVER SHEET PILING

Consider a cantilever sheet piling wall, as shown in Figure 9.1(a), to retain earth of depth z below ground. It is to analyze the minimum depth of embedment required to retain the earth. Let d be the embedment of wall below the excavation line. The whole active earth pressure behind the wall must be resisted by the development passive pressure in the soil in front of wall. Applying the static equilibrium conditions:

Σ forces acting on the member $= 0$

Σ moments acting on the member $= 0$

Figure 9.1(a) shows the distribution, by Rowe [9.2], of active and passive pressures on both sides of the wall assuming a uniform soil density γ and assuming no hydrostatic pressure.

So, the active earth pressure

$$p_a = K_a \times \gamma \times (z + d)$$

and the passive earth pressure

$$p_p = K_p \times \gamma \times d$$

Let

p_a = total active earth pressure acting at a height $(z + d)/3$ from toe of wall

p_p = total passive earth pressure acting at a height $d/3$ from toe of wall.

Consider that the wall sustains a very slight angular rotation about some point O at a distance y above the toe of the wall C. Passive resistances will be mobilized in front of the wall upto the level O and also behind the wall below this point.

In front of wall: Passive pressure

$$p_{p,1} = K_p \times \gamma \times (d - y)$$

and passive resistance

$$p_{p,1} = \frac{1}{2} \times p_{p,1} \times (d - y)$$

Behind the wall: Passive pressure

$$p_{p,2} = K_p \times \gamma \times (z + d)$$

and passive resistance

$$R_2 = P_{p,2} = \frac{1}{2} \times p_{p,2} \times (z + d) \qquad \text{[see Figure 9.1(b)]}$$

The minimum driving depth d for equilibrium can be determined by solving two equations simultaneously in which d and y are unknown. The first equation is formed as:

Algebraic sum of the active forces and passive forces on the wall = 0

and the second equation

Sum of moments of these active and passive forces about the toe = 0

It is laborious to solve these equations involving two unknowns. The solution can be simplified by assuming the passive reaction behind the wall to act as a concentrated force R_1 at the toe of wall [see Figure 9.1(c)].

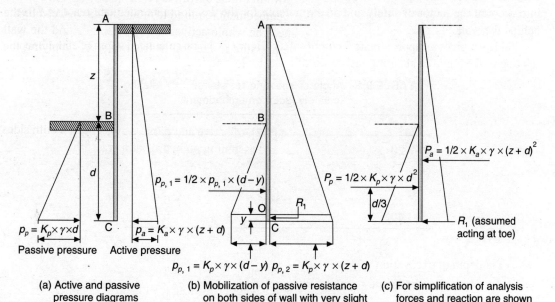

(a) Active and passive pressure diagrams

(b) Mobilization of passive resistance on both sides of wall with very slight angular rotation about point O

(c) For simplification of analysis forces and reaction are shown as above

FIGURE 9.1 Sheet piling foundation: Analysis of cantilever sheet piling.

Then, for equilibrium the moments of the active pressure on the right and the moments of the passive resistance about the point of action of R_2 must balance.

So,

$$P_a = K_a \times \gamma \times \frac{1}{2} \times (z + d)^2$$

and

$$P_p = K_p \times \gamma \times \frac{1}{2} \times d^2$$

Taking moments about toe (R_2)

$$P_p \times \frac{d}{3} - P_a \frac{(z + d)}{3} = 0 \tag{9.11}$$

Substituting the value of P_a and P_p in Eq. (9.11), we get

$$K_p \times \gamma \times \frac{1}{2} \times d^2 \times \frac{d}{3} - K_a \times \gamma \times \frac{1}{2} \times (z + d)^2 \frac{(z + d)}{3} = 0$$

or

$$K_p \times d^3 - K_a \times (z + d)^3 = 0$$

or

$$\frac{d}{(z + d)} = \left(\frac{K_a}{K_p} \right)^{1/3} \tag{9.12}$$

With known values of z and K_a and K_p for soil, the solution of equation will give the minimum depth of embedment required. The depth determined should be increased by at least 20% to take into account the factor of safety and an extra depth for the development adequate reactive force behind the wall.

Table 9.1 gives an approximate factor of safety (Henry [9.3]) on calculated depth of embedment relating to the angle of shearing resistance of cohesionless soil.

TABLE 9.1   Angle of shearing resistance (ϕ') relating to safety factor on embedment

ϕ'	d/z
20	2
25	1.5
30	1.2
35	0.9
40	0.7

where

     z = depth of excavation

     d = depth of embedment.

Note: The above values were obtained from Henry [9.3].

In factor of embedment method: A factor of safety 1.5 in permanent works and 1.2 in temporary works is recommended (CIRIA report 104).

9.8   DESIGN EXAMPLE 1

The sheet piling wall is to retain 5 m of earth above the excavation level. Determine the minimum depth of embedment in soil with a safety factor 1.5 in permanent construction. Design the section of steel sheet piling. The geotechnical soil parameters are as follows:

γ_b = 20 kN/m^3; ϕ' = 30°; δ = 2/3 ϕ' (1/2 ϕ' on active and passive sides, respectively)

Using Figures 39 and 40 of CIRIA report 104

K_a = 0.28 and K_p = 4.6 [Hydrostatic pressure (assumed) = 0]

9.8.1   To Determine the Depth of Embedment and to Design the Section

Based on BS code 8004:1986 [9.4]

To determine the depth of embedment: Referring to Eq. (9.12)

Let d = Minimum depth of embedment and z = 5 m
Then,

$$\frac{d}{(z+d)} = \left(\frac{K_a}{K_p}\right)^{1/3} = \left(\frac{0.28}{4.6}\right)^{1/3} = 0.4$$

$$\left[\left(\frac{D}{5+d}\right) = 0.4; \text{ therefore, } d = 3.33 \text{ with factor of safety} = 1.5\right]$$

Hence, design depth of embedment

$$d = 3.33 \times 1.5 = 5.0 \text{ m} \qquad [\text{see Figure 9.2(a)}]$$

To calculate the maximum bending moment in the sheet piling: Maximum bending moment in the member will occur where the shear force is zero. Let the maximum BM occur at a depth d_0 from the excavation (formation) level
Active pressure

$$p_a = K_a \times \gamma \times (5 + d_0) = 0.28 \times 20 \times (5 + d_0) = 5.6 \times (5 + d_0)$$

Active force

$$P_a = \frac{1}{2} \times p_a \times (5 + d_0) = 2.8 \times (5 + d_0)^2$$

Passive pressure,

$$p_p = K_p \times \gamma \times d_0 = 4.6 \times 20 \times d_0 = 92 \times d_0$$

Passive force

$$P_p = \frac{1}{2} \times p_p \times d_0 = 46 \times d_0^2$$

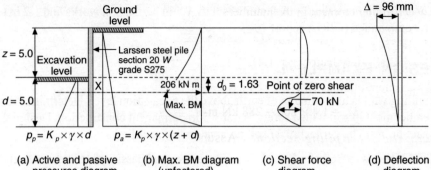

(a) Active and passive pressures diagram

(b) Max. BM diagram (unfactored)

(c) Shear force diagram (unfactored)

(d) Deflection diagram

Geotechnical soil data:
Cohesionless soil: $\phi' = 30°$
$\delta = 2/3 \ \phi'$; ϕ and $1/2\phi'$ for active and passive sides, respectively.
Groundwater table is below formation level.
Factor of embedment: 1.5 for permanent works
Partial safety factor for ULS method: 1.4

FIGURE 9.2 Showing pressure, BM, SF and deflection diagrams of sheet piling foundation: Design of a cantilever sheet piling to retain 5 m earth.

For maximum BM

$$P_a - P_p = 0$$

$$2.8 \times (5 + d_0)^2 = 46 \times d_0^2$$

$$\left[\frac{(5 + d_0)}{d_0}\right]^2 = \frac{46}{2.8}$$

$$\left[\frac{(5 + d_0)}{d_0}\right] = \sqrt{\left(\frac{46}{2.8}\right)} = 4.05$$

$$(5 + d_0) = 4.05 \times d_0$$

$$5 + d_0 - 4.05 \times d_0 = 0$$

Therefore,

$$d_0 = \frac{5}{3.05} = 1.63 \text{ m}$$

Moment due to active pressure about X

$$M_a = P_a \times \frac{(5 + 1.63)}{3} = 2.8 \times \frac{(5 + 1.63)^3}{3} = 272 \text{ kN m}$$

Moment due to passive pressure about X

$$M_p = P_p \times \frac{1.63}{3} = 46 \times \frac{1.63^3}{3} = 66 \text{ kN m}$$

Net maximum bending moment in the member

$$M_{net} = (272 - 66) = 206 \text{ kN m}$$

(Assuming a partial safety factor, $\gamma_f = 1.4$)

Therefore, maximum ultimate BM

$$M_u = 1.4 \times 206 = 288 \text{ kN m} \qquad [\text{see Figure 9.2(b)}]$$

To calculate the sheet piling section: Assuming a steel grade S275, design strength $p_y = 275 \text{ N/m}^2$

$$Z_{reqd} = 288 \times \frac{10^6}{\dfrac{275}{10^3}} = 1047 \text{ cm}^3$$

Try Larssen steel piling section 16 W, $Z = 1601 \text{ cm}^3/\text{m} > Z_{reqd}$
Hence, adopt: higher Larssen steel piling section 20 W, 10 m long, grade S275 to limit the deflection to the allowable value as will be shown in the deflection calculations later on.
To check for shear: Consider a section 3.3 m below formation level. Since at any section the passive resistance must be equal to active pressure for equilibrium, so total active force for 10 m depthis

$$= \frac{1}{2} \times p_a \times 10 = \frac{1}{2} \times 56 \times 10 = 280 \text{ kN}$$

The passive resistance to be developed for equilibrium = 280 kN
Let p_p = passive pressure at 5 m below formation level.
Assume maximum shear occurs at a depth of 3.3 m below formation level.
Passive pressure at 5 m depth below formation level

$$p_p = 280 \times \frac{2}{5} = 112 \text{ kN/m}^2$$

Passive pressure at 3.3 m depth below formation level

$$p_{p1} = 112 \times \frac{3.3}{5} = 74 \text{ kN/m}^2$$

Active pressure at 10 m depth

$$p_a = 56 \text{ kN/m}^2$$

Active pressure at 8.3 m depth,

$$p_{a1} = 56 \times \frac{8.3}{10} = 46.5 \text{ kN/m}^2$$

Therefore, net shear at 3.3 m depth below formation level

$$V_a = \frac{1}{2} \times 1.7 \times (74 + 112) - \frac{1}{2} \times 1.7 \times (47 + 56) = 70 \text{ kN}$$

With a partial safety factor = 1.4
Maximum ultimate shear,

$$V_u = 1.4 \times 70 = 98 \text{ kN}$$

With selected piling section web area = 2993 mm², shear stress

$$v_u = 98 \times \frac{10^3}{2993} = 33 \text{ N/mm}^2$$

Allowable shear stress = $0.6 \times p_y$ = 0.6×275 = 165 N/mm² $\gg v_u$ **(Satisfactory)** [see Figure 9.2(c)].

To check for deflection: Active pressure at a depth 10 m below GL

$$p_a = K_a \times \gamma \times (z + d) = 0.28 \times 20 \times 10 = 56 \text{ kN/m}^2$$

Total force due to active pressure

$$P_a = \frac{1}{2} \times p_a \times (z + d) = \frac{1}{2} \times 56 \times 10 = 280 \text{ kN}$$

Passive pressure at a depth 5 m from formation level

$$p_p = \frac{1}{2} \times K_p \times \gamma \times d = \frac{4.6}{2} \times 20 \times 5 = 230 \text{ kN/m}^2$$

(the value of K_p is reduced to $\frac{1}{2} K_p$ to assume the flexibility of sheet piling)

Total passive force

$$\frac{1}{2} \times p_p \times d = \frac{1}{2} \times 230 \times 5 = 575 \text{ kN}$$

Deflection due to active force

$$\Delta a = \frac{P_a \times (z + d)^3}{(15 \times E \times I)} = \frac{280 \times 10^3 \times 10000^3}{(15 \times 205000 \times 27857 \times 10^4)} = 327 \text{ mm}$$

Deflection due to passive force

$$\Delta p = \frac{575 \times 10^3 \times 5000^3 \times \dfrac{1 + 5 \times 5}{4 \times 5}}{15 \times 205000 \times 27857 \times 10^4} = 189 \text{ mm}$$

Net deflection

$$\Delta = \Delta a - \Delta p = 327 - 189 = 138 \text{ mm}$$

Allowable deflection

$$\Delta a = \frac{L}{100} = 100 \text{ mm for permanent works} < \Delta$$

So, increase the sheet piling section to Larssen section 20 W, $I_x = 40180 \text{ cm}^4$

With increased section, deflection due to active force

$$\Delta a = \frac{280 \times 10^3 \times 10000^3}{(15 \times 205000 \times 40180 \times 10^4)} = 227 \text{ m}$$

Deflection due to passive force

$$\Delta p = \frac{189 \times 27857}{40180} = 131 \text{ mm}$$

Net deflection,

$$\Delta = (227 - 131) \text{ mm} = 96 \text{ mm} < \text{allowable} \qquad [\text{see Figure 9.2(d)}]$$

Therefore, adopt increased Larssen section 20 W.

Based on Eurocode 7: 2004 [9.5]

To determine the depth of embedment: Referring to Eq. (9.12)

$$\frac{d}{(z+d)} = \left(\frac{K_a}{K_p}\right)^{1/3}$$

where

d = design depth of embedment

z = height of embankment = 5.0 m.

Design value of effective angle of shearing resistance

$$\sin \phi'_d = \sin \frac{\phi'}{\gamma_{\phi'}} = \frac{30}{1.25} = 24°$$

(where $\gamma_{\phi'}$ = partial factor for soil parameter of ϕ' = 1.25).

Assuming, structure-ground interface friction angle, $\delta = 2/3 \times \sin \phi'_d$ behind the wall and $\delta = 1/2 \times \sin \phi'_d$ in front of wall, and referring to Figures 39 and 40 of CIRIA Report 104:

$$K_a = 0.36 \text{ and } K_p = 3.2$$

$$\frac{d}{(z+d)} = \left(\frac{0.36}{3.2}\right)^{1/3} = 0.49$$

$$\frac{d}{(5+d)} = 0.49$$

$$d = 0.49 \times (5+d) = 2.45 + 0.49 \, d$$

Therefore, $d = 4.8$ m.

The partial safety factor on soil parameter is considered in the above calculations. Only an extra depth for the development of adequate reactive force behind the wall may be added. So, increase the depth by about 20%.

Therefore, the design depth

$$d = 4.8 \times 1.2 = 5.76 \text{ m} \qquad \text{(say 6.0 m)}$$

Compared to the depth (5.0 m) derived from BS code 8004, we find that Eurocode 7 result gives higher depth (6.0 m).

9.9 ANALYSIS OF ANCHORED SHEET PILING WALL

In anchored sheet piling wall, the sheet pile is anchored near the top by a tie bar back into the stable ground beyond the line of rapture. In anchored sheet piling wall, the passive resistance does not play a major role in the stability of wall because of the anchoring of the sheet pile applying an opposite force against the active force. So, the depth of embedment of sheet pile is reduced. There are two methods of analyzing the anchored sheet piling wall as given in the following:

9.9.1 Methods of Support

Free earth support method: In this method, the wall is freely supported by anchorage force near the top and by the passive resistance of soil below ground level.

Fixed earth support method: In this method, the lower part of the wall is assumed to be fixed as in the case of cantilever wall. This method is more complex in analysis. So, we analyze the free earth support method.

9.9.2 Analysis of Anchored Sheet Piling Wall by Free Earth Method

Let ABCD be the anchored sheet piling wall (see Figure 9.3).
Assume,

Minimum depth of embedment	$= d$
Point of anchorage from GL	$= h$
Depth of excavation from GL	$= z$
Bulk density of soil	$= \gamma$ kN/m^3
Active pressure coefficient	$= K_a$
Passive pressure coefficient	$= K_p$

Then active force

$$P_a = \frac{1}{2} \times K_a \times \gamma \times (z + d)^2 \qquad \text{(acting at a depth 2/3 } (z + d) \text{ from GL)}$$

Passive force

$$P_p = \frac{1}{2} \times K_p \times \gamma \times d^2$$

Let the anchorage force $= T$ (acting at a depth h from GL)
Take moments about the anchorage force at B. Then,

$$P_p \left[\left(\frac{2}{3} \times d + z - h \right) \right] = P_a \left[\frac{2}{3} \times (z + d) - h \right]$$

$$= \frac{1}{2} \times K_p \times \gamma \times d^2 \times \left[\frac{2}{3}d + z - h\right] = \frac{1}{2} \times K_a \times \gamma \times (z+d)^2 \times \left[\frac{2}{3} \times (z+d-h)\right]$$

or

$$\frac{\left[\frac{2}{3} \times (z+d)^3 - h \times (z+d)^2\right]}{\left[\frac{2}{3} \times d^3 + z \times d^2 - h \times d^2\right]} = \frac{K_p}{K_a} \tag{9.13}$$

By solving this cubic equation by trial and error method, the value of depth of embankment can be found.

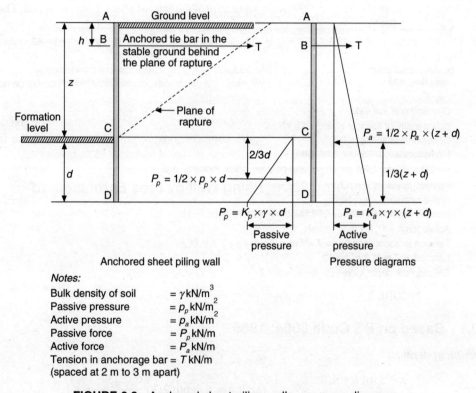

FIGURE 9.3 Anchored sheet piling walls; pressure diagrams.

9.10 DESIGN EXAMPLE 2

Referring to the previous example with same design data and assuming that the anchorage tie bar is placed at a depth 1.0 m from ground level, determine the depth of embedment assuming the sames geotechnical data. Calculate the force in the tie bar, bending moment and section of steel piling section (see Figure 9.4).

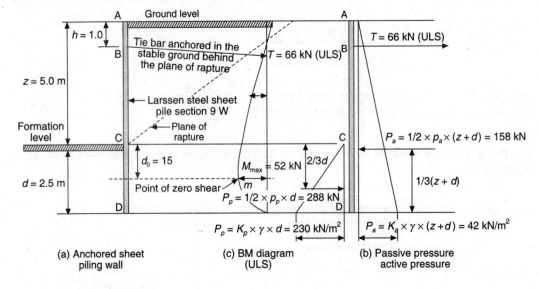

Geotechnical soil data

Bulk density of soil $= \gamma$ kN/m^3 = 20 kN/m^3

Cohesionless soil, $\phi' = 30°$

(no hydrostatic pressure assumed)

$\gamma = 2/3 \times \phi'$ and $1/2\phi'$ for active and passive sides, respectively

Passive pressure $= p_p$ kN/m^2

Active pressure $= p_p$ kN/m^2

Passive force $= P_p$ kN/m = 288 kN

Active force $= P_a$ kN/m = 158 kN

Tension in anchorage bar $= T$ kN/m = 66 kN ($\gamma_f = 1.4$ in ULS)

(spaced at 2 m to 3 m apart)

Embedment depth increased by a factor 2

FIGURE 9.4 Anchores sheet piling wall; pressures and BM diagram.

9.10.1 Based on BS Code 8004: 1986

Embedment depth:

$$z = 5 \text{ m}; \ h = 1 \text{ m}; \ K_p = 4.6; \ K_a = 0.28; \ K_p/K_a = 4.6/0.28 = 16.4$$

Let d = depth of embedment

Referring to Eq. (9.13)

Try $d = 2$ m

Then,

$$\frac{\left[\left(\frac{2}{3} \times (5+2)^3 - 1 \times (5+2)^2\right)\right]}{\left[\frac{2}{3} \times 2^3 + 5 \times 2^2 - 1 \times 2^2\right]} = 8.5 < 16.4$$

Next, try $d = 1.25$

$$\frac{\left[\left(\frac{2}{3} \times 6.25^3 - 6.25^2\right)\right]}{\left[\frac{2}{3} \times 1.25^3 + 5 \times 1.25^2 - 1 \times 1.25^2\right]} = 16.49$$

Therefore, $d = 1.25$ m; Increase the depth by a factor of 2
Therefore, adopt $d = 2.5$ m below formation level [see Figure 9.4 (a)].

Force in the anchorage bar:
Let $T =$ force in the anchorage tie bar
Active pressure

$$p_a = K_a \times \gamma \times (z + d) = 0.28 \times 20 \times 7.5 = 42 \text{ kN/m}^2$$

Total active force

$$P_a = \frac{1}{2} \times 42 \times 7.5 = 158 \text{ kN}$$

Take moments about the line of action of passive force

$$T \times (5.7) = 158 \times 1.7 \qquad (T = 47 \text{ kN/m of wall})$$

with a partial safety factor $\gamma_f = 1.4$
Therefore, ultimate tensional force in the anchorage bar

$$T_u = 1.4 \times 47 = 66 \text{ kN/m of wall} \qquad \text{[see Figure 9.4(b)]}$$

Bending moment: Maximum bending moment will occur at a section where shear force is zero.
Let $d_0 =$ depth below excavation level where shear force is zero.

$$P_p = \frac{1}{2} \times K_p \times \gamma \times d_0^2 = \frac{1}{2} \times 4.6 \times 20 \times d_0^2$$

$$P_a = \frac{1}{2} \times K_a \times \gamma \times (5 + d_0)^2 = \frac{1}{2} \times 0.28 \times 20 \times (5 + d_0)^2$$

$$\text{(For } \Sigma F = 0)$$

Therefore,

$$P_a - T - P_p = 0$$

$$\frac{1}{2} \times 0.28 \times 20 \times (5 + d_0)^2 - 47 - \frac{1}{2} \times 4.6 \times 20 \times d_0^2 = 0$$

Divide both sides by 10. Then,

$$0.28 \times (5 + d_0)^2 - 4.7 - 4.6 \times d_0^2 = 0$$

Try, $d_0 = 1.15$

$$0.28 \times 6.15^2 - 4.7 - 4.6 \times 1.15^2 = 0 \qquad \text{(approx.)}$$

Therefore, maximum bending moment will occur at a depth 1.15 from formation level.

P_p at 6.15 from GL

$$42 \times \frac{6.15}{7.5} = 34 \text{ kN/m}^2$$

$$P_p = \frac{1}{2} \times 34 \times 6.15 = 105 \text{ kN}$$

For equilibrium

$$P_p - 47 = P_a$$

So,

$$P_a = 105 - 47 = 58 \text{ kN}$$

P_p at 1.15 from formation level $= 58 \times \dfrac{1.15}{2.5} = 26.7 \text{ kN}$

Take moments about the line of zero shear
Therefore, Max. B.M

$$= P_p \times \left(\frac{1}{3} \times 6.15\right) - P_p \times \left(\frac{1}{3} \times 1.15\right) - 47 \times 5.15$$

$$= 105 \times 2.05 - 26.7 \times 0.38 - 47 \times 5.15 = -37 \text{ kN m}$$

(with a partial safety factor $\gamma_f = 1.4$)
Therefore,

$$\text{ultimate } M_u = -1.4 \times 37 = -52 \text{ kN m} \qquad \text{[see Figure 9.4(c)]}$$

Design of section of steel sheet pile:
Assuming steel grade S275

$$p_y = 275 \text{ N/mm}^2$$

$$Z_{\text{required}} = 52 \times \frac{10^6}{\frac{275}{10^3}}^{\!3} = 189 \text{ cm}^3/\text{m}$$

Try Larssen steel piling section 9 W;

$$Z = 902 \text{ cm}^3 > 189 \text{ cm}^3$$

Therefore, adopt Larssen steel section 9 W, 7.5 m long.
Thus, we find that with anchored tie bar we need much smaller steel pile section.

9.10.2 Based on Eurocode 7: 2004

Embedment depth: Referring to Eq. (9.13) as stated before:

$$\frac{\left[\dfrac{2}{3}(z+d)^3 - h(z+d)^2\right]}{\left[\dfrac{2}{3} \times d^3 + z \times d^2 - h \times d^2\right]} = \frac{K_p}{K_a}$$

where

K_a = design active earth pressure coefficient $= \dfrac{\left[1 - \sin\left(\dfrac{\phi'}{\gamma_{\phi'}}\right)\right]}{\left[1 + \sin\left(\dfrac{\phi'}{\gamma_{\phi'}}\right)\right]}$

K_p = design passive earth pressure coefficient $= \dfrac{\left[1 + \sin\left(\dfrac{\phi'}{\gamma_{\phi'}}\right)\right]}{\left[1 - \sin\left(\dfrac{\phi'}{\gamma_{\phi'}}\right)\right]}$

ϕ' = angle of shearing resistance in terms of effective stress = 30°

Hence,

$$\frac{\phi'}{\gamma_{\phi'}} = \frac{30}{1.25} = 24°$$

$\gamma_{\phi'}$ = partial safety factor of soil parameter = 1.25   [see Table A.2 of EC 7, partial factors for soil parameter (γ_m)]

Angle of shearing resistance = $\gamma_{\phi'}$ = 1.25; this factor applied to tan ϕ'

Undrained shear strength = γ_{c_u} = 1.4

Effective cohesion = $\gamma_{c'}$ = 1.25

Assuming,

wall friction δ behind the sheet pile $= \dfrac{2}{3} \times \sin \dfrac{2}{3} \times \sin \dfrac{\phi'}{\gamma_{\phi'}}$

and in front of sheet pile $= \dfrac{1}{2} \times \sin \dfrac{\phi'}{\gamma_{\phi'}}$

Referring to Table 39 of CIRIA Report 104,

$$K_a = 0.36 \text{ and } K_p = 3.2 \text{ and } \frac{K_p}{K_a} = \frac{3.2}{0.36} = 8.9$$

z = height of embankment = 5 m
Try, depth of embankment, $d = 2$ m
Then,

$$\frac{\left[\dfrac{2}{3}(5+2)^3 - 1(5+2)^2\right]}{\left[\dfrac{2}{3} \times 2^3 + 5 \times 2^2 - 2^2\right]} = \frac{179}{21.3} = 8.4$$

which is nearly 8.9.
Therefore, $d = 2$ m.

Referring to Table A.13 of Eurocode 7

Partial resistance factor for earth pressure, $\gamma_{re} = 1.4$

Therefore, design depth of embedment

$$d_{design} = d \times \gamma_{re} = 2 \times 1.4 = 2.8 \quad \text{(say 3.0 m)}$$

and, based on BS 8004, design depth = 2.5 m

Thus, we find that the embedment depth by Eurocode 7 results higher depth.

Force in the anchorage bar:

Let T = safe tensional force in the anchorage bar.

Design active pressure

$$p_a = K_a \times \gamma' \times (z + d) = 0.36 \times 20 \times 8 = 57.6 \text{ kN/m}^2$$

Total design active force

$$P_a = \frac{1}{2} \times p_a \times (z + d) = \frac{1}{2} \times 57.6 \times 8 = 230 \text{ kN}$$

Take moments about the line of action of passive force

$$T \times \left(z + \frac{2}{3} \times d - 1 \right) = \frac{P_a \left[(d + z) \right]}{3 - \dfrac{d}{3}} = 230 \left(\frac{8}{3} - \frac{3}{3} \right) = 230 \times \frac{5}{3}$$

Therefore, safe tensional force in the anchorage bar,

$$T = \frac{383.3}{6} = 63.9 \text{ kN} \quad \text{(say 64 kN)}$$

Assuming a partial safety factor $\gamma_f = 1.4$.

Therefore, ultimate tensional force in the anchorage bar

$$T_u = 64 \times 1.4 = 90 \text{ kN}$$

which is higher than the value (66 kN) obtained by BS code 8004: 1986.

REFERENCES

[9.1] CIRIA report 104: Design of retaining walls embedded in stiff clays.

[9.2] Rowe, P.W., Cantilever sheet piling in cohesionless soil, *Engineering*, 172:316, 1951.

[9.3] Henry, F.D.C., The design and construction of engineering foundations, *Spon*, 1956.

[9.4] BS 8004: 1986: British Standard Code of Practice for Foundations.

[9.5] Eurocode 7: 2004: Geotechnical design: Part 1: General rules.

[9.6] Piling Handbook: by British Steel plc., London, 1988.

Chapter 10

Retaining Walls

10.0 DESCRIPTIONS

The retaining wall is the substructure that retains and provides the lateral support with a mass of soil of backfill behind their back. The stability of the wall depends on its own self-weight and the weight of the mass of soil resting directly on its base. It acts as an inseparable part of many foundations (see codes of practice for earth retaining structures BS 8002, 1994 [10.1]).

10.1 CLASSIFICATION OF RETAINING WALL

The retaining wall may be classified as follows:

1. Gravity retaining wall
2. Cantilever retaining wall
3. Counterfort retaining wall.

Gravity retaining wall: In olden times, the gravity wall was usually constructed of stone masonry. After the introduction of concrete, the gravity retaining wall is being constructed with plain or reinforced concrete, as shown in Figure 10.1(a).

Cantilever retaining wall: The cantilever retaining wall is constructed in reinforced concrete. It consists of vertical stem and base slab. The soil mass is supported horizontally by the vertical stem and vertically by the base slab. The stem and the base is thinner compared to the gravity wall as they are of reinforced concrete construction, as shown in Figure 10.1(b).

Counterfort retaining wall: The counterfort retaining wall of reinforced concrete consists of vertical wall and base slab with counterforts at certain intervals forming an integral part with the wall and the base. The wall and the base slab are considered continuous over the counterforts [Figure 10.1(c)]. The introduction of counterforts reduces the thickness of wall and the base slab. The counterfort retaining wall is used generally where the retained soil mass is considerably high.

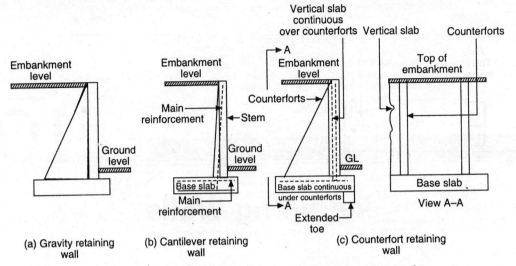

(a) Gravity retaining wall   (b) Cantilever retaining wall   (c) Counterfort retaining wall

FIGURE 10.1 Types and general arrangement of retaining walls.

10.2 CONCEPT OF DEVELOPMENT OF EARTH PRESSURE

The backfill is always deposited after the structure is completed. During the process of backfill the pressure develops due to the fill and the wall yields. The end results of the value of pressure is dependent not only on the type of soil and the height of wall, but also on the amount of yield that the wall sustains. If the wall is of very high stiffness so that the yield is almost zero (no movement), then the pressure exerted on the wall is the full value of retaining the earth behind it for infinite period, and is considered as *the earth pressure at rest.*

If the wall yields, i.e. the wall moves away from the backfill, then the whole mass of retained soil transforms from the state of rest to the active state of plastic equilibrium. The earth pressure decreases in a continuous manner until, at a specific amount of wall movement, a slip occurs in the backfill along an inclined, slightly curved surface of sliding, as shown in Figure 10.2.

At this stage the shearing strength σ is fully mobilized along the surface of sliding, and the direction of the shearing forces is such as to reduce the earth pressure. Hence, at this stage, the earth pressure reduces to the minimum value termed as *the active earth pressure.*

Any further outward movement of wall does not significantly alter the value of the active pressure. So, we consider the case when the wall is subjected to active earth pressure with the yield or deformation of wall but not the failure of wall. From the laboratory test results it was shown that the movement required to reduce the earth pressure to the value of the active earth pressure is in the region of 0.1% of the height of wall.

10.3 RANKINE'S THEORY OF EARTH PRESSURE OF COHESIONLESS SOIL AGAINST RETAINING WALLS

10.3.1 When the Embankment Surface is Horizontal

In the derivation of Rankine's theory, [10.2] the following assumptions were made:

- The surface of vertical wall is smooth without any wall friction.

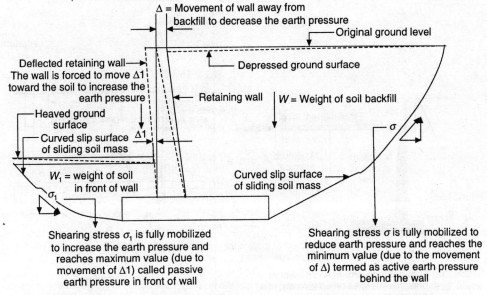

FIGURE 10.2 Concept of development of earth pressure against wall.

- The backfill of soil is perfectly dry. The bulk density = γ kN/m^3
- The wall yields under the influence of the earth pressure and the soil fails by shear along two planes rising from the heel at angles of $45° + \phi/2$ with the horizontal. Within the wedge-shaped zone between these two planes, the soil is in the active Rankine state.

Consider an element of soil at a depth z subjected to two principal stresses, namely

1. The maximum principal stress = Equal to the weight of column of soil at a depth, $z = \gamma \times z$
2. The minimum principal stress = Active pressure = p_a

The ratio between these two principal stresses will be determined by means of Mohr's circle as drawn in Figure 10.3.

The resultant stress on a plane shall have an obliquity equal to the angle of internal friction ϕ of soil as shown by the lines OT and OR. Therefore, those lines represent the limiting tangents within which the Mohr's circle shall be inscribed.

Referring to Figure 10.3, OP_1/OP_3 represent the ratio of maximum and minimum principal stresses so that $OP_1 = \gamma z$ and $OP_3 = p_a$

$$\sin \phi = \frac{TC}{OC} = \frac{\frac{1}{2}(\text{difference of principal stresses})}{\frac{1}{2}(\text{sum of principal stresses})}$$

or

$$\frac{p_a}{\gamma z} = \frac{(1 - \sin \phi)}{(1 + \sin \phi)} = \tan^2\left(45° - \frac{\phi}{2}\right)$$

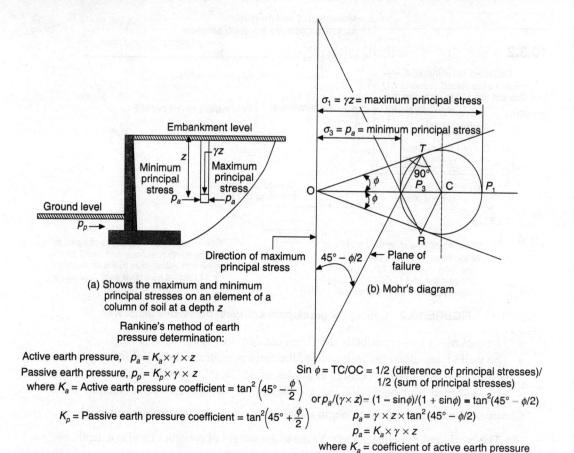

(a) Shows the maximum and minimum
principal stresses on an element of a
column of soil at a depth z

(b) Mohr's diagram

Rankine's method of earth
pressure determination:

Active earth pressure, $p_a = K_a \times \gamma \times z$

Passive earth pressure, $p_p = K_p \times \gamma \times z$

where K_a = Active earth pressure coefficient = $\tan^2\left(45° - \dfrac{\phi}{2}\right)$

K_p = Passive earth pressure coefficient = $\tan^2\left(45° + \dfrac{\phi}{2}\right)$

$\text{Sin }\phi = TC/OC = 1/2$ (difference of principal stresses)/
1/2 (sum of principal stresses)

or $p_a/(\gamma \times z) = (1 - \sin\phi)/(1 + \sin\phi) = \tan^2(45° - \phi/2)$

$p_a = \gamma \times z \times \tan^2(45° - \phi/2)$

$p_a = K_a \times \gamma \times z$

where K_a = coefficient of active earth pressure

FIGURE10.3   Rankine's method of analysis of earth pressures on retaining wall in cohesionless soil.

Therefore,

$$p_a = \gamma z \times \tan^2\left(45° - \frac{\phi}{2}\right)$$

Let

$$\tan^2\left(45° - \frac{\phi}{2}\right) = K_a \qquad \text{(coefficient of active earth pressure)}$$

Then, active earth pressure

$$p_a = K_a \times \gamma \times z \qquad\qquad\qquad (10.1)$$

And total active thrust on a vertical wall of height z

Average pressure × height

$$P_a = \frac{1}{2} \times K_a \times \gamma \times z^2 \qquad\qquad\qquad (10.2)$$

10.3.2 Rankine's Method when the Embankment is Inclined to the Horizontal

Let the embankment surface be inclined upwards to an angle β to the horizontal. The active earth pressure is solved analytically. Thus,

$$p_a = \dfrac{\gamma z \cos \beta}{\dfrac{\cos \beta - \sqrt{(\cos^2 \beta - \cos^2 \phi)}}{\cos \beta + \sqrt{(\cos^2 \beta - \cos^2 \phi)}}} \qquad (10.3)$$

10.4 RANKINE'S METHOD OF ANALYSIS OF PASSIVE RESISTANCE OF COHESIONLESS SOIL

10.4.1 When the Embankment Surface is Horizontal

It has already been explained that a slight deflection of the wall in a direction away from the retained soil mass of embankment results in the development of active earth pressure and, at the same time, this slight deflection towards the mass of soil in front of wall brings into play a force to resist such movement. This resisting force is known as passive resistance (P_p). The analytical solution for passive resistance by Rankine's method with horizontal embankment may be given as

$$p_p = \text{passive eath pressure} = \gamma \times z \times \tan^2 \left(45° + \frac{\phi}{2} \right) \qquad (10.4)$$

10.4.2 When the Embankment Surface is Inclined to the Horizontal

Let β be the upward inclination of embankment surface to the horizontal. Then,

$$p_p = \dfrac{\gamma z \cos \beta}{\dfrac{\cos \beta + \sqrt{(\cos^2 \beta - \cos^2 \phi)}}{\cos \beta - \sqrt{(\cos^2 \beta - \cos^2 \phi)}}} \qquad (10.5)$$

10.5 BELL'S [10.3] METHOD OF ANALYSIS OF EARTH PRESSURE OF COHESIVE SOIL

10.5.1 Active Pressure Analysis

Refer to Figure 10.4 as follows:

Consider that the embankment surface is horizontal. Assume the general case when the soil has got the properties of both cohesion c and angle of shearing resistance ϕ. Active pressure can be determined by means of Mohr's circle. As the soil posses cohesion of fixed value for a given soil, Mohr's circle shall be drawn to scale. Consider that the limiting tangent to the Mohr's circle is RT, as shown in Figure 10.4(a). The ordinate OR measures the value of cohesion c. When the tangent

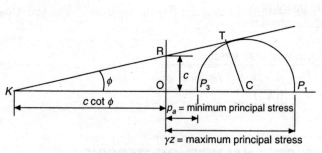
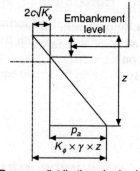

(a) Mohr s circle for active
pressure of cohesive soil

(b) Pressure distribution of cohesive
soil on the vertical wall

Active pressure, $p_a = K_\phi \times \gamma \times z\ 2 \times c \times \sqrt{K_\phi}$
where K_ϕ = coefficient for cohesive soil = $\tan^2 (45°\ \phi/2)$
c = cohesion in kN/m^2
z = depth below embankment surface in metre
γ = bulk density of soil in kN/m^3

FIGURE 10.4   Analysis of active pressure of cohesive soil.

is extended back, it meets the *x*-axis at a distance $c \times \cot \phi$. OP$_3$ represents the active pressure p_a and OP$_1$ represents the vertical pressure γz. Then,

$$\frac{OP_3}{OP_1} = \frac{(c \times \cot \phi + p_a)}{(c \times \cot \phi + \gamma z)} = \frac{(1 - \sin \phi)}{(1 + \sin \phi)} = \tan^2 \left(45° - \frac{\phi}{2}\right)$$

Let

$$\tan^2 \left(45° - \frac{\phi}{2}\right) = K_\phi = \text{coefficient of earth pressure for cohesive soil.}$$

Hence,

$$p_a = K_\phi \gamma z + (K_\phi - 1) \times c \cot \phi$$

Let

$$(K_\phi - 1) = \frac{(1 - \sin \phi)}{(1 + \sin \phi)} - 1 = -\frac{(2 \sin \phi)}{(1 + \sin \phi)}$$

Multiply both sides by $\cot \phi$. Then,

$$(K_\phi - 1) \cot \phi = -\frac{(2 \sin \phi \times \cos \phi)}{(1 + \sin \phi)} = -\frac{2 \cos \phi}{1 + \sin \phi} = 2 \tan \left(45° - \frac{\phi}{2}\right) = -2\sqrt{(K_\phi)}$$

Therefore,

$$p_a = K_\phi \times \gamma \times z - 2c \sqrt{(K_\phi)} \tag{10.6}$$

In the analysis no wall friction on the back of wall is considered.

From the above, we find that the active pressure of cohesive soil is less by the amount $2c\sqrt{(K_\phi)}$ compared to cohesionless soil of same density and angle of shearing resistance.

The active pressure distribution on wall is shown in Figure 10.4(b), in which upto a certain depth from embankment surface the pressure is negative, i.e. no pressure is exerted on the wall.

Let z_c be critical depth from the embankment surface at which the active pressure starts to exert on the wall.

By equating the above equation to zero with $z = z_c$

So,

$$K_\phi \times \gamma \times z_c = 2c \times \sqrt{(K_\phi)}$$

$$z_c = \frac{2c}{\gamma\sqrt{(K_\phi)}} = \frac{2c}{\gamma \times \left[\tan\left(45° + \dfrac{\phi}{2}\right)\right]}$$

The tension crack developed in soil behind the wall is generally filled with water. This water pressure compensates approximately the value $2c\sqrt{(K_\phi)}$.

Therefore, generally in the calculation of earth pressure of cohesive soil, the value of $2c\sqrt{(K_\phi)}$ in Eq. (10.6) may be neglected. During the construction of embankment with cohesive soil, the pore pressure in the soil undergoes little change. So, in the stability analysis during and just after the completion of embankment, total stress condition of the soil is assumed without the deduction of pore pressure. In the case of fully saturated soil (say clay), the angle of shearing resistance of soil is assumed zero, i.e. $\phi = 0$. In long-term stability of the wall, effective stress analysis is carried out without the consideration of pore pressure and full development of angle of shearing strength of soil.

10.5.2 Passive Pressure Analysis

Applying the same Bell's method by drawing the Mohr's circle, we arrive at the following expression for passive pressure of cohesive soil:

$$p_p = \gamma z \tan^2\left(45° + \frac{\phi}{2}\right) + 2c \times \tan\left(45° + \frac{\phi}{2}\right) \tag{10.7}$$

From Eq. (10.7), we find that the passive pressure of cohesive soil is greater than that of cohesionless soil of same density and angle of shearing resistance.

10.6 DESIGN EXAMPLE 1

A long continuous retaining wall is to be constructed to retain an earth embankment of 9.0 m high from ground level. The embankment is to support the unloading platform for heavy vehicular wheel loads (16 t laden loader). The embankment shall be constructed of compacted granular fill. Adequate drainage system is to be provided to avoid any possibility of developing hydrostatic pressure behind the wall. Beyond the retaining wall, two wing walls shall be provided to retain side slopes of the embankment. We are to design the structural elements of the retaining wall.

Basic assumptions of proportions and sizing of structural members: Refer to Figure 10.5 as follows:

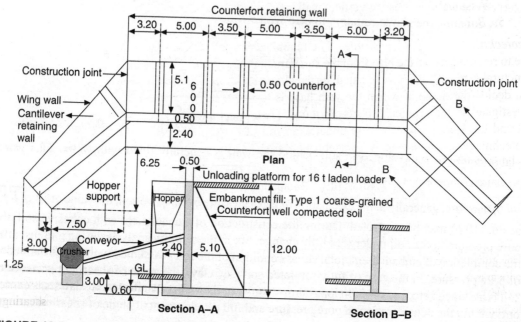

FIGURE 10.5 General arrangement: To support material unloading platform for a 16 t laden loader to primary crusher.

1. *Type of retaining wall:* The wall is subjected to heavy horizontal pressures due to high embankment and surcharge. In general, when the embankment exceeds 6 m, it is more economical to adopt counterfort retaining wall which will reduce the thickness of vertical stem and also the base slab. So, adopt the counterfort retaining wall with counterforts spaced at 5 m max.

2. *Width of base slab:* In deciding the width of the base, two important factors should be considered:

   - The eccentricity of the resultant force, measured from the central line of base should not exceed one-sixth the width of base.
   - The maximum pressure should not exceed the allowable soil pressure.

   Based on the above considerations, the width of base varies from 0.6 to 0.65 of height. In our case, assume the base is founded at a depth 3 m from the ground level. So, width of base assumed,

   $$B = 0.65 \times (9 + 3) = 7.8 \text{ m} \qquad \text{(say 8.0 m)}.$$

3. *Projection of toe:* Assumed, projection of toe from front face of wall = 0.3 × width of base = 2.4 m.

4. *Thickness of vertical wall:* The wall is considered to be a continuous slab over counterforts. Minimum thickness should be

$$\frac{1}{26} \times \text{Counterfort spacing} = \frac{5}{26} = 0.2 \text{ m}$$

Assume: thickness of vertical wall = 0.5 m.

5. *Base thickness:* Continuous under counterforts. Assume thickness = 0.6 m.

Geotechnical data of the ground: The retaining wall is subjected to heavy horizontal pressure due to retaining earth and also from the surcharge of heavily laden loader. So, before designing the structural elements, we have to calculate the allowable bearing capacity of soil, and based on it, we can decide the depth at which the wall base is to be taken below ground level. So, we have to investigate the geotechnical aspects of ground. Therefore, the site ground explorations were carried out and the laboratory tests were undertaken from field soil samples. From the test results, the geotechnical soil parameters were established, as shown in Table 10.1. Basic soil data from site and the laboratory test results are taken.

TABLE 10.1 Geotechnical soil parameters

Soil type	Depth below GL (m)	Bulk density γ_b (kN/m^3)	ϕ' (degree)	δ (degree)	K_a	K_p	K_o	N	N_q
Made ground	0.0	18	0	0	0	0	0	0	0
Loose to medium silty clayey sand	1.0	18	25	18					12
Medium to dense clayey silty sand	3.0	21	30	22.5					20
Very dense clayey silty sand	15.5	21	35	26					30

where

ϕ' = angle of shearing resistance of soil in degrees.

δ = angle of friction between soil and back of wall in degrees.

N_q = bearing capacity factor whose value is dependant on the angle of shearing resistance of soil.

10.6.1 To Calculate the Bearing Capacity of Soil under the Base Slab

Based on BS code 8004: 1986 [10.4]

Terzaghi investigated the ultimate bearing capacity of soil under a shallow strip footing allowing friction and cohesion between the base and the soil. He derived Eq. (2.4) as follows, resulting the shear failure (see Chapter 2)

$$q_u = C_u \times N_c + \gamma_b \times z \times N_q + 0.5 \times \gamma_b \times B \times N_y$$

where

C_u = undrained shear strength of cohesive soil in kN/m^2

γ_b = bulk density of soil in kN/m^3

z = depth of foundation below ground level (in m)

B = width of foundation (in m).

N_c, N_q, N_y = the bearing capacity factors. The values of bearing capacity factors are obtained from the graphs in Figure 2.5, Chapter 2.

Before the construction started, the soil is removed from the foundation trenches. This soil has oiginally applied a pressure equal to the weight at the level of the base of the footing. If the soil is deducted from the ultimate bearing capacity, the net ultimate bearing capacity is given by Eq. (2.6) as follows:

$$q_{u\,net} = C_u \times N_c + \gamma_b \times z \times (N_q - 1) + 0.5 \times \gamma_b \times B \times N_y$$

To obtain the safe bearing capacity of soil, the above expression is divided by a safety factor (F), and then the weight of column of soil, removed from the excavation, is added to obtain the total safe bearing capacity of soil under the foundation level. Thus, the total safe bearing capacity of soil, i.e. Eq. (2.7)

$$q = \frac{[C_u \times N_c + \gamma \times z \times (N_q - 1) + 0.5 \times \gamma \times B \times N_y]}{F} + \gamma \times z$$

To determine the depth at which the base is to be founded and the width of foundation base, we have to consider the following points:

- The height of embankment
- The surcharge
- The actual toe pressure which should be equal or less than the allowable bearing capacity of soil to prevent excessive tilting
- The resultant of all the forces should intersect the base within the middle third
- The factor of safety against sliding must be adequate, preferably 1.5.

In our case, considering the above points, as the height of embankment is high and heavy surcharge on the embankment, it will be wise to found the base on the stratum of medium to dense clayey silty sand at a depth of 3.0 m below ground level to keep the soil pressure at toe within allowable bearing capacity of soil.

Therefore, assume that the depth of base below ground level = 3.0 m (Total height of wall = 9 + 3 = 12 m).

To keep the resultant within middle third of base, assume that the width $B = 0.65 \times H = 0.65 \times 12 = 8.0$ m (say). (see Figure 10.5).

Referring to Figure 2.5 in Chapter 2) (of Terzaghi's bearing capacity factors):

With $\phi' = 30°$, $\gamma_b = 21$ kN/m^3 and the groundwater table almost at the ground level, submersed weight of soil

$$\gamma_s = 21 - 10 = 11 \text{ kN/m}^3$$

$$Z = 3 \text{ m}$$

Since $C_u = 0$, $N_c = 0$; $N_q = 22$; and $N_y = 20$

$$q_u = \gamma_s \times z \times (N_q - 1) + 0.5 \times \gamma_s \times B \times N_y$$

$$= 11 \times 3 \times (22 - 1) + 0.5 \times 11 \times 8 \times 20 = 1573 \text{ kN/m}^2$$

Assuming a safety factor = 2.5

Hence, safe bearing capacity of soil at a depth of 3 m below ground level

$$q = \frac{q_u}{2.5} + 3 \times 11 = 662 \text{ kN/m}^2$$

Based on Eurocode 7: 2004 [10.5]

As explained before, the foundation base slab is placed on soil of medium to dense clayey silty sand at a depth 3.0 m from the ground level (for geotechnical soil parameters, see Table 10.1).

Effective density of soil, $\gamma' = (21 - 10) = 11$ kN/m³

Effective angle of shearing resistance of soil, $\phi' = 30°$

Referring to Annex D.4 (analytical method for bearing resistance calculation) of Eurocode 7:

In drained conditions, the design bearing stress may be calculated from the following expression:

$$q_b = c' \times N_c \times b_c \times n_c \times i_c + q' \times N_q \times b_q \times s_q \times i_q + 0.5 \times \gamma' \times B' \times N_\gamma \times b_\gamma \times s_\gamma \times i_\gamma$$

Since $c' = 0$, the first quantity = 0

N_q and N_y are the bearing capacity factors

$$N_q = e^{\pi \times \tan\left(\frac{\phi'}{\gamma_{\phi'}}\right)} \times \tan^2 \times \left(45 + \frac{\phi'/\gamma_{\phi'}}{2}\right)$$

where, $\gamma_{\phi'}$ = Partial factor for soil parameter of angle of shearing resistance = 1.25

$$\frac{\phi'}{\gamma_{\phi'}} = \frac{30}{1.25} = 24°$$

Hence,

$$N_q = e^{(\pi \times \tan 24)} \times \tan^2 57 = 9.6$$

and

$$N_\gamma = 2 \times (N_q - 1) \times \tan 24 = 2 \times (9.6 - 1) \times \tan 24 = 7.7$$

b_q and b_γ are the inclination factors for foundation base

$$b_q = b_\gamma = (1 - \alpha \times \tan 24) = 1 \qquad (\text{since } \alpha = 0)$$

s_q and s_γ are the foundation shape factors

$$s_q = 1 + \frac{B'}{L'} \times \sin 24$$

(where B' = effective width of foundation base = 8 m ; L' = effective length of foundation base = 28.4)

Therefore,

$$s_q = 1 + \frac{8}{28.4} \times \sin 24 = 1.1$$

$$i_q = \left[1 - \frac{H}{\left[V + A' \times c' \times \cot\left(\dfrac{\phi'}{\gamma_{\phi'}}\right) \right]} \right]^m \qquad \text{since } c' = 0, \; i_q = 1$$

$$i_\gamma = \left[1 - \frac{H}{\left[V + A' \times c' \times \cot\left(\dfrac{\phi'}{\gamma_{\phi'}}\right) \right]} \right]^{(m+1)} \qquad \text{since } c' = 0, \; i_\gamma = 1$$

$$s_\gamma = 1 - 0.3 \times \frac{B'}{L'} = 1 - 0.3 \times \frac{8}{28.4} = 0.92$$

where

$$m = m_b = \frac{2 + (B'/L')}{1 + (B'/L')}$$

when H acts in the direction of B'

$$m = m_L = \frac{2 + (L'/B')}{1 + (L'/B')}$$

when H acts in the direction of L'
B' and L' are effective width and length of foundation base.
Therefore, allowable bearing stress of soil

$$q_b = 3 \times (21 - 10) \times 9.6 \times 1 \times 1.1 \times 1 + 0.5 \times (21 - 10)$$
$$\times 8 \times 7.7 \times 1 \times 0.92 \times 1 = 348 + 312 = 660 \text{ kN/m}^2$$

Thus, we find that using Eurocode 7 gives the allowable bearing stress (660 kN/m²), whereas, using BS code 8004 gives almost the same value of allowable capacity (662 kN/m²).

10.6.2   To Determine the Geotechnical Characteristics and Selection of Backfilled Material

The type of backfill soil shall have to be selected before calculating the soil pressure on the wall. Generally, as specified by Terzaghi, five types of backfill soil as classified in the following may be used:

- *Type 1:*   Coarse-grained soil without admixture of fine soil particles (very permeable).
- *Type 2:*   Coarse-grained soil of low permeability due to admixture of silt size particles.
- *Type 3:*   Residual soil with stones, fine silty sand, and granular materials with conspicuous clay content.
- *Type 4:*   Very soft or soft clay, organic silts, or silty clays.
- *Type 5:*   Medium or stiff clay, deposited in chunks and protected in such a way that a negligible amount of water enters the spaces between the chunks during floods or heavy rain. If this condition cannot be satisfied, the clay should not be used as a backfill material as the backfill material with increasing stiffness of clay is dangerous to the wall, because in this situation, infiltration of water increases rapidly.

Considering the geotechnical characteristics of all the above types of soil, we adopt type 1 backfill material.

Now, assume, angle of shearing resistance of type 1 backfill soil, $\phi' = 30°$

Maximum effective wall friction, $\delta = \frac{2}{3} \times \phi' = 20°$ (suggested by Caquot and Kerisel)

Bulk density of fill material, $\gamma_b = 21$ kN/m³
With the above values of ϕ' and δ, and referring to Figure 10.6:

$$K_a = 0.28$$

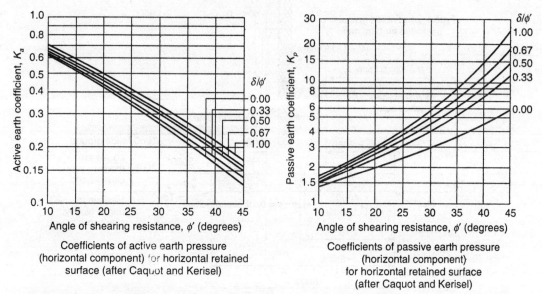

FIGURE 10.6 Coefficients of active and passive earth pressures (after Caquot and Kerisel).

10.6.3 Analysis of Retaining Wall

Refer to Figure 10.7.

The retaining wall shall be analyzed on the following aspects:

1. To check the ground pressure at the toe does not exceed the safe capacity of soil.
2. To check the stability of structure against overturning.
3. To check the structure against sliding.

Based on BS code 8004: 1986

1. *To check the ground pressure at the toe of the structure:* To determine the CG of the self-weight of the structure and the soil over the heel of base, see Table 10.2 as follows:

TABLE 10.2 Showing all vertical loads

Description	Weight/m (in kN)		Distance from heel length (in m)	Moment about heel (in kN m)
Base	$8 \times 1 \times 0.6 \times 24 =$	115.2	4.0	460.8
Wall	$11.4 \times 0.5 \times 24 =$	136.8	5.35	731.9
Counterfort	$1/2 \times 5.1 \times 11.4 \times 24/5 =$	139.5	$2/3 \times 5.1$	474.3
Soil over the heel	$5.1 \times 11.4 \times 21 =$	1221	5.1/2	3113.4
	Total weight, $W = 1613$			Total moment = 4780.4

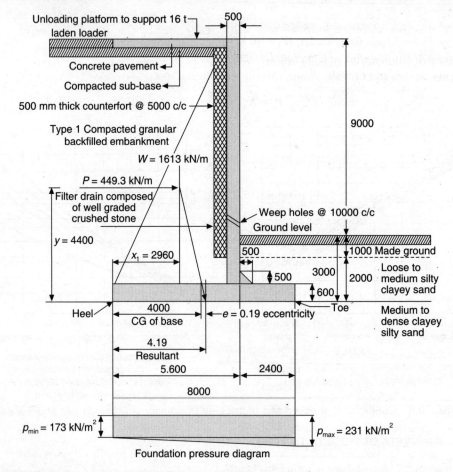

FIGURE 10.7 Analysis of foundation pressures due to earth and surcharge pressures.

Therefore, distance of CG of self-weight and soil from heel

$$x_1 = \frac{4780.4}{1613} = 2.96 \text{ m} \qquad \text{(see Figure 10.7)}$$

Calculation the CG of all the horizontal forces due to earth pressures from the base slab containing the following steps:

- To calculate the horizontal earth pressure due to granular fill:
  Assumed that effective drainage system has been provided behind the wall.
  Active earth pressure coefficient

$$K_a = 0.28 \qquad \text{(already obtained from Figure 10.6)}$$

Therefore, horizontal pressure at a depth 12 m

$$p_1 = K_a \times \gamma_b \times z = 0.28 \times 21 \times 12 = 70.6 \text{ kN/m}^2$$

Total horizontal pressure,

$$p_1 = \frac{1}{2} \times 70.6 \times 12 = 424 \text{ kN} \qquad \left(\text{acting at } \frac{1}{3} \times 12 = 4 \text{ m from base} \right)$$

- To calculate horizontal pressure due to surcharge of 16 t laden loader:

Each wheel load from loader, $W_1 = 90$ kN

Referring to *Reinforced Concrete Designer's Handbook* by Reynolds and Steedman [10.7]:

Line load/m run of wall

$$P_s = K_a \times \frac{W_1}{\left(d + \dfrac{b}{2}\right)}$$

where

d = distance of wheel from wall edge = 1 m

B = width of tyre = 0.5 m (assumed) $= 0.28 \times \dfrac{90}{\left(1 + \dfrac{0.5}{2}\right)} = 20.2$ kN/m

With assumed 25% increase due to impact.

Therefore, effective line load/m run of wall

$$P_{sc} = 20.2 \times 1.25 = 25.3 \text{ kN} \left[\text{acting at} \left(\frac{z-d}{1.2}\right) = 11.2 \text{ m} \right] \quad \text{(from base).}$$

Now, take moments of all the horizontal forces about base (see Table 10.3).

TABLE 10.3 Showing horizontal forces and moments

Description	Forces (in kN/m)	Height from base (in m)	Moment about base (in kN m)
Horizontal soil pressure	$P_1 = 424$	4.0	1696
Surcharge from loader	$P_{sc} = 25.3$	11.2	283.4
	Total, $P = 449.3$		Total = 1979.4

Therefore, the resultant is acting at a height from base, $y = 1979.4/449.3 = 4.4$ m (from base). Let x be the shift of resultant vertical force due to horizontal thrust. Taking moment of all the resultant horizontal and vertical forces about the point where the resultant cuts the base:

$$x \times W = P \times 4.4; \ x \times 1613 = 449.3 \times 4.4; \ x = 1.22 \text{ m}$$

Therefore, eccentricity

$$e = 1.22 + 2.96 - 4 = 0.19 \text{ m} \quad \text{(from right of CG of base area)}$$

Hence, maximum soil pressure at toe

$$f_{max} = \frac{W}{A} + W \times \frac{e}{Z}$$

where

A = base area = 8 m^2

Z second modulus $= \dfrac{8^2}{6} = 10.7$ m^3

Thus,

$$f_{max} = \frac{1613}{8} + 1613 \times \frac{0.19}{10.7} = 202 + 29 = 231 \text{ kN/m}^2 < q$$

(Allowable bearing capacity = 662 kN/m^2)   **(Satisfactory)**.

Minimum soil pressure at heel

$$f_{min} = 173 \text{ kN/m}^2 \quad \text{(see Figure 10.7)}$$

2. *To check against overturning:*   Taking moments about toe:
   Overturning moment, OTM = 1979.4 kN m
   Stabilizing moment, STM   = 1613 × 3.82 = 6162 kN m

   Therefore, factor of safety against overturning is $\dfrac{6162}{1979.4} = 3.1 > 1.5$ (**Satisfactory**).

3. *To check against sliding:*   Total horizontal forces

$$P = 449.3 \text{ kN}$$

Forces resisting sliding:

- The shearing resistance generated between the soil and the base.
- The passive earth pressure of the soil in contact with the front of the structure below the ground level.

The shearing resistance between the base and the soil is highly dependent on the geotechnical characters of soil and also the roughness of the surface of concrete in contact with soil. If the surface is rough, higher frictional resistance will be achieved. Thus, the total shearing resistance between the base and the soil that derives most of its strength from the angle of shearing strength of soil may be taken equal to the summation of all normal vertical forces multiplied by the coefficient of friction of soil.

Therefore, total shearing resistance

$$R_{sh} = \Sigma V \times \mu$$

where

ΣV = total vertical forces on the base area

$\mu = \tan \phi'$ = coefficient of friction.

The following values of coefficient of friction may be taken for various types of soil (as suggested by Peck, Hansen and Thornburn):

μ for:

coarse a grained soil without silt = 0.55

coarse a grained soil with silt = 0.45

silt = 0.35

In our case, the base is founded on medium to dense clayey sand with $\phi' = 30°$

Hence, coefficient of friction $\mu = \tan 30° = 0.58$

Assume a lower value of μ since the soil is of silty character.

Adopt $\mu = 0.45$

Therefore, total frictional resistance

$$R_{sh} = \Sigma V \times \mu = 161 \times 0.45 = 726 \text{ kN}$$

and total horizontal force

$$P = 449.3 \text{ kN}$$

Therefore, actual factor of safety against sliding is $\dfrac{726}{449.3} = 1.62$.

and minimum allowable factor of safety against sliding is usually taken to be $1.5 < 1.62$. Therefore, the structure is safe against sliding.

Based on Eurocode 7: 2004 [10.5]

To check the actual ground pressure at foundation base

1. *To calculate the CG of all vertical loads from heel:*
   Total vertical weight of structure + Soil over the heel, $W = 1613$ kN

   Total moment about heel = 4780.4 kN m

   The distance of CG of vertical from heel = 2.96 m

   (From previous calculations. The effect of surcharge of 0.3 kN/m^2 on base due to 16 t laden loader at the top of embankment is neglected)

2. To calculate the CG of all the horizontal forces due to earth pressures from the base slab

   - *To calculate the horizontal earth pressure on wall due to granular fill:* Assumed that the effective drainage system is provided behind the wall.

   $$\phi' = 30°; \ \gamma_{\phi'} = 1.25$$

   Therefore,

   $$\phi'_d = \text{design value of } \phi' = \frac{\phi'}{\gamma_{\phi'}} = \frac{30}{1.25} = 24°;$$

   $$\delta = \frac{2}{3}\phi'_d = 16°$$

   Referring to graph in Figure 10.6;

   $$K_a = 0.36 \text{ and } K_p = 3.2$$

   Therefore, horizontal pressure at a depth 12 m

   $$p_{a,\,12} = K_a \times \gamma' \times z = 0.36 \times 21 \times 12 = 91 \text{ kN/m}^2$$

   Total horizontal pressure

   $$P_{a,\,12} = \frac{1}{2} \times p_{a,12} \times z = \frac{1}{2} \times 91 \times 12 = 546 \text{ kN}$$

   $$\left(\text{acting at } \frac{1}{3} \times 12 = 4 \text{ m from base} \right)$$

   - *To calculate the horizontal pressure due to surcharge of 16 t laden loader on embankment:* Each wheel load from loader, $W_1 = 90$ kN
   Referring to *Reinforced Concrete Designer's Handbook* by Reynolds and Steedman [10.7]:
   Line load/m run of wall

   $$P_s = K_a \times \frac{W_1}{\left(d + \dfrac{b}{2} \right)}$$

where

d = distance of wheel from the edge of wall = 1 m

b = width of tier = 0.5 m (assumed)

Therefore, line load/m run of wall

$$P_s = 0.36 \times \frac{90}{\left(1 + \dfrac{0.5}{2}\right)} = 25.9 \text{ kN/m}$$

with assumed 25% increase due to impact, effective line load/m run

$$P_{sc} = 1.25 \times 25.9 = 32 \text{ kN}$$

acting at ($z - d/1.2 = 11.2$ m from base).

Now, take moments of all the horizontal forces about the base (see Table 10.4).

TABLE 10.4 Horizontal forces about the base

Description	Forces of wall (in kN/m)	Height from base (in m)	Moment about base (in kN m)
Horizontal soil pressure	$P_{a,\,12}$ = 546	4	$546 \times 4 = 2184$
Surcharge from loader	P_{sc} = 32	11.2	$32.2 \times 11.2 = 361$
	Total P = 578.0		Total M = 2545

Therefore, the resultant of all horizontal forces is acting at a height from base

$$y = \frac{2545}{578} = 4.4 \text{ m}$$

Let x m be the shift of resultant vertical force due to resultant horizontal thrust.

- *To calculate the actual ground pressures under the foundation base:* Taking moments of all the resultant horizontal and vertical forces about the point where the resultant cuts the base:

$$x \times W = P \times 4.4$$

Therefore,

$$x = 578 \times \frac{4.4}{1613} = 1.58 \text{ m}$$

So, the eccentricity

$$e = 1.58 + 2.96 - \frac{8}{2} = 0.54 \text{ m}$$

from right of CG of base area.

Hence, maximum soil pressure at toe

$$f_{max} = \frac{W}{A} + W \times \frac{e}{Z}$$

where A = base area = 8 m^2

$$Z = \frac{8^2}{6} = 10.7 \text{ m}^3 = \frac{1613}{8} + 1613 \times \frac{0.54}{10.7} = 202 + 81 = 283 \text{ kN/m}^2$$

which is less than allowable bearing capacity of soil

$$q_d = 660 \text{ kN/m}^2 \quad \textbf{(Satisfactory)}.$$

Minimum soil pressure at heel

$$f_{min} = 121 \text{ kN/m}^2 \quad \text{[see Figure 10.7(a)]}$$

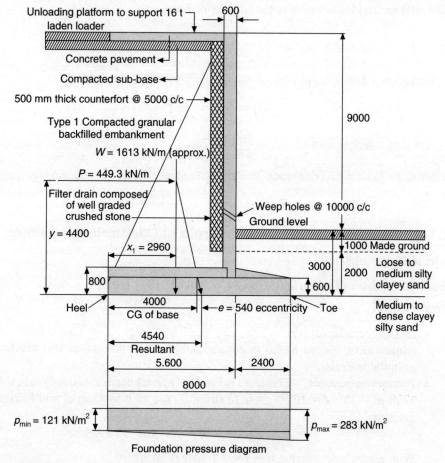

FIGURE 10.7(a)   Analysis of foundation pressures due to earth and surcharge pressures (Based on Eurocode code 7: 2004).

To check against overturning: Take moments of all the forces about toe:

Overturning moment, OTM = 2545 kN m

Stabilizing moment, STM   = 1613 × (8 − 2.96) = 8130 kN m

Therefore, factor of safety against overturning $= \dfrac{8130}{2545} = 3.19 > 1.4$ (see Table A.13 of Eurocode 7)

(**Satisfactory**).

To check against sliding: Total horizontal force

$$P = 578 \text{ kN}$$

Total shearing resistance against sliding

$$R_d = \Sigma V \times \mu$$

where
$\Sigma V =$ total vertical loads acting at the foundation base

$$\mu = \tan \left(\frac{\phi'}{\gamma_{\phi'}} \right) = \tan \left(\frac{30}{1.25} \right) = \tan 24 = 0.45$$

Therefore, total design frictional resistance

$$R_d = 1613 \times 0.45 = 726 \text{ kN}$$

So, factor of safety against sliding $= \dfrac{726}{578} = 1.26$

Referring to Table A.13 (Eurocode 7): Partial resistance factor for retaining wall against sliding

$$\gamma_{rh} = 1.1 < 1.26 \qquad (\textbf{Satisfactory}).$$

10.6.4   Design of Reinforced Concrete of Counterfort Retaining Wall

Refer to Figure 10.8.

Based on British code of practice BS 8110: Part 1: 1997 [10.6]

Vertical wall

- *Design considerations:*   The wall shall be designed as a slab continuous over the counterforts, spaced at 5.0 m c/c and subjected to horizontal soil pressure of backfill granular material.
- *Pressure calculations:*   Consider 1 m height of wall at a depth, $z = 10$ m from top of embankment. With $\phi' = 30°$; $\delta = 20°$; $K_a = 0.28$ (from Figure 10.6 by Caquot and Kerisel), horizontal pressure

$$p_a = K_a \times g \times z = 0.28 \times 21 \times 10 = 58.8 \text{ kN/m}^2$$

With partial safety factor $\gamma_f = 1.4$, ultimate pressure

$$p_u = 1.4 \times 58.8 = 82.3 \text{ kN/m}^2$$

- *Moments:*   The slab may be regarded as continuous:
Maximum BM

$$M_u = \pm \frac{1}{12} \times p_u \times \frac{l^2}{12} = \pm \frac{1}{12} \times 82.3 \times 5^2 = \pm 171.5 \text{ kN m}$$

where $l =$ spacing of counterfort in metres.

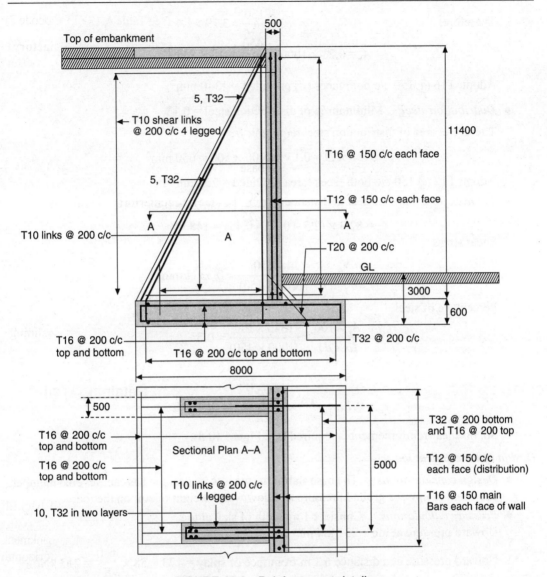

FIGURE 10.8 Reinforcement details.

- *Design of section:* With $f_{cu} = 40$ N/mm^2 and $f_y = 460$ N/mm^2

  Assuming $D = 500$ mm; $d = 500 - 40$ (cover) $- 10$ (half bar diameter) $= 450$ mm

$$\frac{M_u}{(b \times d^2)} = \frac{171.5 \times 10^6}{(1000 \times 450^2)} = 0.85$$

Referring to Chart 2 of BS 8110: part 3: 1985

$$100 \times \frac{A_s}{(b \times d)} = 0.23$$

Therefore,

$$A_s = 0.23 \times 1000 \times \frac{450}{100} = 1035 \text{ mm}^2$$

Adopt: T16 @ 150 c/c both faces (A_s provided = 1340 mm²)

- *Distribution steel:*   Minimum % of distribution steel = 0.13

Therefore, area of distribution steel required

$$0.13 \times b \times D = 0.13 \times 1000 \times 500 = 650 \text{ mm}^2$$

Adopt: T12 @ 150 c/c both faces (area provided = 754 mm²)

- *To check for shear:*   Shear at distance d from the face of counterfort

$$V_u = 82.3 \times (2.5 - 0.25 - 0.45) = 148 \text{ kN}$$

Shear stress

$$v_u = \frac{V_u}{(b \times d)} = \frac{148 \times 10^3}{(1000 \times 450)} = 0.33 \text{ N/mm}^2$$

Percentage of steel

$$p = \frac{A_s \times 100}{(b \times d)} = \frac{1340 \times 100}{(1000 \times 450)} = 0.3$$

$$v_c = 0.79 \times p^{0.33} \times \frac{\left(\frac{f_{cu}}{25}\right)^{0.33}}{1.25} = 0.50 > 0.33$$

So, no shear reinforcement is required (see Figure 10.8).

Design of base slab at toe

- *Design considerations:*   The base slab at the toe is to be designed as cantilevered member, subjected to upward ground pressure and downward weight of soil on the toe.
- *Pressure calculations:*   Consider 1 m width of slab at toe.
Upward pressure at toe = 231 kN/m²

Upward pressure at a distance 6.1 m from face of splay = $173 + 58 \times \dfrac{6.1}{8} = 217$ kN/m²

Average upward pressure $= \dfrac{1}{2} \times (217 + 231) = 224 \text{kN/m}^2$

Downward load: weight of slab = $0.6 \times 24 = 14.4$ kN/m²

Weight of soil (submersed)   = $(18 - 10) \times 2.4 = 19.2$ kN/m²

Total = 33.6 kN/m²

Therefore,

$$\text{net upward pressure} = 224 - 33.6 = 190.4 \text{ kN/m}^2/\text{m}$$

- *Moment:*   With partial safety factor $\gamma_f = 1.4$, and with 500×500 splay at the face vertical wall

Ultimate moment at the face of splay

$$M_u = 1.4 \times 190.4 \times \frac{1.9^2}{2} = 480 \text{ Nm/m}$$

- *Design of section:* Assumed:

$D = 600$ mm; $d = 600 - 40$ (cover) $- 10$ (half bar diameter) $= 550$ mm

$$\frac{M_u}{(b \times d^2)} = \frac{480 \times 10^6}{(1000 \times 550^2)} = 1.6$$

Referring to Chart 2 of BS 8110: part 3: 1985

$$100 \times \frac{A_s}{b \times d} = 0.42$$

$$A_s = 0.42 \times 1000 \times \frac{550}{100} = 2310 \text{ mm}^2$$

Adopt T32 @ 200 c/c bottom (A_s provided = 4021 mm²)
And top = 0.0013 × 1000 × 600 = 780 mm²;
Adopt T16 @ 200 c/c (distribution: same)

- *To check for shear:* Shear at a distance d from face of splay

$$V_u = 1.4 \times 190.4 \times (1.9 - .55) = 360 \text{ kN}$$

Shear stress

$$v_u = \frac{V_u}{(b \times d)} = \frac{360 \times 1000}{(1000 \times 550)} = 0.65 \text{ N/mm}^2$$

$$p = 100 \times \frac{A_s}{(b \times d)} = \frac{100 \times 4021}{(1000 \times 550)} = 0.73$$

$$v_c = 0.79 \times 0.73^{0.33} \times \frac{\left(\frac{40}{25}\right)^{0.33}}{1.25} = 0.67 \text{ N/mm}^2 > 0.65 \text{ N/mm}^2$$

So, no shear reinforcement is required.

Design of base slab at heel

- *Design considerations:* The slab is to be designed as continuous over counterforts spaced 5 m apart, and subjected to upward soil pressure and downward weights (of soil and self-weight of slab).

- *Soil pressure calculations:* Consider 1 m width of slab at a distance 4.6 m from heel.

Upward pressure at a distance 4.6 m from heel = $173 + 58 \times \dfrac{4.6}{8} = 206 \text{ kN/m}^2$

Deduct: downward weight of soil = $11.4 \times 21 = 239$ kN/m^2

downward weight of slab = $0.6 \times 24 = 14.4$ kN/m^2

Net downward pressure

$$w = 206 - 239 - 14.4 = -47.4 \text{ kN/m}^2$$

- *Moment calculations:* With a partial safety factor $\gamma_f = 1.4$
  Ultimate moment

$$M_u = \pm w \times \frac{l^2}{12} = 1.4 \times 47.4 \times \frac{5^2}{12} = 138 \text{ kN m}$$

where l = spacing of counterfort in metres.

- *Section design:* Assumed: $D = 600$ mm; $d = 550$ mm

$$\frac{M_u}{b \times d^2} = \frac{138 \times 10^6}{1000 \times 550^2} = 0.46$$

Referring to Chart 2 of BS8110: part 3: 1985

$$100 \times \frac{A_s}{(b \times d)} = 0.105$$

$$A_s = 0.105 \times 1000 \times \frac{550}{100} = 578 \text{ mm}^2$$

Adopt: T16 @ 200 c/c top and bottom (area provided = 1005 mm^2)

- *Distribution steel:* Minimum = $0.0013 \times 1000 \times 600 = 780$ mm^2
  Provide T16 @ 200 c/c top and bottom (area provided = 1005 mm^2)
- *To check for shear:* Shear at a distance d from the face of counterfort

$$V_u = 1.4 \times 47.4 \times (2.5 - 1.05) = 96 \text{ kN/m}^2$$

Shear stress

$$v_u = \frac{V_u}{(b \times d)} = 0.17 \text{ N/mm}^2$$

$$p = \frac{A_s}{(b \times d)} \times 100 = \frac{1005 \times 100}{(1000 - 550)} = 0.18$$

$$v_c = \frac{0.79}{1.25 \times p^{0.33}} \times \left(\frac{40}{25}\right)^{0.33} = 0.42 \text{ N/mm}^2 > v_u$$

So, no shear reinforcement is required.

Design of counterfort

- *Design considerations:* The counterfort shall be designed as cantilever fixed at base slab and subjected to horizontal earth pressure.
- *Pressure calculations:* Maximum horizontal soil pressure due to granular fill at a depth 11.4 m from top

$$K_a \times \gamma_b \times z = 0.28 \times 21 \times 11.4 = 67 \text{ kN/m}^2$$

And at ground level $= 0 \text{ kN/m}^2$

With 5 m spacing of counterforts, total pressure

$$P = \frac{1}{2} \times 67 \times 11.4 \times 5 = 382 \times 5 = 1910 \text{ kN}$$

Acting at a height $\dfrac{11.4}{3}$ from top of base slab

Surcharge load from 16 t loader, $P_s = 25.3 \text{ kN/m}$ run

Total pressure $= 25.3 \times 5 = 126.5 \text{ kN}$

Acting at a height $(11.2 - 0.6) = 10.6 \text{ m}$ from top of base slab.

- *Ultimate moments:*

M_u due to earth pressure $= 1.4 \times 1910 \times \dfrac{11.4}{3} = 10161 \text{ kN m}$

M_u due to surcharge $= 1.4 \times 126.5 \times 10.6 = 1877 \text{ kN m}$

Total $M_u = (10161 + 1877) = 12038 \text{ kN m}$

- *Section design:*   Assume the depth of cantilever, $D = 5600 \text{ mm}$ at the base. Effective depth

$$d = 5600 - 40 \text{ (cover)} - 32 \times 1.5 \text{ (2 layers of bars)} = 5512 \text{ mm}$$

Thickness of counterfort, $b = 500 \text{ mm}$

$$\frac{M}{(b \times d^2)} = \frac{12038 \times 10^6}{(500 \times 5512^2)} = 0.8$$

Referring to Figure 2 of BS 8100: part 3: 1985

$$100 \times \frac{A_s}{(b \times d)} = 0.23$$

Therefore,

$$A_s = 0.23 \times 500 \times \frac{5512}{100} = 6340 \text{ mm}^2$$

Length along rib $= (5.1^2 + 11.4^2)^{0.5} = 12.5 \text{ m}$

Therefore,

$$A_s \text{ along rib} = 6302 \times \frac{12.5}{11.4} = 6910 \text{ mm}^2$$

Adopt, 10 nos. T 32 bars in two layers (area provided $= 8042 \text{ mm}^2$)

Curtail inner layer at about mid height (see Figure 10.8).

- *To check for shear:*   Consider the shear at a height d from base, i.e. 5480 mm from base. Soil pressure at 5.92 from top

$$K_a \times \gamma_b \times z = 0.28 \times 21 \times 5.92 = 34.8 \text{ kN/m}^2$$

Total force for 5 m length of wall

$$P_h = \frac{1}{2} \times 5.92 \times 34.8 \times 5 = 515 \text{ kN}$$

Total surcharge due to loader for 5 m length of wall

$$P_s = 25.3 \times 5 = 126.5 \text{ kN}$$

Therefore, total ultimate shear

$$V_u = 1.4 \times (515 + 126.5) = 898 \text{ kN}$$

Total depth of counterfort at 5.92 m from top

$$D = 5.1 \times \frac{5.92}{11.4} + 0.5 = 3.15 \text{ m}$$

Effective depth

$$d = 3150 - 40 - 1.5 \times 32 = 3062 \text{ mm}$$

Shear stress

$$v_u = \frac{V_u}{(b \times d)} = \frac{898 \times 10^3}{(500 \times 3062)} = 0.59 \text{ N/mm}^2$$

$$p = 100 \times \frac{A_s}{(b \times d)} = \frac{100 \times 8042}{(500 \times 3062)} = 0.53$$

$$v_c = \frac{0.79}{1.25} \times p^{0.33} \times \left(\frac{f_{cu}}{25}\right)^{0.33} = \frac{0.79}{1.25} \times 0.53^{0.33} \times \left(\frac{40}{25}\right)^{0.33} = 0.60 \text{ N/mm}^2 > v_u$$

So minimum shear steel is to be provided.

Using spacing of links, $s_v = 200$ mm c/c, area of shear steel required

$$A_{sv} = 0.4 \times b \times \frac{sv}{(0.95 \times f_{yv})} = 0.4 \times 500 \times \frac{200}{(0.95 \times 460)} = 92 \text{ mm}^2$$

Adopt: T10 @ 200 c/c, 4 legged for the whole height of counterfort.
(area of shear steel provided = 4 × 78.5 = 314 mm²) (see Figure 10.8).

Based on Eurocode 2 and Eurocode 7: 2004 [10.8]

Refer to Figure 10.8(a).

Vertical wall

- *Design considerations:* The wall shall be designed as a slab continuous over the counterforts spaced at 5.0 m, and subjected to horizontal soil pressure of backfill granular material.

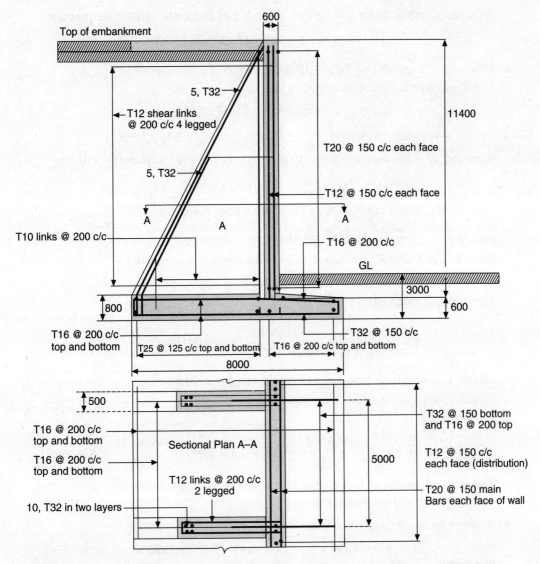

FIGURE 10.8(a) Reinforcement details (for GA, see Figure 10.7) (based on Eurocode).

- *Pressure calculations:*
  Consider 1 m height of wall at a depth $z = 10$ m from top of embankment.

  With design $\phi'_d = \dfrac{\phi'}{\gamma_{\phi'}} = 30/1.25 = 24°$; and $\delta = \dfrac{2}{3}\phi'_d$

  $K_a = 0.36$ (from graphs of Figure 10.6 by Caquot and Kerisel)
  Horizontal pressure

  $$p_{a,10} = K_a \times \gamma' \times z = 0.36 \times 21 \times 10 = 76 \text{ kN/m}^2$$

With partial safety factor $\gamma_f = 1.5$ (see Table A.3 of Eurocode 7), ultimate pressure

$$p_u = 1.5 \times 76 = 114 \text{ kN/m}^2$$

- *Moments:* The slab may be considered continuous over counterforts. Maximum ultimate moment at mid of 1st span

$$0.075 \, p_u \times l^2 = 0.075 \times 114 \times 5^2 = 214 \text{ kN m}$$

- *Design of section:* Assumed: $f_{ck} = 30 \text{ N/mm}^2$; and $f_{yk} = 500 \text{ N/mm}^2$

Assumed: $D = 500 \text{ mm}$; $d = 500 - 40 \text{ (cover)} - 10 \text{ (half bar diameter)} = 450 \text{ mm}$

$$K = \frac{M_u}{(b \times d^2 \times f_{ck})} = \frac{214 \times 10^6}{(1000 \times 450^2 \times 30)} = 0.035$$

$$K' = 0.6 - 0.18 - 0.21 = 0.21$$

Since K is less than K', no compression reinforcement is required.

$$z = 0.95 \, d$$

Therefore, A_s required

$$\frac{M_u}{(f_{yk} \times z)} = \frac{214 \times 10^6}{(500 \times 0.95 \times 450)} = 1001 \text{ mm}^2$$

Adopt: T20 @ 150 c/c both faces (Area provided = 2094 mm²).

- *Distribution steel:* Minimum % of distribution (secondary) reinforcement = 20% of $A_{s, \, min}$ where

$$A_{s, \, min} = 0.26 \times 0.3 \times f_{ck}^{2/3} \times \frac{b \times d}{f_{yk}} = 0.26 \times 0.3 \times 30^{2/3} \times \frac{1000 \times 550}{500} = 828 \text{ mm}^2$$

Therefore, minimum area of distribution steel = 0.2 × 828 = 166 mm²
Adopt: T12 @ 150 c/c both faces.

- *To check for shear:* Shear at a distance d from the face of support

$$V_u = 0.6 \times 114 \times 5 - 114 \times (0.45 + 0.25) = 262 \text{ kN}$$

Shear stress

$$v_u = \frac{V_u}{(b \times d)} = \frac{262 \times 10^3}{(1000 \times 450)} = 0.58 \text{ N/mm}^2$$

Allowable shear stress

$$v_{rd} = 0.12 \times k \times (100 \times \rho \times f_{ck})^{0.33}$$

where

$$\rho = \frac{A_s}{b \times d} = \frac{2094}{(1000 \times 450)} = 0.0047$$

and

$$k = 1 + \left(\frac{200}{d}\right)^{0.5} = 1 + \left(\frac{200}{450}\right)^{0.5} = 1.67$$

Therefore,

$$v_{rd} = 0.12 \times 1.67 \times (100 \times 0.0047 \times 30)^{0.33} = 0.48 \text{ N/mm}^2 < v_u$$

So, increase the thickness of wall to 600 mm. With increase section:

$$d = 550 \text{ mm}$$

$$V_u = 0.6 \times 114 \times 5 - 114 \times 0.8 = 251 \text{ kN}$$

$$v_u = \frac{V_u}{(b \times d)} = \frac{25 \times 10^3}{(1000 \times 550)} = 0.46 \text{ N/mm}^2$$

$$\rho = \frac{A_s}{b \times d} = \frac{2094}{(1000 \times 550)} = 0.0038$$

$$k = 1 + \left(\frac{200}{550}\right)^{0.5} = 1.6$$

$$v_{rd} = 0.12 \times 1.6 \times (100 \times 0.0038 \times 30)^{0.33} = 0.43 \text{ N/mm}^2 < v_u$$

but may be allowed.

From the above calculations based on Eurocode 2, we require higher thickness and increased diameter of main reinforcement. Therefore, adopt thickness of wall = 600 mm and T20 @ 150 c/c both faces.

To design the base slab at toe

- *Design considerations:* The base slab at toe shall be designed as cantilever member subjected to upward ground pressure and downward weight of soil and self-weight of toe.
- *Pressure calculations:* Consider 1 m width of slab.

Upward soil pressure at the toe	$= 283 \text{ kN/m}^2$
Upward soil pressure at the heel	$= 121 \text{ kN/m}^2$

$$\text{Upward soil pressure at the front face of wall} = 121 + 162 \times \frac{5.6}{8} = 234 \text{ kN/m}^2$$

Downward load:
Self-weight of slab

$$2.4 \times 0.6 \times 24 = 34.6 \text{ kN} + \frac{1}{2} \times 2.4 \times 0.1 \times 24 = 2.9 \text{ kN}$$

Weight of soil

$$2.4 \times 2.3 \times (18 - 10) + \frac{1}{2} \times 2.4 \times 0.1 \times 8 = 44.2 + 1 = 43.2 \text{ kN}$$

- *Moment at the face of wall:*
Upward moment due to soil pressure

$$234 \times \frac{2.4^2}{2} + \frac{1}{2} \times 49 \times 2.4 \times \frac{2}{3} \times 2.4 = 768 \text{ kN m}$$

With a partial safety factor $\gamma_f = 1.5$
Ultimate moment = $1.5 \times 786 = 1152$ kN m
Downward moment due to weight of slab

$$34.6 \times \frac{2.4}{2} + 2.9 \times \frac{2.4}{3} = 43.8 \text{ kN m}$$

Downward moment due to weight of soil

$$44.2 \times \frac{2.4}{2} + 1 \times 2.4 \times \frac{2}{3} = 54.6 \text{ kN m}$$

With a factor of safety, $\gamma_f = 1.35$
Total ultimate downward moment due to weight of slab and soil

$$1.35 \times (43.8 + 54.6) = 133 \text{ kN m}$$

Therefore, net ultimate moment

$$M_u = 1152 - 133 = 1019 \text{ kN m}$$

- *Design of section:*   Assumed: depth $D = 700$ mm; $d = 700 - 40$ (cover) −
16 (1/2 bar diameter) = 644 mm

$$K = \frac{M_u}{(b \times d^2 \times f_{ck})} = \frac{1019 \times 10^6}{(1000 \times 644^2 \times 30)} = 0.08$$

$$K' = 0.6 \times 0.18 - 0.21 = 0.21$$

Since $K < K'$, no compression reinforcement is required.
Lever arm $z = 0.95\,d$

$$A_s = \frac{M_u}{(f_{yk} \times z)} = \frac{1019 \times 10^6}{(5000 \times 644 \times 0.9)} = 3516 \text{ mm}^2$$

Adopt: T32 @ 200 c/c bottom (A_s provided = 4021 mm²)
And top: $0.0015 \times 1000 \times 644 = 966$ mm²
Adopt: T16 @ 200 c/c top (area provided = 1006 mm²)
Distribution: T16 @ 200 c/c top and bottom
- *To check for shear:*   Total upward soil pressure at a distance d from face of wall

$$1.576 \times 247 + \frac{1}{2} \times 36 \times 1.576 = 418 \text{ kN}$$

Total ultimate upward soil pressure (with $\gamma_f = 1.5$) = $1.5 \times 418 = 626$ kN

Total downward weight of slab = $\dfrac{1}{2} \times 1.756 \times (0.6 + 0.673) \times 24 = 29$ kN

Total downward weight of soil = $\dfrac{1}{2} \times 1.756 \times (2.327 + 2.4) \times 8 = 33$ kN

Total ultimate downward load (with $\gamma_f = 1.35$) = $1.35 \times (29 + 33) = 84$ kN

Therefore, net ultimate upward load

$$V_u = 626 - 84 = 542 \text{ kN}$$

Shear stress

$$v_u = \frac{V_u}{(b \times d)} = \frac{542 \times 1000}{(1000 \times 617)} = 0.87 \text{ N/mm}^2$$

Allowable shear stress

$$v_{rd} = 0.12 \times k \times (100 \times \rho \times f_{ck})^{1/3}$$

where

$$k = 1 + \left(\frac{200}{617}\right)^{0.5} = 1.57$$

$$\rho = \frac{A_s}{b \times d} = \frac{4021}{(1000 \times 617)} = 0.0065$$

Therefore,

$$v_{rd} = 0.12 \times 1.57 \times (100 \times 0.0065 \times 30)^{1/3} = 0.51 \text{ N/mm}^2 < 0.87 \text{ N/mm}^2$$

Increase the depth at the face of wall to 800 mm and decrease the spacing of the main reinforcement to 150 mm c/c.

So, increased effective depth $d = 682$ mm

And area of $A_s = 5362$ mm^2

$$\rho = \frac{A_s}{(b \times d)} = \frac{5362}{(1000 \times 682)} = 0.0079$$

and

$$k = 1 + \left(\frac{200}{682}\right)^{0.5} = 1.54$$

Therefore,

$$v_{rd} = 0.12 \times 1.54 \times (100 \times 0079 \times 30)^{1/3} = 0.53$$

and

$$v_u = \frac{542}{682} = 0.79 \text{ N/mm}^2 > v_{rd}$$

So, provide shear reinforcement.

Using, T16 shear links @ 200 c/c

$$A_{sw} = \frac{V_u \times b \times s}{(0.9 \times d \times f_y)} = \frac{542 \times 1000 \times 200}{(0.9 \times 682 \times 500)} = 353 \text{ mm}^2$$

Provide: T16 shear links @ 200 c/c 2 legged (A_{sw} = 402 mm^2)
Adopted: depth = 800 mm at face of wall reduced to 600 mm at toe,
And T32 @ 150 mm c/c bottom.

To design the base slab at heel

- *Design considerations:* The slab shall be designed as continuous over the counterfort spaced at 5 m apart, and subjected to upward soil pressure and downward weights of soil and self-weight.
- *Soil pressure calculations:* Consider 1 m width of slab at the heel [see Figure 10.7(a)].
  Ultimate upward soil pressure (with γ_f = 1.5) = 1.5 × 121 = 182 kN/m^2
  Ultimate downward pressure (with γ_f = 1.35) = 1.35 × 283.4 = 342 kN/m^2

  Therefore, net ultimate pressure on soil = 342 – 182 = 160 kN/m^2

- *Ultimate moment:* Ultimate + moment

$$M_u = 0.1 \times w_l^2 = 0.1 \times 160 \times 5^2 = 400 \text{ kN m}$$

- *Design of section:* Assumed: thickness of slab, D = 600 mm; d = 550 mm

$$K = \frac{M_u}{(b \times d^2 \times f_{ck})} = \frac{400 \times 10^6}{(1000 \times 550^2 \times 30)} = 0.04$$

$$K' = 0.6 - 0.18 - 0.21 = 0.21 > K;$$

So compression reinforcement is required.
Lever arm, z = 0.95 d
Therefore, A_s required

$$\frac{M_u}{(f_{yk} \times z)} = \frac{400 \times 10^6}{(500 \times 0.9 \times 550)} = 1616 \text{ mm}^2$$

Minimum percentage of main steel = 0.0015 × 550 × 1000 = 825 mm^2

- *To check for shear:* Shear at a diatance d from the face of counterforts

$$V_u = 160 \times 0.6 \times 5 - 0.8 \times (1.35 \times 253.4 - 1.5 \times 121) = 352 \text{ kN}$$

$$v_u = \frac{V_u}{(b \times d)} = \frac{352 \times 10^3}{(1000 \times 550)} = 0.64 \text{ N/mm}^2$$

$$\rho = \frac{A_s}{(b \times d)} = \frac{2094}{(1000 \times 550)} = 0.0038$$

and

$$k = 1 + \left(\frac{200}{550}\right)^{0.5} = 1.6$$

$$v_{rd} = 0.12 \times k \times (100 \times \rho \times f_{ck})^{1/3} = 0.43 < v_u$$

Increase the depth of section to 800 mm; $d = 750$ mm and reinforcement T25 @ 125 c/c (3927 mm^2)

$$V_u = 160 \times 0.6 \times 5 - 1.0 \times (1.35 \times 253.4 - 1.5 \times 121) = 319 \text{ kN}$$

$$v_u = \frac{V_u}{(b \times d)} = \frac{319 \times 10^3}{(1000 \times 750)} = 0.0.425 \text{ N/mm}^2$$

$$\rho = \frac{A_s}{(b \times d)} = \frac{3927}{(1000 \times 750)} = 0.0052$$

and

$$k = 1 + \left(\frac{200}{750}\right)^{0.5} = 1.52$$

Therefore,

$$v_{rd} = 0.12 \times 1.52 \times (100 \times 0.0052 \times 30)^{1/3} = 0.46 \text{ N/mm}^2 > v_u$$

Therefore, adopt: thickness of slab = 800 mm, and T25 @ 125 c/c top and bottom.

Design of counterfort

- *Design considerations:* The counterfort shall be designed as a cantilever beam fixed at the base, and subjected to soil pressure of embankment.
- *Pressure calculations:* Due to soil pressure

Maximum horizontal pressure at a 11.2 m from top of embankment

$$p_a = K_a \times \gamma' \times z = 0.36 \times 21 \times 11.2 = 84.7 \text{ kN/m}^2$$

Total pressure/m of wall $= \dfrac{1}{2} \times 84.7 \times 11.2 = 474$ kN/m

Spacing of counterfort = 5 m

Therefore, total pressure on each counterfort due to soil pressure $= 474 \times 5 = 2370$ kN

acting at a height $\dfrac{11.2}{3}$, i.e. 3.73 m from base.

Due to surcharge from loader:

Maximum horizontal pressure, $P_s = 32$ kN/m run

Total horizontal pressure $= 32 \times 5 = 160$ kN

Acting at a height 10.4 m from base (see previous calculations)

- *Ultimate moment:*

M_u due to soil pressure $= 1.5 \times 2370 \times 3.73 = 13260$ kN m

M_u due to surcharge = $1.5 \times 160 \times 10.4 = 2496$ kN m

Therefore,

$$\text{Total } M_u = 13260 + 2496 = 15756 \text{ kN m}$$

- *Design of section:*

Total depth, $D = 5600$ mm; $d = 5500$ mm

Thickness of counterfort, $b = 500$ mm

$$A_s = \frac{M_u}{f_y \times 0.95 \times d} = \frac{15756 \times 10^6}{(500 \times 0.95 \times 5500)} = 6030 \text{ mm}^2$$

A_s along the rib = $6030 \times \dfrac{12.5}{11.4} = 6612$ mm^2

Adopt: 10 nos. T32 bars in two tiers (area provided = 8042 mm^2)

- *To check for shear:*   Depth of counterfort at a height 5.5 m from base

$$5.5 \times \frac{5.7}{11.2} = 2.8 \text{ m}$$

Earth pressure at a depth 5.7 m from top

$$K_a \times z \times \gamma' = 0.36 \times 5.7 \times 21 = 43 \text{ kN/m}^2$$

Total soil pressure/m run = $\dfrac{1}{2} \times 43 \times 5.7 = 123$ kN

Pressure due to surcharge = 32 kN/m

Spacing of counterfort = 5.0 m

Total pressure = $(123 + 32) \times 5 = 775$ kN

With a partial safety factor, $\gamma_f = 1.5$

Total ultimate shear (pressure)

$$V_u = 1.5 \times 775 = 1163 \text{ kN}$$

Depth of section, $D = 2800$ mm; $d = 2700$ mm; $b = 500$ mm

$$v_u = \frac{1163 \times 10^3}{(b \times d)} = \frac{1163 \times 10^3}{(500 \times 2700)} = 0.86 \text{ N/mm}^2$$

$$\rho = \frac{A_s}{(b \times d)} = \frac{8042}{(500 \times 2700)} = 0.0095$$

$$v_{rd} = 0.12 \times k \times (100 \times \rho \times f_{ck})^{1/3}$$

$$k = 1 + \left(\frac{200}{d}\right)^{0.5} = 1 + \left(\frac{200}{2700}\right)^{0.5} = 1.27$$

$$v_{rd} = 0.12 \times 1.27 \times (100 \times 0.0095 \times 30)^{1/3} = 0.47 \text{ N/mm}^2 < v_{rd}$$

So, shear links (stirrups) to be provided.

Using, spacing of links = 200 mm c/c

Area of shear steel required

$$\frac{s \times v_u \times b_w}{0.9 \times d \times f_y \times \cot 45} = \frac{200 \times 0.86 \times 500}{0.9 \times 500 \times 1} = 191 \text{ mm}^2$$

Adopt: T12 shear links @ 200 c/c, 2 legged (area provided = $2 \times 113 = 226$ mm^2)

And, T10 links @ 200 c/c vertically [see Figure 10.8(a)].

REFERENCES

[10.1]   Codes of practice for earth retaining structures, BS 8002: 1994.

[10.2]   Rankine, W.J.M., On the stability of loose earth. *Phil. trans. Royal Soc.*, p. 147, 1897.

[10.3]   Bell, A.L., *The lateral pressure and resistance of clay and the supporting power of clay foundation*, Proc. I.C.E., 199 (1915), 233.

[10.4]   BS 8004: 1986: British Standard Code of Practice for Foundations.

[10.5]   Eurocode 7: 2004: Geotechnical design. Part 1: General rules.

[10.6]   BS 8110: 1997: Structural use of concrete. Part 1. Code of practice for design and construction.

[10.7]   Reynolds and Steedman, *Reinforced Concrete Designer's Handbook*, E & FN Spon, London, 1995.

[10.8]   Eurocode 2: 2004: Design of Concrete Structures Part – I: General rules and rules for buildings.

Chapter 11

Lateral Supports in Open Cuts

11.0 GENERAL

Generally, open temporary vertical cuts are made to install the pipelines for sewerage, water mains, and gas and oil transportation system. The open cuts are strutted depending on the depth of the excavation. The open cuts are strutted at an interval of 1.5 to 2 m vertically and 3 m horizontally.

11.1 TYPES OF OPEN CUTS

Depending on the depth of excavation, the open cut trenches may be classified into two types, namely (i) shallow cuts, and (ii) deep cuts.

Shallow cuts

In shallow open cut trenches, the depth is limited to 6 m. In cohesive soils the maximum theoretical depth of excavation (Z_c) that may be carried out without any horizontal struts varies on the soil parameters. In soft clays, the excavation depth (Z_c) cannot be more than 1.5 m without any strut. In medium clay the excavation depth (Z_c) may be taken up to 4 m without the introduction of the strut. In cohesive sand the depth of excavation (Z_c) depends on the value of cohesion. In practice the depth of excavation may be extended to 3.5 m. In cohesive soil, the tension cracks are likely to occur on the top portion of vertical sides of trenches after a few hours or days of excavation. In this case, the strut at the top of excavation should be inserted to prevent collapse of trench sides. When the depth of open cut excavation exceeds 1/2 Z_c, the bracing system should be applied as the excavation progresses.

Deep cuts

The deep cut trenches are applied when the excavation exceeds 6 m. In deep cut trenches, the bracing system is applied as the excavation proceeds. As the excavation progresses, inwards ground movement takes place before the bracing system is installed. The depth of excavation increases and the movement of ground inwards also increases, because the struts are inserted after the excavation.

11.2 METHOD OF CONSTRUCTING OPEN CUTS

For shallow open cuts

In shallow open cut construction, the depth of narrow trench should not exceed 6.0 m as previously stated. Normally, the installation of bracing system starts when the excavation exceeds 1/2 the total design depth. The sequence of excavation and installation of bracing system [see Figure 11.1(a)] is as follows:

- *Step 1:* Excavate to a depth not exceeding half of the maximum theoretical depth (Z_c) without the insertion of strut.
  Note: If the soil is of clayey character and may develop tension crack and possible collapse of sides of trench, it will be wise to install a strut just below ground level.
- *Step 2:* Place the 'laggings' (timber sheeting boards of 150 to 200 mm) horizontally on the vertical excavated faces.
- *Step 3:* Place the vertical 'soldier beams' at about 2 to 2.5 m centres bearing against the horizontal laggings.
- *Step 4:* Install the horizontal struts at about 1.5 to 2 m vertical space against the solder beams.
  Step 5: Tighten the struts at both ends by wedges against the solder beams.
- *Step 6:* Continue to follow the above sequence of excavation and installation of bracing system until the final depth is reached when no strut may be needed.

For deep open cut excavation

- *Step 1:* Drive down the vertical steel sheeting piles to the design depth.
- *Step 2:* Excavate about half a metre deep.
- *Step 3:* Place the horizontal member known as wales.
- *Step 4:* Install the horizontal member called strut, tighten it against the wales at the ends by means of the wedges.
- *Step 5:* Excavate to depth about half a metre below the 2nd strut level.
- *Step 6:* Place the wales at a depth same as the depth of the 2nd strut.
- *Step 7:* Install the 2nd strut, and tighten it against the wales by means of wedges.
- *Step 8:* Continue the above sequence of operation until the final depth is reached.

For deep open cut excavation upto 4 m wide

200 × 200 wooden struts and wales may be used upto a depth of 10 m in cohesionless soil and upto the depth of 3 m in excess of half the designed depth.

In excess of 10 m depth and 4 m wide open cut excavation, metal struts and wales are economical to use [see Figure 11.1(b)].

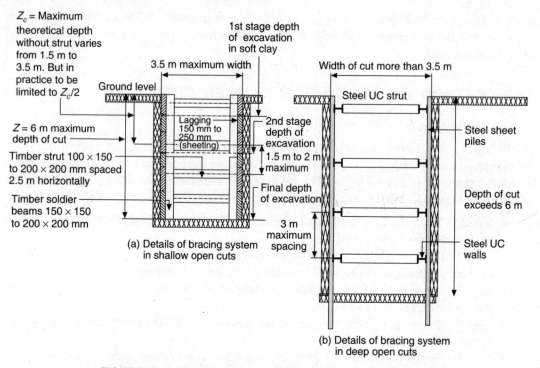

Z_c = Maximum theoretical depth without strut varies from 1.5 m to 3.5 m. But in practice to be limited to $Z_c/2$

Ground level

3.5 m maximum width

1st stage depth of excavation in soft clay

Width of cut more than 3.5 m

Steel UC strut

Z = 6 m maximum depth of cut

Timber strut 100 × 150 to 200 × 200 mm spaced 2.5 m horizontally

Timber soldier beams 150 × 150 to 200 × 200 mm

Lagging 150 mm to 250 mm (sheeting)

2nd stage depth of excavation
1.5 m to 2 m maximum

Final depth of excavation

3 m maximum spacing

Steel sheet piles

Depth of cut exceeds 6 m

Steel UC walls

(a) Details of bracing system in shallow open cuts

(b) Details of bracing system in deep open cuts

FIGURE 11.1 Bracing support system in open cut excavation.

11.3 PRESSURE DISTRIBUTION ON STRUTS IN OPEN CUT TRENCHES

In open cut excavation the installation of struts proceeds the progress of excavation, as described before, and the inward movement of the soil takes place on vertical faces before the insertion of struts. Just below the ground surface the first (uppermost) strut is installed. The movement of soil is negligible. So, the state of stress in the soil is virtually unaltered at this stage before the excavation proceeds downwards. As the excavation proceeds downwards, the gradual inward movement of soil takes place before the installation of struts, with the development of a roughly parabolic distribution of pressure on the excavated surface and reaches the maximum value at about the mid depth of excavation.

The fundamental differences of the behaviour of struts in open cuts and the retaining wall are the following:

- Pressure distribution on the open cut trench faces is of parabolic shape, whereas on the retaining wall the pressure increases in proportion to the depth as in the case of hydrostatic pressure of triangular distribution of pressure.
- In open cut, the failure of any strut induces the increment of load on the neighbouring struts and thus bringing the progressive failure of entire bracing system, whereas the retaining wall forms a structural unit and fails as a whole member. The variation of intensities of pressures from designed pressure distribution due to improper consolidation in construction does not have significant effect in the failure of structure (see Figure 11.2).

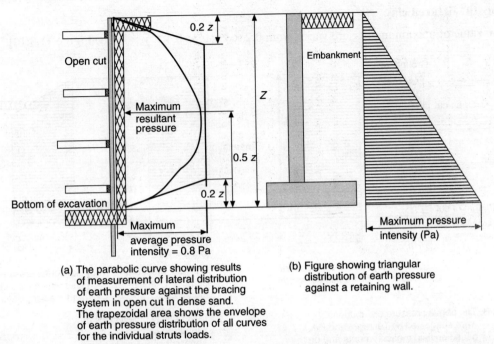

(a) The parabolic curve showing results of measurement of lateral distribution of earth pressure against the bracing system in open cut in dense sand. The trapezoidal area shows the envelope of earth pressure distribution of all curves for the individual struts loads.

(b) Figure showing triangular distribution of earth pressure against a retaining wall.

FIGURE 11.2 Lateral bracing support system in open cut excavation: Comparison of behaviour of horizontal pressures against the vertical faces between open cuts and cantilever wall.

11.3.1 Analysis of Pressure on the Strut

No theoretical analysis has been carried out in the pressure calculations on the struts. Based on the measurements of loads on trench sheeting, and on the results of model tests, Terzaghi and Peck [11.1] suggested the following pressure distribution on the vertical surface of open cut excavation:

For sandy soil:

The intensity of pressure distribution, $p_h = 0.65 \times K_a \times \gamma \times Z$, and is uniform for the whole depth. where

K_a = coefficient of active earth pressure

γ = bulk density of soil

Z = depth of excavation below ground level   [see Figure 11.3(a)].

For soft and medium clays, Peck [11.2]

The maximum intensity of pressure distribution

$$p_{max} = \gamma \times Z - 4 \times m \times c \quad \text{[see Fig.11.3(c)]}$$

where

$m = 1$, except for normally consolidated clays having $\gamma \times Z/c > 4$ in which case the value of m may be significantly less than 1

c = apparent cohesion in terms of total stress.

The intensity of maximum pressure decreases at a height $0.75 \times Z$ from base of trench.

For stiff fissured clay

The value of maximum pressure varies from $0.2 \times \gamma \times Z$ to $0.4 \times \gamma \times Z$ [see Figure 11.3(b)].

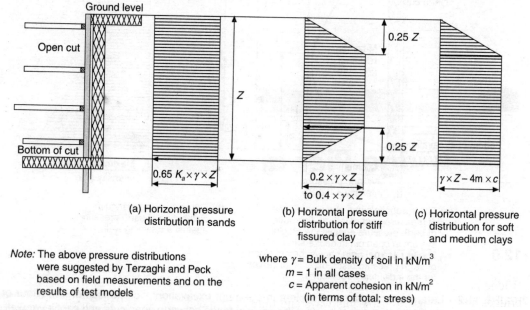

(a) Horizontal pressure distribution in sands

(b) Horizontal pressure distribution for stiff fissured clay

(c) Horizontal pressure distribution for soft and medium clays

Note: The above pressure distributions were suggested by Terzaghi and Peck based on field measurements and on the results of test models

where γ = Bulk density of soil in kN/m^3
m = 1 in all cases
c = Apparent cohesion in kN/m^2
(in terms of total; stress)

FIGURE 11.3 Lateral bracing support system in open cut excavation.

REFERENCES

[11.1] Terzaghi, K. and Peck, R.B., Soil Mechanics in Engineering Practice, Wiley International, New York, 1962.

[11.2] Peck, R.B., Earth pressure measurements in open cuts, Chicago Subway, Tanns. ASCE, vol. 108 (1943), pp. 1008–1036.

Chapter 12

Bridge Pier and Foundation

12.0 DESCRIPTION

Bridge pier and foundation may be described as a substructure to support the superstructure for bridges and viaducts to carry highways and railways. In planning and detail design of pier and foundation below the surface of ground or water, the following aspects should be carefully considered:

1. The type of superstructure either highways or railways, its dimensions, weight and loads.
2. The soil conditions that affect the type, depth and size of foundation.

12.1 TYPES OF SUPERSTRUCTURE

The superstructure for highway bridges is classified for 2 to 4 lane traffics with girders upto 45 m span, and with trusses when the span exceeds 45 m. The bridge deck consists of reinforced concrete construction with 2 sidewalks assumed. The superstructure for railway bridges may be classed as single or double track system. The deck girder construction is adopted upto a span of 30 m in single track system. The half through girder bridges are chosen for single track railway upto a span of 30 m, and upto 40 m span for double track railway system. When the span exceeds 40 m, the trussed girder construction for both single and double track railway system is economical. The wooden slippers are usually used as ties to provide higher cushioning effect from hammering action of high speed moving wheel loads. No ballast is assumed to be provided.

12.2 DIMENSIONS OF SUPERSTRUCTURE

1. *Height of superstructure:* The height of bridges and viaducts depends on the minimum required clear waterway for shipping and also depth of valley over which the viaduct will be built. Thus, high superstructure of bridges and via ducts will be necessary to satisfy the above requirements.

2. *Width of superstructure:* The width of superstructure will vary according to the number of traffic lanes for highway bridges, or number of rail tracks for railway bridges. For higher number of traffic lanes and rail tracks with walkways, the width of superstructure will be quite significant.

3. *Depth of superstructure:* The depth of superstructure depends on the span of bridges and loadings on bridges.

12.3 LOADINGS ON SUPERSTRUCTURE

The bridge superstructure is subjected to the following loading conditions:

1. Dead load on bridges
2. Live load on bridges
3. Wind load on bridges

12.4 GEOTECHNICAL GROUND CONDITIONS

Before we design the bridge pier and foundation, we should study the geotechnical ground conditions. When the superstructure runs over the waterways of river or lakes, we shall investigate the following points:

1. Determine the velocity of current
2. Ascertain the scouring effect (R.W. Stewart [12.1]) of current on the foundation
3. Evaluate the pressure exerted on pier due to crushing, drifting and jamming of ice at waterline in winter time
4. Ground exploration below the bed of river or lake, with adequate soil samples for laboratory tests to find out the geotechnical soil parameters at various depths.

12.5 DESIGN OF BRIDGE PIER

After getting a general knowledge about the superstructure and the ground conditions, we should now proceed with the concept of design of bridge pier on its dimensions, loadings from superstructure, and effects of flow of current and ice under water in waterways. (Dunham [12.2]).

12.5.1 Type and Shape of Bridge Pier

In evaluation of type and shape of pier dimensions, the following points should be taken into account:

Type of pier

The type of pier should be of aesthetically pleasing appearance, keeping harmony with the superstructure, shape and size, and also with the surrounding environment. For large bridges, the pier structure above the water level may consists of high portal frame (in some cases with cantilever at each end to accommodate pedestrian ways) or solid concrete section, and at the portion below water level, the section should be solid with curved noses to allow the streamline flow of water, as shown in Figures 12.1(a) and 12.1(b). For small span bridges the height of pier structure is considerably low and of the same type as for large span bridges.

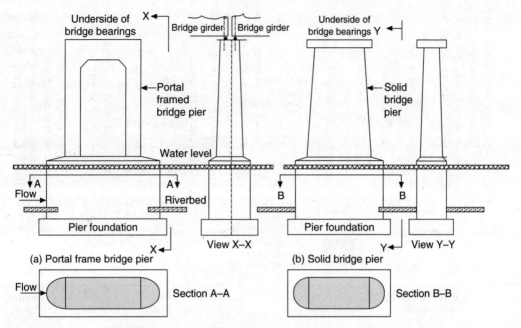

FIGURE 12.1 Bridge pier and foundation: Types of pier.

Shape of pier

- *Shape of nose of pier below water level:* The design of shape of the nose of the pier below water should be given prime importance and a careful study should be made with regard to the flow of water in the waterway. The presence of pier constricts the waterway and increases the velocity of stream. If the nose of the pier is rectangular, as shown in Figure 12.2(a), the sudden increased velocity of water creates swirls and flows past the pier to induce washing away the particles of soil locally. The formation of eddies in the stream tends to suck up the soil particles from the bottom and carry them away. The carried away materials are deposited in slack water beyond the downstream end of pier. The removal of soil by scouring action (R.W. Stewart [12.1]) along the side of pier may endanger the collapse of pier by the shear failure of the ground below the pier due to the reduction of embedment of foundation. So, in order to reduce the chance of shear failure, proper detailing of the nose should be made to streamline the flow.

If the upstream nose is made with a curvature, as shown in Figure 12.2(b), the suddenness of deflection of flow reduces and consequent decrement of washing away of soil particles in front of pier happens. In the same way, if the downstream nose is curved as shown in Figure 12.2(b), the formation of eddies is much reduced. The most effective shape of minimizing the occurrence of scouring action by reducing the resistance of flow is streamlining the shapes of upstream and downstream noses, as shown in Figure 12.2(c).

There is also the possibility of scouring of soil along the sides of pier due to increased flow. It may be advisable to install pile fenders or submerged sheet piles around the foundation of pier to minimize the scouring action. It is difficult to estimate the effectiveness of pile fenders or sheet piles to guard against the scouring of soil. To prevent the dangerous scouring effect, it is rather wise to bring the foundation to a higher depth.

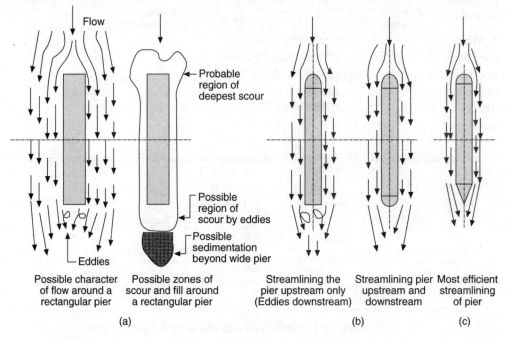

Possible character of flow around a rectangular pier

Possible zones of scour and fill around a rectangular pier

(a)

Streamlining the pier upstream only (Eddies downstream)

Streamlining pier upstream and downstream

Most efficient streamlining of pier

(b)   (c)

FIGURE 12.2   Characteristics of flow around different shapes of pier.

- *The shape of pier above water level:*   The shape may be any section, namly, solid rectangular or rectangular with circular shaped noses, etc . In RC portal frame construction, the two or three columns (depending on the width of pier) are connected by a horizontal member at top to form the support of superstructure. Sometimes, the shape may be of reinforced concrete I-section.

Width of pier

The width of pier depends on the number of lanes in highway bridges or number of tracks in rail road bridges. The pedestrian walkways on either side of main lanes or tracks should be taken into account.

Thickness of pier

The bidge pier is subjected to longitudinal tractive force generated due to moving wheel loads of traffic. This tractive force causes bending moments and shear in minor axis. So, the thickness assumed should be adequate in strength in resisting the bending moment shear. Consideration should also be given to the sizes of bearing plates of bridges to accommodate properly on the top of pier with sufficient allowances for the inspection of bearings.

12.5.2   Forces Acting on Piers

It is difficult to calculate the exact value of forces to be applied on the piers because of the variations of local conditions, shape of superstructure and the loadings on the bridge.

The following estimates of loads due to wave actions, ice, wind, and superstructure, dead and live loadings may be considered for the preliminary analysis of bridge piers (originally prepared by C.W. Dunham [12.2] 'Foundations of structures' and the empirical units are converted to metric units).

1. Wave action: The structure under water is subjected to wave forces when the wind blows over the waterways. The excact magnitude of forces caused by the waves striking on the pier has not been theoretically analyzed. By empirical method the magnitude of the wave forces has been estimated based on the formula given by Paul Anderson [12.3] in his publication *Substructure Analysis and Design*, as shown in Figure 12.3 and in Table 12.1. The original values in empirical units have been converted into metric units in Table 12.1.

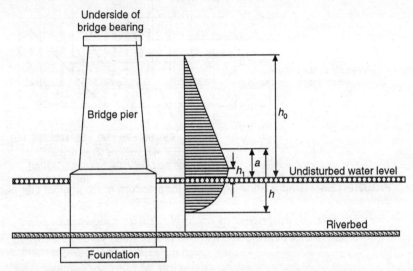

FIGURE 12.3 Bridge pier and foundation: wave pressure diagram on pier.

TABLE 12.1 Showing wave force generated/lin · m thickness of pier due to wind velocity

Wind velocity (km/h)	h_0 (m)	H (m)	a (m)	h_1 (m)	Maximum pressure PM (kN/m²)			Total pressure in pier (kN/lin · m)		
					d = 6 m	d = 9 m	d = 15	D = 6 m	d = 9 m	d = 15 m
48.0	3.0	2.8	1.5	0.34	83.0	103.0	122.0	62.7	77.4	91.9
112.0	5.0	4.3	2.5	0.58	102.7	107.6	122.3	119.2	125.1	142.0
160.0	6.4	5.2	3.2	0.61	107.6	112.5	122.3	152.4	159.3	168.8

The forces on the pier in Table 12.1 may be reduced by 50% if the pier nose is streamlined in rounded or triangular shape. The same reduction may be applied if the wind blows at 45 degrees to the superstructure.

2. Ice actions: The ice on the lakes and waterways has a considerable impact in the design of pier. The floating ice in large cakes crushes against the pier inducing formidable pressure on the pier. Also the drifting ice in the lakes and rivers produces large forces against the pier. Frequently, the floating ice in rivers and lakes forms jam when flows between the piers and this jamming action generates tremendous forces on the pier. So, the nose of the pier should be protected against damage due to the actions of those above forces by providing steel angles or cast iron noses embedded in concrete. The pressures to be considered due to the various actions of ice on the pier structure are given in the following:

- *Crushing of ice against the nose of pier:* The pressure/horizontal metre thickness of upstream end of pier at water line shall be taken from Figure 12.4.

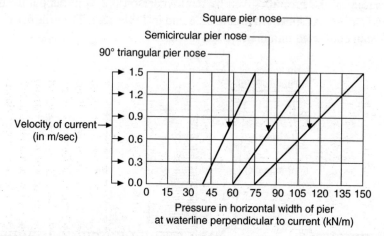

FIGURE 12.4   Graphs showing values for pressure of ice against pier nose.

- *Drifting ice in a lake or waterways at an angle α with long axis of pier:* Total force $F = 15$ kN/horizontal metre of projected width of pier at water level, as shown in Figure 12.5.

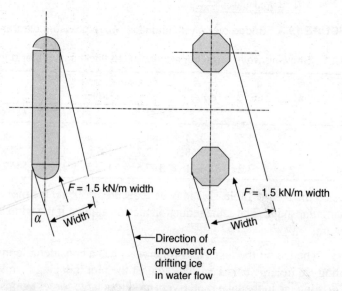

FIGURE 12.5   Pressure of drifting ice on effective width of piers installed obliquely in the direction of flow.

- *Ice jam:*   Ice jamming may occur in spite of provision of ice breakers. The forces that are subjected to the pier may be estimated equal to a static hydraulic head of 1.5 m uniformly distributed over a length of spacing of piers. If this value is less than twice the pressures given in Figure 12.4, then use the value given in Figure 12.4.
- *Forces on the starlings (ice breakers):*   The forces on the starlings are to be taken from Figure 12.4 for rounded or triangular nose multiplied by the sine of slope angle β of the starling with the horizontal.

3. Dead loads from the superstructure bridges: Figure 12.6 shows the values of end reactions of various types of bridges for the estimation of dead loads on the pier (originally prepared by C.W. Dunham [12.2]. The empirical units are converted into metric units):

- Figure 12.6(a) shows the value of end reactions of highway bridges of variable lanes of traffic (2 lane, 3 lane, etc.) with girder and trussed construction.
- Figure 12.6(b) shows the value of end reactions of railroad bridges of single and double tracks and of various types (deck girder, trussed girder, etc.)
- Self-weight of pier. For the portion under the water, the submerged weight to be considered.
- Submerged weight of soil above the projected footing should be taken into account.

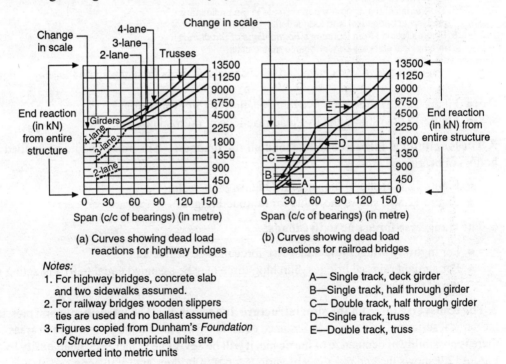

(a) Curves showing dead load reactions for highway bridges

(b) Curves showing dead load reactions for railroad bridges

Notes:
1. For highway bridges, concrete slab and two sidewalks assumed.
2. For railway bridges wooden slippers ties are used and no ballast assumed
3. Figures copied from Dunham's *Foundation of Structures* in empirical units are converted into metric units

A— Single track, deck girder
B—Single track, half through girder
C— Double track, half through girder
D—Single track, truss
E—Double track, truss

FIGURE 12.6   Approximate end reactions of dead loads for highway and railroad bridges.

4. Live loads from the superstructure bridges: Figure 12.7 shows the live load reactions for bridges.

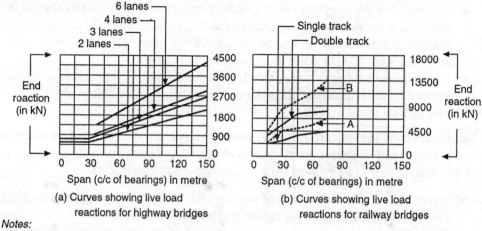

Figure 12.7 Approximate end reactions of live loads for highway and railway bridges.

- Figure 12.7(a) shows the live load reactions of highway bridges.
- Figure 12.7(b) shows the live load reactions of railroad bridges.

5. The longitudinal force due to live load on the bridges: This force should be applied at the bottom of bearings.

- Figure 12.8(a) shows the value for highway bridges.
- Figure 12.8(b) shows the value for railroad bridges.

6. The transverse force due to live loads:

- For highway bridges, the transverse force may be neglected.
- For straight railroad bridges, burching force may be assumed equal to 91 kN acting at the top of the pier.

7. The transverse force on the superstructure due to wind: The intensity of wind pressure on the vertical surface of bridge may be assumed equal to 1.5 kN/m². For large span and in areas where there is possibility of occurance of hurricane, it will be advisable to increase the intensity by 50%. Figure 12.9 shows the end reactions of various types of bridges and of different spans.

8. Longitudinal force due to wind blowing diagonally against the superstructure: Figure 12.10 shows the approximate value of longitudinal forces for highway and railway bridges of varying spans.

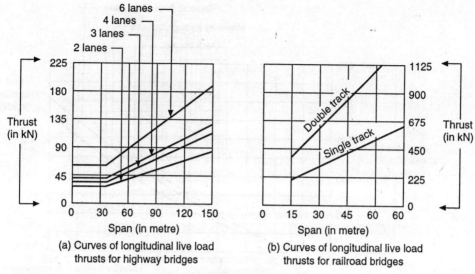

(a) Curves of longitudinal live load thrusts for highway bridges

(b) Curves of longitudinal live load thrusts for railroad bridges

Notes: Figure taken from Dunham's *Foundations of Structures* in empirical units are converted to metric units

FIGURE 12.8 Approximate longitudinal thrusts due to live loads.

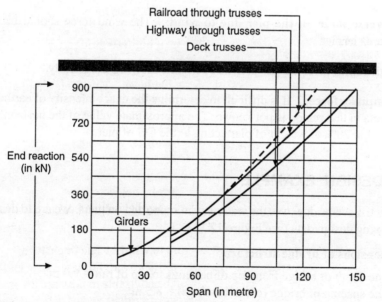

Note: Figure taken from Dunham's *Foundations of Structures* in empirical units are converted to metric units.

FIGURE 12.9 Transverse normal wind reaction on bridge structures.

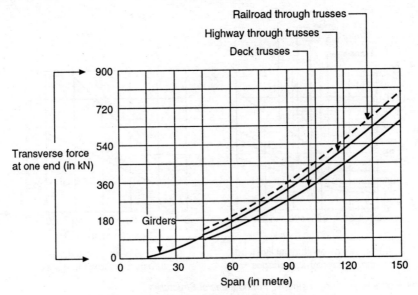

Note: Figure taken from Dunham's *Foundations of Structures*
in empirical units are converted to metric units.

FIGURE 12.10   Transverse and longitudinal wind reactions for 45° on bridge structures.

9. Transverse force on the pier due to wind: The wind force should be calculated on the exposed area of pier.

10. Longitudinal force on the pier due to wind blowing diagonally.

11. Earthquake force: It is difficult to determine the exact intensity of earthquake forces if the seismic data in that region is not known. The approximate value of the horizontal force should be taken equal to 20% of weight of pier acting at the CG of pier.

12.6   DESIGN EXAMPLE 1

A railway trussed bridge over the waterway is supported on piers. We are to design the pier, given the following design data (see Figure 12.11):

The dimensions of bridge structure

- The depth of bridge from top of bearings to top of rail = 9.0 m
- The spacing of bridge (c/c of bearings) = 8.5 m
- The spacing of bearings = 1.14 m

Design data

1. Max. (DL + LL + Impact) on two bearings at each side of pier = 10000 kN
2. Braking force at top of rail = 1090 kN

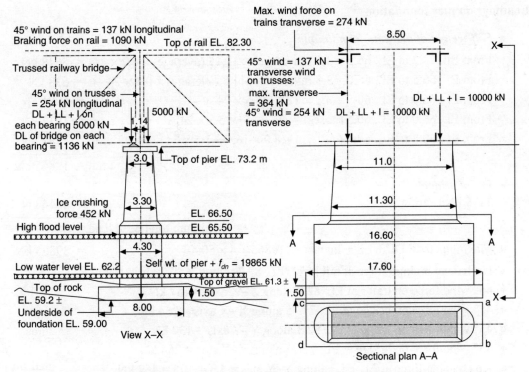

FIGURE 12.11 General arrangement and loadings.

3. *Wind load on trains:*
   Maximum transverse on pier = 274 kN
   45° wind transverse = 137 kN
   Longitudinal = 137 kN
4. *Wind load on trussed bridge:*
   Maximum transverse = 364 kN
   45° wind transverse = 254 kN
   Longitudinal = 254 kN
5. Dead load of bridge on each bearing = 1136 kN
6. Velocity of current at flood = 1.33 m/sec
7. *Heavy crushing of ice on pier in spring floods:*   Referring to Figure 12.4, horizontal pressure/m width of pier = 105 kN at water line
8. Elevation at top of pier = EL. 73.17 m ±
9. Approximate flood level = EL. 65.55 m ±
10. Approximate low water level = EL. 62.20 m ±
11. Approximate level of bottom of basin = EL. 61.28 m ±
12. Geotechnical ground profile: Refer Figure 12.11.

Preliminary dimensioning of pier

Before the analysis of pier, we have to make the preliminary dimensioning of pier. Figure 12.11 shows the preliminary dimensions of pier. The upstream and downstream noses are shaped circular to streamline the water flow.

Loadings on pier foundation

- *Self-weight of pier and foundation:*
  From EL. 73.2 to EL. 66.5 = 3.15 (average) × 11.15 (average) × 6.7 × 24 = 5648 kN
  From EL. 66.5 to EL. 66.0 = 3.8 (average) × 11.8 (average) × 0.5 × 24 = 538 kN
  From EL. 66.0 to EL. 60.5 = 4.3 × 12.3 × 5.5 × 24 = 6981 kN
  From EL. 66.0 to EL. 60.5 (noses) = $\pi \times 2.15^2 \times 5.5 \times 24$ = 1917 kN
  From EL. 60.5 to EL. 59.0 ($f_{dn,\,base}$) = 8.0 × 16.6 × 1.5 × 24 = 4781 kN

  Total = 19865 kN

- DL *of bridge:*
  1136 kN/bearing × 4 = 4544 kN

  Maximum total dead load = 24409 kN

- Maximum total DL + LL + Impact = (19865 + 4 × 5000) = 39865 kN
- Horizontal braking force at rail level (EL. 82.3) along X–X axis = 1090 kN
- 45° wind force on trains at EL. 82.3 along X–X axis = 137 kN
- 45° wind force on bridge at EL. 77.75 along X–X axis = 254 kN
- 45° wind force on trains at EL. 82.3 along Y–Y axis = 137 kN
- 45° wind force on bridge at EL. 77.75 along Y–Y axis = 254 kN
- Ice crushing force at EL. 65.5 along Y–Y axis = 4.3 – 105 = 452 kN

Foundation pressures

Refer to Figure 12.12 on next page.

Moments of all horizontal forces about foundation level

- *About X–X axis of foundation base:*
  Moment due to braking force = 1090 × (82.3 – 59.0) = 25397 kN m
  Moment due to wind force on train = 137 × (82.3 – 59.0) = 3192 kN m
  Moment due to wind force on bridge = 254 × (77.75 – 59.0) = 4763 kN m

  Total moment about X–X, M_x = 33352 kN m

- *About Y–Y axis of foundation base:*
  Moment due to wind force on train = 137 × (82.3 – 59.0) = 3192 kN m
  Moment due to wind force on bridge = 254 × (77.75 – 59.0 = 4763 kN m
  Moment due crushing ice force on pier = 452 × (65.5 – 59.0) = 2938 kN m

  Total moment about Y–Y, M_y = 10893 kN m

Area of foundation base = 8 × 17.6 = 140.8 m^2

Section modulus about X–X axis = $17.6 \times \dfrac{8^2}{6}$ = 187.7 m^3

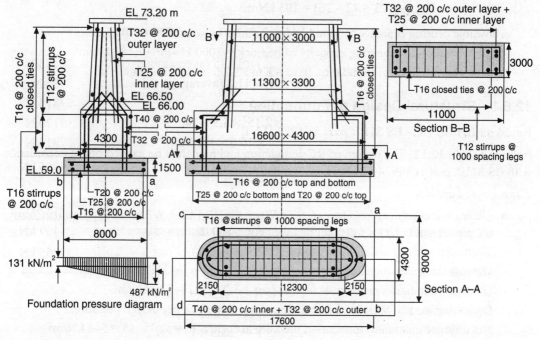

Notes:

1. For general arrangement, see Figure 12.11
2. Minimum cover = 50 mm
3. Concrete cube strength f_{cu} = 40 N/mm²
4. Reinforcement strength f_y = 460 N/mm²
5. Designed on ultimate limit state method.

FIGURE 12.12 Bridge pier; reinforcement details.

Section modulus about Y–Y axis $= 8 \times \dfrac{17.6^2}{6} = 413 \text{ m}^3$

- *Foundation pressure with max. DL + LL + Impact:*

$$\frac{W}{A} + \frac{M_x}{Z_x} + \frac{M_y}{Z_y} = \frac{39865}{14.8} + \frac{33352}{187.7} + \frac{10893}{413} = (283 + 178 + 26) \text{ kN/m}^2 = 487 \text{ kN/m}^2$$

P at corner $b = 283 - 178 + 26 = 131$ kN/m²
P at corner $c = 283 + 178 - 26 = 435$ kN/m²

$$P_{\min} \text{ at corner } d = \frac{W}{A} - \frac{M_x}{Z_x} - \frac{M_y}{Z_y} = 79 \text{ kN/m}^2$$

- *Foundation pressure with DL only*

$$\frac{W}{A} + \frac{M_x}{Z_x} + \frac{M_y}{Z_y} = \frac{24409}{140.8} + \frac{(33352 - 25397)}{187.7} + \frac{10893}{413} = (173 + 42 + 26) = 241 \text{ kN/m}^2$$

$$P_{min} = (173 - 42 - 26) = 105 \text{ kN/m}^2$$

Allowable bearing capacity of sound bedrock varies between 2000–4000 kN/m²

Assume an allowable bearing capacity of bedrock = 2000 kN/m² >> 487 kN/m²

Hence, adopt the size of foundation base = 8 m × 17.6 m × 1.5 m thick.

12.6.1 Structural Design of Foundation

Based on British code BS 8110: part 1: 1997 [12.4]

(refer to Figure 12.12) The design of RC foundation and pier shall be carried out in accordance with BS 8110: part 1: 1997 [12.4] in ULS method.

Foundation base slab

- *Ultimate upward foundation pressure:* When the DL + LL + WL are acting simultaneously, the partial safety factor (γ_f) shall be taken equal to 1.2.

  Therefore, with a partial safety factor = 1.2

  Ultimate maximum foundation pressure, p_{max} = 1.2 × 487 = 584 kN/m² at one extreme corner 'a'

  Ultimate foundation pressure at face of pier = 1.2 × 322 = 386 kN/m²

  Deducting the self-weight of foundation slab,1.5 m thick net design pressure:

  Net ultimate maximum foundation pressure at corner 'a' = 584 – 36 = 548 kN/m²

  Net ultimate foundation pressure at face of pier = 322 – 36 = 286 kN/m²

- *Bending moment:* Consider 1 m width of base slab along short side of pier. Cantilever projection on short side = 1.85 m

$$M_u \text{ at face of pier} = 1.2 \left(322 \times \frac{1.85^2}{2} + \frac{1}{2} \times 1.85 \times 165 \times \frac{2}{3} \times 1.85 \right) = 887 \text{ kN m}$$

- *Design of section:* Assumed thickness, D = 1500 mm

  Effective depth, $D - 75 \text{ (cover)} - \dfrac{1}{2} \times 25 \text{ (bar diameter)} = 1412 \text{ mm}$

  With f_{cu} = 40 N/mm² and f_y = 460 N/mm²;

$$d/D = \frac{1412}{1500} = 0.94$$

Referring to Chart no. 2 of BS 8110: part 3:1985

$$\frac{M_u}{(b \times d^2)} = \frac{887 \times 10^6}{1000 \times 1412^2} = 0.44$$

$$100 \times \frac{A_s}{b \times d} = 0.11$$

$$A_s = 0.11 \times 1000 \times \frac{1412}{100} = 1553 \text{ mm}^2$$

But min % of steel to be provided = 0.0013 × 1500 × 1000 = 1950 mm²

Provide, T25 @ 200 c/c bottom (area provided = 2454 mm²)

And T20 @ 200 c/c top; distribution T16 @ 200 c/c

- *Check for shear:* Shear shall be checked at a distance d from the face of pier.

So, pressure at distance 1412 mm from the face of pier = 448 kN/n²

Total ultimate shear

$$V_u = 1.2 \left[\left(\frac{448 + 487}{2} \right) \times (1.85 - 1.41) \right] = 247 \text{ kN}$$

Shear stress

$$v_u = \frac{V_u}{(b \times d)} = \frac{247 \times 10^3}{(1000 \times 1412)} = 0.17 \text{ N/mm}^2$$

% of steel

$$p = 100 \times \frac{A_s}{(b \times d)} = \frac{100 \times 2454}{(1000 \times 1412)} = 0.17$$

Allowable shear stress

$$v_c = 0.79 \times p^{0.33} \times \frac{\left(\dfrac{f_{cu}}{25} \right)^{0.33}}{1.25} = 0.41 \text{ N/mm}^2 > v_u$$

So, no shear reinforcement is required.

Structural design of pier: Consider the section at EL. 60.5 m

- *Loadings:*

Vertical (DL + LL + Impact) = 20000 kN

DL of bridge = 1136 × 4 = 4544 kN

Self-weight of pier = [(19865 – 4781 (base)] = 15084 kN

Maximum vertical (DL + LL + Impact + self-weight) = 20000 + 15084 = 35084 kN

Minimum vertical (DL bridge + self-weight) = 4 × 1136 + 15084 = 19628 kN

- *Moment:*

Moment due to braking force = 1090 × (82.3 – 60.5) = 23762 kN m

Moment due to 45° wind on bridge = 137 × 21.8 = 2987 kN m

Moment due to 45° wind on truss

$$254 \times \frac{(82.3 - 73.2)}{2} + (73.2 - 60.5) = 4382 \text{ kN m}$$

Moment due cruching ice force = 452 (65.5 – 60.5) = 2260 kN m

$$\Sigma(23762 + 2987 + 4382 + 2260) \text{ kNm} = 33391 \text{ kN m}$$

- *Design of section:*

With γ_f = 1.2, since (dead + live + wind) loads are acting simultaneously.

Ultimate vertical load = $1.2 \times 35084 = 42100$ kN

Ultimate moment = $1.2 \times 33391 = 40069$ kN m

Width of pier = 14 m (average)

Therefore, ultimate vertical load/m $= \dfrac{42100}{14} = 3007$ kN

Ultimate moment/m $= \dfrac{40069}{14} = 2862$ kN m

Thickness of pier, $D = 4300$ mm

Effective thickness $= 4300 - 50 - \dfrac{32}{2}$ (bar diameter) $= 4232$ mm

$$d/D = \frac{4234}{4300} = 0.98$$

Referring the Chart no. 39 of BS 8110: part 3: 1985

$$\frac{M_u}{(b \times D^2)} = \frac{2862 \times 10^6}{(1000 \times 4300^2)} = 0.15$$

$$\frac{N}{(b \times D)} = \frac{3007 \times 10^3}{(1000 \times 4300)} = 0.7$$

$$100 \times \frac{A_{sc}}{(b \times D)} = 0.4$$

$$A_{sc} = 0.4 \times 1000 \times \frac{4300}{100} = 17200 \text{ mm}^2$$

On each face

$$\frac{A_{sc}}{2} = \frac{17200}{2} = 8600 \text{ mm}^2$$

Adopt: T40 @ 200 c/c outer layer + T32 @ 200 c/c inner layer
[Area of steel provided = 6283 + 4021 mm² = 10304 mm²]

- *Check for shear:*
Total shear = (1090 + 254 + 137 + 452) kN = 1933 kN
Ultimate shear = $1.2 \times 1933 = 2320$ kN
Ultimate shear/m width

$$V_u = \frac{2320}{14} = 166 \text{ kN}$$

Shear stress

$$v_u = \frac{166 \times 10^3}{(1000 \times 4234)} = 0.04 \text{ N/mm}^2 \qquad \textbf{(Negligible)}$$

So, theoretically no shear reinforcement is required.
Provide nominal shear reinforcement.

$$A_{sv} = \frac{0.4 \times bv \times sv}{(0.95 \times f_{yv})}$$

Using T16 @ 200 c/c; $sv = 200$ mm; $bv = 1000$

$$A_{sv} = \frac{0.4 \times 1000 \times 200}{(0.95 \times 460)} = 183 \text{ mm}^2$$

Using T16 @ 200 c/c with 2 legs; A_{sv} provided = 402 mm^2 > 183 mm^2 (see Figure 12.12).

Next, consider the section at EL. 66.5 m:

- Vertical self-weight of pier = (5648 + 538) = 6186 kN
  Vertical (DL + LL + Impact) from superstructure = 20000 kN
  Total vertical load = (6186 + 20000) kN = 26186 kN

- *Moment:*
  Moment due to braking force = 1090 × (82.3 – 66.5) = 17222 kN m
  Moment due to wind on trains = 137 × (82.3 – 66.5) = 2165 kN m
  Moment due to wind on trusses = 254 × (77.8 – 66.5) = 2870 kN m
  Total moment   = (17222 + 2165 + 2870) kN m = 22257 kN m

  Assuming a partial safety factor, $\gamma_f = 1.2$
  Ultimate moment = 1.2 × 22257 = 26709 kN m

- *Design of section:*
  Ultimate vertical load = 1.2 × 26186 = 31423 kN

  Ultimate vertical load/m width $= \dfrac{31423}{11.3} = 2781 \text{ kN}$

  Ultimate moment = 26709 kN m

  Ultimate moment/m width $= \dfrac{26709}{11.3} = 2364 \text{ kN m}$

  Assumed thickness of pier, $D = 3300$ mm
  Effective thickness

$$d = D - 50 - \frac{1}{2} \times 32 \text{ (bar diameter)} = 3234 \text{ mm}$$

$$d/D = \frac{3234}{3300} = 0.98$$

Referring to Chart no. 39 of BS 8110: part 3: 1985

$$\frac{M_u}{(bD^2)} = \frac{2364 \times 10^6}{(1000 \times 3300^2)} = 0.22$$

$$\frac{N}{bD} = \frac{2781 \times 10^3}{(1000 \times 3300)} = 0.84$$

$$100 \times \frac{A_{sc}}{bD} = 0.4$$

Therefore,

$$A_{sc} = 0.4 \times 1000 \times \frac{3300}{100} = 13200 \text{ mm}^2$$

$$A_{sc}/2 \text{ per face} = \frac{13200}{2} = 6600 \text{ mm}^2$$

Adopt: T32 @ 200 c/c outer layer + T25 @ 200 c/c inner layer

(area of steel provided = 6475 mm² < 6600 mm² but **OK**)

- *Check for shear:*

Shear = (1090 + 254 + 137) = 1481 kN

Ultimate shear = 1.2 × 1481 = 1777 kN

Ultimate shear per m width

$$= V_u = \frac{1777}{11.3} = 157 \text{ kN}$$

Shear stress

$$v_u = \frac{V_u}{bd} = \frac{157 \times 10^3}{(1000 \times 3234)} = 0.5 \text{ N/mm}^2 \quad \textbf{(Negligible)}$$

Provide minimum shear steel,

$$A_{sv} = \frac{0.4 \times bv \times sv}{0.95 \, f_{yv}}$$

Assuming a spacing, $sv = 200$ mm

and breadth of section, $bv = 1000$ mm

$$A_{sv} = \frac{0.4 \times 1000 \times 200}{(0.95 \times 460)} = 183 \text{ mm}^2$$

Use: T12 @ 200 c/c links 2 legged (area provided = 226 mm²) (see Figure 12.12).

Based on Eurocode 2: 2004 [12.5]

Foundation base slab

1. *Ultimate upward foundation pressure:*

- Due to dead load:

Total self-weight of pier and foundation = 19865 kN

(from previous calculations)

Dead weight of bridge = 4544 kN

Total dead load = 19865 + 4544 = 24409 kN

Therefore, upward foundation pressure due to dead load

$$\frac{24409}{(8 \times 17.6)} = 173 \text{ kN/m}^2$$

with a partial safety factor, $\gamma_f = 1.35$.

Ultimate upward foundation due to dead load = 1.35 × 173 = 234 kN/m²

- Due to live load (with impact):

Total live load = (20000 − 4544) = 15456 kN

(from design data)

Therefore, upward foundation pressure due to live load

$$\frac{15456}{(8 \times 17.6)} = 110 \text{ kN/m}^2$$

with a partial safety factor, $\gamma_f = 1.5$.

Ultimate upward foundation pressure due to live load = 1.5 × 110 = 165 kN/m².

- Due to all horizontal forces (wind, braking forces and ice crushing):

Moment about X–X axis of foundation base, $M_x = 33352$ kN m

Moment about Y–Y axis of foundation base, $M_y = 10893$ kN m

(from previous calculations)

Section modulus about X–X axis, $zx = \dfrac{17.6 \times 8^2}{6} = 187.7 \text{ m}^3$

Section modulus about Y–Y axis, $zy = \dfrac{8 \times 17.6^2}{6} = 413 \text{ m}^3$

Pressure about X − X axis, $\dfrac{M_x}{zx} = \pm\dfrac{33352}{187.7} = \pm 178 \text{ kN/m}^2$

Pressure about Y − Y axis, $\dfrac{M_y}{zy} = \pm\dfrac{10893}{413} = \pm 26 \text{ kN/m}^2$

Referring to Figure 12.11, and with a partial safety factor, $g_f = 1.5$

Ultimate pressure at corner 'a' = 1.5 × (178 + 26) = + 1.5 × 204 kN/m² = 306 kN/m²

Ultimate pressure at corner 'b' = 1.5 × (− 178 + 26) = − 228 kN/m²

Ultimate pressure at corner 'c' = 1.5 × (+ 178 − 26) = + 228 kN/m²

Ultimate pressure at corner 'd' = 1.5 × (− 178 − 26) = − 306 kN/m²

Therefore, maximum ultimate upward pressure at corner 'a'

$(234 + 165 + 306) \text{ kN/m}^2 = 705 \text{ kN/m}^2 < 2000 \text{ kN/m}^2$ (**Satisfactory**)

Ultimate upward pressure at corner 'b' = $234 + 165 - 228 = 171 \text{ kN/m}^2$

Minimum ultimate upward pressure at corner 'd' = $234 + 165 - 306 = 93 \text{ kN/m}^2$.

2. *Ultimate bending moment:* Consider 1 m width of base slab along short side of pier. The projection of cantilever base slab = 1.85 m

Ultimate upward pressure at the face of pier = $171 + 531 \times \dfrac{6.15}{8} = 579 \text{ kN/m}^2$

Assume the base slab thickness $D = 1.5$ m

Net ultimate upward pressure = $579 - 36 = 543 \text{ kN/m}^2$

Net ultimate upward pressure at edge 'a' = $705 - 36 = 669 \text{ kN/m}^2$

Therefore, ultimate moment at the face of pier

$$\frac{543 \times 1.5^2}{2} + \frac{1}{2} \times 126 \times 1.5 \times \frac{2}{3} \times 1.5 = 705 \text{ kN m}$$

3. *Design of section:*

Effective depth, $d = 1500 - 75 - \dfrac{1}{2} \times 25 = 1412$ mm

With $f_{ck} = 30 \text{ N/mm}^2$ and $f_y = 500 \text{ N/mm}^2$

$$Z = 0.95d$$

$$A_s = \frac{M_u}{z \times f_y} = \frac{705 \times 10^6}{0.95 \times 1000 \times 500} = 1051 \text{ mm}^2$$

$$A_{s,\,min} = 0.0015 \times b \times d = 0.0015 \times 1000 \times 1412 = 2118 \text{ mm}^2$$

Adopt: T25 @ 200 c/c bottom (area provided = 2454 mm²)

and T25 @ 200 c/c top

Distribution steel: T16 @ 200 c/c.

4. *To check for shear:* Ultimate pressure at a distance d from the face of pier

$$171 + 534 \times \frac{7.56}{8} = 676 \text{ kN/m}^2$$

Ultimate shear at a distance d from face of pier

$$V_u = \frac{1}{2} \times 0.44 \times (676 + 705) = 304 \text{ kN}$$

Design shear stress

$$v_u = \frac{V_u}{(b \times d)} = \frac{304 \times 10^3}{(1000 \times 1412)} = 0.22 \text{ N/mm}^2 \qquad (\textbf{Negligible})$$

So, no shear reinforcement is required.

Structural design of pier: Consider the section at EL. 60.5 m.

- *Loadings:* Vertical loads:
  Total ultimate dead loads $= 24409 \times 1.35 = 32952$ kN
  Total ultimate live loads $= 15456 \times 1.5 = 23184$ kN

- *Ultimate moments:* Total ultimate moments (due to breaking force, wind, crushing ice)
  $$33391 \times 1.5 = 50087 \text{ kN m} \qquad \text{(from previous calculations)}$$

- *Design of section:*
  Width of pier, $B = 14$ m (average)
  Thickness of pier, $D = 4300$ mm
  Consider 1 m width of pier.
  Therefore,

$$\text{Ultimate vertical load per m} = \frac{(32952 + 23184)}{14} = 4010 \text{ kN/m}$$

$$\text{Ultimate moment per m} = \frac{50087}{14} = 3578 \text{ kN m/m}$$

Effective depth of pier

$$d = \frac{4300 - 50 - 40}{2} \text{ (half bar diameter)} - 16 \text{ (link diameter)} = 4214 \text{ mm}$$

$$\frac{d}{D} = \frac{4214}{4300} = 0.98$$

Referring to Figure 9 of Eurocode 2

$$\frac{M_u}{(bh^2 f_{ck})} = \frac{3578 \times 10^6}{(1000 \times 4300^2 \times 30)} = 0.0065$$

$$\frac{N_u}{(b \times h \times f_{ck})} = \frac{4010 \times 10^3}{(1000 \times 4300 \times 30)} = 0.03$$

Minimum reinforcement to be provided

$$\frac{0.1 \times N_u}{f_y} = \frac{0.1 \times 4010 \times 10^3}{500} = 802 \text{ mm}^2$$

or

$$0.002 \times A_c = 0.002 \times 4300 \times 1000 = 8600 \text{ mm}^2$$

Adopt: T40 @ 200 c/c outer layer and T32 @ 200 c/c inner layer
(Total steel provided $= (6283 + 4021) = 10304$ mm^2) (see Figure 12.12)

- *To check for shear:*
  Braking force   = 1090 kN
  Wind force   = 137 + 254 = 391 kN
  Ice crushing force = 452 kN

Total ultimate shear = $1.5 \times (1090 + 391 + 452) = 2900$ kN

Therefore, ultimate shear per m width

$$V_u = \frac{2900}{14} = 207 \text{ kN/m}$$

Design shear stress

$$v_u = \frac{207}{4214} = 0.05 \text{ N/mm}^2 \quad \textbf{(Negligible)}$$

Provide minimum shear steel

$$A_{sw} \frac{0.4 \times b_w \times s}{0.9 \, f_{ywd}}$$

Assuming a spacing of shear links, $s = 200$ mm, and width, $b_w = 1000$ mm

$$A_{sw} = \frac{0.4 \times 1000 \times 200}{(0.9 \times 500)} = 178 \text{ mm}^2$$

Use: T12 @ 200 c/c links 2 legged (area provided = 226 mm²) (see Figure 12.12).

REFERENCES

[12.1] Stewart, R.W., Safe foundation depths for bridges to protect from scour, *Civil Engineering*, June, 1939.

[12.2] Dunham, C.W., Foundations of Structures, McGraw-Hill, New York, 1950.

[12.3] Anderson, Paul: Substructure Analysis and Design, Irwin-Rarnham Publishing, Chicago, 1948.

[12.4] BS 8110: part 1: 1997: Structural use of concrete, code of practice for design and construction.

[12.5] Eurocode 2: 2004: Design of concrete structures.

Chapter **13**

Underpinning

13.0 DESCRIPTION

The term *underpinning* in foundation engineering is defined as the method of operation of transferring the load from the wall of an existing foundation to the temporary supports and then finally to the new foundation, capable of sustaining higher load bearing capacity due to the increase in load on the existing column and wall, and also modifications of the existing structure.

The underpinning is applied in the following circumstances and conditions (Dunham [13.1]).

1. New construction of basement in an existing building
2. New construction of tunnels, sewer lines, water mains and electrical ducts under or near the structure, columns or walls
3. New construction of tanks, pits, sumps or elevator pit in the existing plant or process building
4. The construction of deeper foundation near the side of existing foundation of neighbouring structure.

13.1 GENERAL PHILOSOPHY OF UNDERPINNING

The underpinning is an operation (Tomlinson [13.2]) which requires a lot of engineering judgement and expertise. Before we start the underpinning operation, the geotechnical ground condition, watertable, etc. should be investigated in the proposed area. The condition of the structure, the loading of the existing column or wall to be properly evaluated. The supporting members to be used in the underpinning operation shall have to be designed in strength and deflection to carry the existing loads to be temporarily supported.

The underpinning operation is a slow, steady and time-consuming process. It involves a great deal of manual labour in hand-digging and handpicking of dug out materials. The operation should be carried out in a cautious way not allowing undue movement or deflection of the supporting members to take place that may develop cracks in the existing wall causing damage to the structure.

Adjustment to the proper elevation is essential to transfer the load by means of wedges, hydraulic jacks, bolts,turnbuckle, and threaded rods.

The groundwater sometimes creates problems in underpinning operations. So, to control groundwater, sumps and pumps shall be used, and well points may be installed if and when necessary. Before starting the underpinning operation, a careful examination of the structures of the neighbouring properties, adjacent to the property under consideration, should be carried out and adequate photographs to show the present condition of structure and foundation (if possible) should be taken. A report with all details and photographs shall be prepared, and should be submitted to a competent and independent authority for review and approval. This is to avoid any unjust claims by the owner of the neighbouring property for damages caused by the underpinning operation.

13.2 UNDERPINNING OPERATIONS OF VARIOUS STRUCTURAL ELEMENTS, DUNHAM [13.1]

13.2.1 Underpinning of Columns

Consider the column of an industrial building that will be subjected to an increased loading due to the addition of floors. The column is resting on an isolated footing which is not capable of resisting this increased loading. So, the existing foundation will have to be replaced by a new one capable of carrying this increased loading.

The sequence of underpinning operation to replace the existing footing by the new one is given by the following steps (see Figure 13.1).

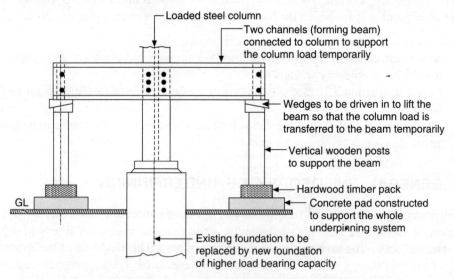

FIGURE 13.1   Underpinning: Column foundation.

Step 1:   Before starting the operation, investigate the geotechnical condition of ground, calculate the allowable bearing capacity from the geotechnical data obtained from laboratory test results. Design and detail the size and strength of the new foundation with increased loading and with allowable bearing capacity.

Step 2: Prepare two concrete pads of adequate strength on solid ground on either side of the column under consideration.

Step 3: Install hardwood timber 'mud sills' on top of the concrete pads.

Step 4: Install two channels (of adequate strength) bolted on the existing steel column.

Step 5: Erect two hardwood wooden posts (of adequate strength) below the projected ends of channels (connected together with bolts).

Step 6: Insert wedges (or jacks) between the cap of the post and the channel base.

Step 7: Apply forces very slowly by the jacks or hammering the wedge in so that the channel member is raised allowing the load on the column is transferred to the channel member.

Step 8: Now, remove the existing foundation and construct the new foundation.

Step 9: When the new foundation acquires adequate strength, lower down the jacks or release the wedge slowly so that the column base is placed on the new foundation with proper adjustments and finally grouting the column base.

13.2.2 Underpinning of Walls

A vehicular subway is to be built near and along the existing foundation of an old building. The existing foundation wall is to be replaced by an extended new foundation wall to serve the wall of the proposed subway. The underpinning operation shall be carried out in the following sequence (see Figure 13.2).

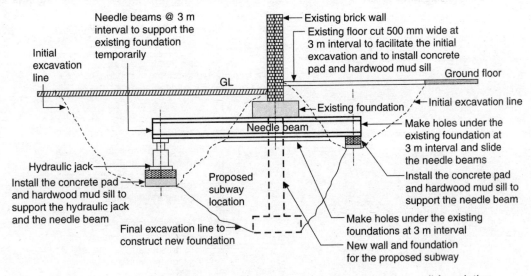

FIGURE 13.2 Details showing the underpinning operation of existing wall foundation.

Step 1: Cut a series of holes at a spacing of 2 m to 3 m on the existing floor slab along the length of the inside of the building, 500 mm wide and 1500 long from the face of wall.

Step 2: Excavate 500 mm deep and 500 mm wide at a spacing of 2 m to 3 m on either side of the wall.

Step 3: Prepare the concrete pad on the hard base of excavated ground to receive the hardwood block (mud sill) to support the hydraulic jacks.

Step 4:   Install the hardwood blocks on the concrete pads.

Step 5:   Install the hydraulic jacks on the outer hardwood blocks.

Step 6:   Make holes under the wall footing at about 2 m to 3 m interval to slide the needle beams.

Step 7:   Insert needle beams through the holes, the outer ends being supported on the jacks and the inside ends resting on the hardwood blocks.

Step 8:   Activate the jacks so that the outer ends of the needle are raised slowly and the full load of wall is transferred to a series of needle beams.

Step 9:   Now, excavate under the existing old foundation for the whole length of wall.

Step 10:   Construct the new wall with footing and allow time to reach adequate strength to support the existing wall.

Step 11:   Release the hydraulic jacks slowly so that the load from the needle beams are transferred to the new foundation wall.

Step 12:   Remove the needle beams and jacks. So, the underpinning operation of existing wall foundation is complete.

REFERENCES

[13.1]   Dunham, C.W., Foundation of Structures, McGraw-Hill, New York, 1950.

[13.2]   Tomlinson, M.J., Foundation Design and Construction, Longman Scientific & Technical, Essex, England, 1995.

Chapter 14

Caisson Foundation

14.0 DESCRIPTION

The word *caisson* may be expressed as the hollow substructure to act as a protective member during the operation of excavation and construction of deep foundation. After the construction of foundation on the caisson is complete, the caisson remains in position to behave as part of the foundation to carry the load in conjunction with the foundation. The shape of caisson may be circular, rectangular, oval with single or multiple cavities (cells), and the thickness of cavity wall varies, generally made of reinforced concrete. The size and depth of the caisson depends on the load carrying capacity of foundation. Figure 14.1 shows various shapes and sizes of caisson.

The caisson is sunk due to its own weight as the excavation within the caisson progresses. The design, construction and sinking of caisson form an integral part of foundation engineering, which requires several years professional experience and expertise.

14.1 TYPES OF CAISSONS

There are mainly two types of caissons (Dunham [14.1]) which are as follows:

1. Open ended caisson is simply open on both top and bottom and the soil is scooped out by means of mechanical digger operated at the ground level.
2. Closed type pneumatic caisson in which an air lock working chamber is created at the bottom end and excavation is carried out by manual digging within the chamber.

14.1.1 Method of Operation of Sinking Open Ended Caisson

Refer to Figure 14.2 as follows: Before the operation of sinking the open ended caisson, a thorough soil investigation at the site should be carried out. With reference to borehole logs the drawing showing soil profile shall be drawn. Based on data of the laboratory test results, the structural design and detail drawings of the caisson shall be carried out of shell thickness and depth of

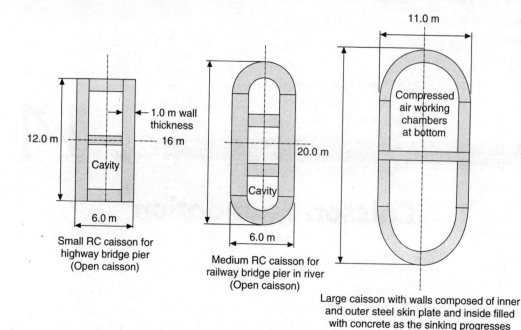

FIGURE 14.1 Caisson foundation: types, shapes and sizes.

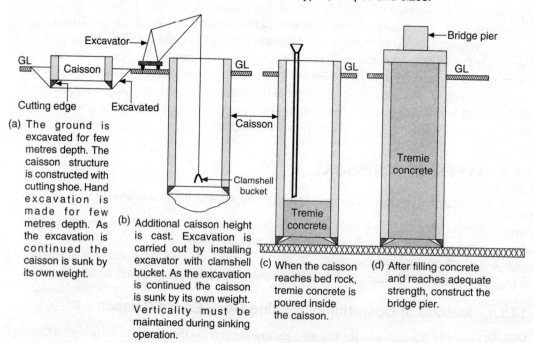

(a) The ground is excavated for few metres depth. The caisson structure is constructed with cutting shoe. Hand excavation is made for few metres depth. As the excavation is continued the caisson is sunk by its own weight.

(b) Additional caisson height is cast. Excavation is carried out by installing excavator with clamshell bucket. As the excavation is continued the caisson is sunk by its own weight. Verticality must be maintained during sinking operation.

(c) When the caisson reaches bed rock, tremie concrete is poured inside the caisson.

(d) After filling concrete and reaches adequate strength, construct the bridge pier.

FIGURE 14.2 Caisson foundation: Sequence of sinking operation of open ended caisson.

penetration required for the loadings. After all the design and detail drawing is complete, the operation of sinking of caisson will start. The sequence of operations of sinking of open ended caisson shall be followed as follows:

Step 1: Locate the exact location of pier where the sinking of caisson will commence. Excavate the ground for a small depth. Cast at site a couple of metres of caisson with the cutting edge and time to bring it to the required strength. Hand excavation is carried out. As the excavation continues, the caisson sinks by its own weight [see Figure 14.2(a)].

Step 2: Install the mechanical digger on the ground level. Cast additional height of caisson. Excavate within the shell by mechanical digger and scoop out the excavated soil by clamshell buckets.

Step 3: As the digging and scooping operation continues, the caisson goes on sinking due to its own weight. When the portion of caisson sinks and the top of it comes to ground level another additional section of caisson is cast to the top of the previous one [see Figure 14.2(b)].

During the digging and sinking operation, there may be sometimes the tendency of tilting the caisson due to the encounter of any hard object at one side of cutting edge. In this situation, heavy weight to the higher side shall have to be added to counterbalance the tilting position and bring it to the straightened verticality. So, from the early stage of sinking operation, a careful observation should be given to avoid the tilting of caisson which is always a difficult task to correct the tilting at the later stage.

Step 4: Thus, the digging and sinking operations continue until the bottom end reaches the designed depth. Sometimes, the caisson has to be sunk to reach the rock in order to obtain the required bearing capacity.

Step 5: After the sinking operation of caisson is complete, the hollow portion of caisson is filled with tremie concrete which replaces the water that existed inside the caisson [see Figure 14.2(c)].

Step 6: When the concrete reaches adequate strength, the bridge pier foundation and pier are constructed on the top of caisson. Thus, the caisson forms an integral part of pier to take up the designed loadings on the pier [for details, see Figure 14.2(d)].

14.1.2 Pneumatic Caisson

The pneumatic caisson is generally used in river foundation pier with very high loadings from the superstructure, and where the foundation is taken to the bedrock. Before the operation of sinking of pneumatic caisson, the shell of pneumatic caisson is designed, normally made up of designed inner and outer skin of steel plates with horizontal steel girders spaced at certain vertical spacing to form boxed shell structure with bottom cutting edge and fabricated on ground. An air-compressed working chamber with fabricated steel roof about 3 m high from bottom is connected to the inside of caisson shell. The ventilation shafts to locks are attached to the roof. The sequence of operations of sinking the caisson is as follows (see Figure 14.3) (E.P. Swateck, JR [14.2]).

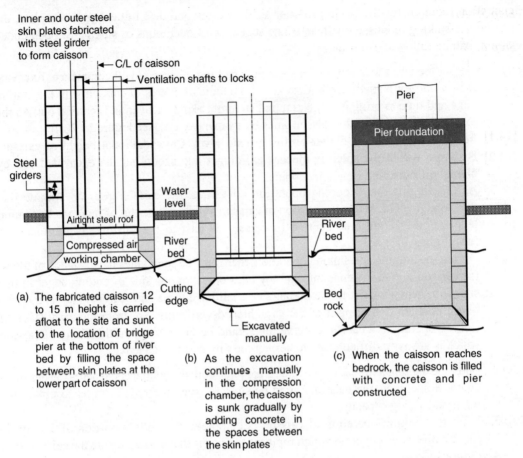

FIGURE 14.3 Caisson foundation: Sequence of sinking operation of pneumatic caisson.

Step 1: The fabricated unit of caisson of approximately 12 to 15 m is carried afloat to the site and is sunk to the exact location of bridge pier. The caisson is then gradually lowered down to the bottom of river bed by filling the space between skin plates of shell with concrete at the lower part of caisson. The caisson is vertically aligned [see Figure 14.3(a)].

Step 2: The compressed air through the tubular shafts with air locks is injected in the working chamber to a pressure not to allow the ingrace of the soil (mainly silt and sand) in the chamber.

Step 3: The men are then brought inside the compressed air chamber, and starts digging manually.

Step 4: As the excavation continues, the caisson is sunk gradually by adding more concrete in the space of shell and the addition of annular steel shell connecting to the existing one. As the excavation stops and the people leave the compression chamber, the air pressure is reduced to an extent not to allow the sand coming inside the chamber [see Figure 14.3(b)].

The operation of excavation is a slow process and time consuming. The men after leaving the compression chamber have to go to the decompression chamber to avoid any air bubbles going into the blood stream causing serious health hazard.

Step 5: After the caisson is sunk to the required design depth (to bed rock), the compression chamber and the entire height of caisson is filled with concrete.

Step 6: When the concrete reaches the required strength, the bridge pier is constructed [Figure 14.3(c)].

REFERENCES

[14.1] Dunham, C.W., Foundations of Structures, McGraw-Hill, New York, 1950.

[14.2] Sweteck, E.P., Foundation Engineering Handbook Edited by H.F. Winterton & H. Yang Fang, Van Nostrand Reinhold Company, New York, 1975.

Annex D of Eurocode 7 (Informative)

EN 1997-1: 2004

A SAMPLE ANALYTICAL METHOD FOR BEARING RESISTANCE CALCULATION

D.1 Symbols used in Annex D

1. The following symbols are used in Annex D.

$A' = B' \times L'$	the design effective foundation area
b	the design values of the factors for the inclination of the base, with subscripts, c, q and γ
B	the foundation width
B'	the effective foundation width
D	the embedment depth
e	the eccentricity of the resultant action, with subscripts B and L
i	the inclination factors of the load, with subscripts cohesion c, surcharge q and weight density γ
L	the foundation length
L'	the effective foundation length
m	exponent in formulas for the inclination factor i
N	the bearing capacity factors, with subscripts for c, q and γ
q	overburden or surcharge pressure at the level of the foundation base
q'	the design effective overburden pressure at the level of the foundation base
s	the shape factors of the foundation base, with subscripts for c, q and γ
V	the vertical load
α	the inclination of the foundation base to the horizontal
γ'	the design effective weight density of the soil below the foundation level
θ	direction angle of H

2. The notations used in this method are given in Figure D.1.

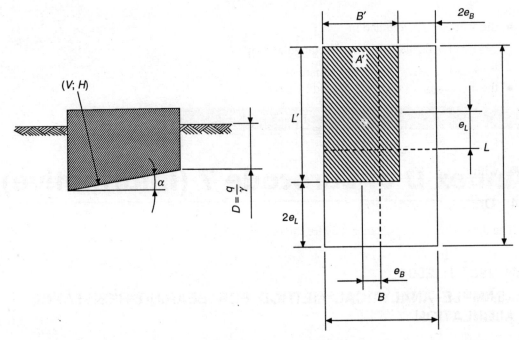

FIGURE D.1 Notations.

D.2 General

1. Approximate equations for the design of vertical bearing resistance, derived from plasticity theory and experimental results, may be used. Allowance should be made for the effects of the following:

- The strength of the ground, generally represented by the design values of C_u, c' and ϕ'
- Eccentricity and inclination of design loads
- The shape, depth and inclination of the foundation
- The inclination of the ground surface
- Groundwater pressures and hydraulic gradients
- The variability of the ground, especially layering.

D.3 Undrained Conditions

1. The design bearing resistance may be calculated from

$$\frac{R}{A'} = (\pi + 2)\, C_u\, b_c\, s_c\, i_c + q$$

with the dimensionless factors for:

- the inclination of the foundation base

$$b_c = 1 - \frac{2\alpha}{(\pi + 2)}$$

- the shape of the foundation

  $s_c = 1 + 0.2\,(B'/L')$, for a rectangular shape

  $s_c = 1, 2,$ for a square or circular shape.
- the inclination of the load, caused by a horizontal load H:

$$i_c = \frac{1}{2}\left(1 + \sqrt{1 - \frac{H}{A'C_u}}\right)$$

with $H \le A'\,C_u$.

D.4   Drained Conditions

1. The design bearing resistance may be calculated from

$$\frac{R}{A'} = c'\,N_c\,b_c\,s_c\,i_c + q'\,N_q\,b_q\,s_q\,i_q + 0.5\,\gamma'\,B'\,N_\gamma\,b_\gamma\,s_\gamma\,i_\gamma$$

with the design values of dimensionless factor for:
- the bearing resistance

$$N_q = e^{\pi \tan \phi'} \tan^2\left(45° + \frac{\phi'}{2}\right)$$

$$N_c = (N_q - 1)\cot\phi'$$

$$N_\gamma = 2(N_q - 1)\tan\phi', \text{ where } \delta \ge \frac{\phi'}{2} \text{ (rough base)}$$

- the inclination of the foundation base

$$b_c = b_q - \frac{(1 - b_q)}{(N_c \cdot \tan\phi')}$$

$$b_q = b_\gamma = (1 - \alpha\cdot\tan\phi)^2$$

- the shape of foundation

$$s_q = 1 + \left(\frac{B'}{L'}\right)\sin\phi', \qquad \text{for a rectangular shape}$$

$$s_q = 1 + \sin\phi', \qquad \text{for a square or circular shape}$$

$$s_\gamma = 1 - 0.3\left(\frac{B'}{L'}\right), \qquad \text{for a rectangular shape}$$

$$s_\gamma = 0.7, \qquad \text{for a square or circular shape}$$

- $s_c = \dfrac{(s_q \cdot N_q - 1)}{(N_q - 1)}$, for rectangular, square or circular shape;
- the inclination of the load, caused by horizontal load H:

$$i_c = i_q - \frac{(1 - i_q)}{(N_c \cdot \tan \phi')}$$

$$i_q = \left[1 - \frac{H}{(V + A' \cdot c' \cdot \cot \phi')} \right]^m$$

$$i_\gamma = \left[1 - \frac{H}{(V + A' \cdot c' \cdot \cot \phi')} \right]^{m+1}$$

where

$$m = m_B = \frac{\left[2 + \left(\dfrac{B'}{L'} \right) \right]}{\left[1 + \left(\dfrac{B'}{L'} \right) \right]}, \qquad \text{when } H \text{ acts in the direction of } B'$$

$$m = m_L = \frac{\left[2 + \left(\dfrac{L'}{B'} \right) \right]}{\left[1 + \left(\dfrac{L'}{B'} \right) \right]}, \qquad \text{when } H \text{ acts in the direction of } L'.$$

In case where the horizontal component acts in a direction forming an angle θ with the direction of L', m may be calculated by

$$m - m_\theta = m_L \cos^2 \theta + m_B \sin^2 \theta.$$

Index